NATIONAL NUCLEAR ENERGY SERIES
Manhattan Project Technical Section

Division V—Volume 1

ELECTRONICS

Experimental Techniques

ELECTRONICS
Experimental Techniques

by

WILLIAM C. ELMORE

Associate Professor of Physics
Swarthmore College

and

MATTHEW SANDS

Assistant Professor of Physics
Massachusetts Institute of Technology

First Edition

New York · Toronto · London
McGRAW-HILL BOOK COMPANY, INC.
1949

ELECTRONICS

Experimental Techniques

Copyright, 1949, by the

McGraw-Hill Book Company, Inc.

Printed in the United States of America

Lithoprinted
by
Edwards Brothers, Incorporated
Ann Arbor, Michigan

FOREWORD

The United States program of development of atomic energy has been described by Major General L. R. Groves, who, as Commanding General of the War Department's Manhattan Project, directed the program from mid-1942 until December 31, 1946, as "a generation of scientific development compressed into three years." The tremendous scope of the Manhattan Project Technical Section of the National Nuclear Energy Series, which has been in preparation since 1944, is a tribute to the unprecedented accomplishments of science, industry, government, labor, and the Army and Navy, working together as a team. These volumes can be a firm foundation for the United States atomic energy program which, in the words of the Atomic Energy Act of 1946, is " . . . directed toward improving the public welfare, increasing the standard of living, strengthening free competition in private enterprise, and promoting world peace."

David E. Lilienthal, Chairman
U. S. Atomic Energy Commission

ACKNOWLEDGMENT

The Manhattan Project Technical Section of the National Nuclear Energy Series embodies results of work done in the nation's wartime atomic energy program by numerous contractors, including Columbia University. The arrangements for publication of the series volumes were effected by Columbia University, under a contract with the United States Atomic Energy Commission. The Commission, for itself and for the other contractors who contributed to this series, wishes to record here its appreciation of this service of Columbia University in support of the national nuclear energy program.

PREFACE

This volume is one of a series which has been prepared as a record of the research work done under the Manhattan Project and the Atomic Energy Commission. The name Manhattan Project was assigned by the Corps of Engineers, War Department, to the far-flung scientific and engineering activities which had as their objective the utilization of atomic energy for military purposes. In the attainment of this objective, there were many developments in scientific and technical fields which are of general interest. The National Nuclear Energy Series (Manhattan Project Technical Section) is a record of these scientific and technical contributions, as well as of the developments in these fields which are being sponsored by the Atomic Energy Commission.

The declassified portion of the National Nuclear Energy Series, when completed, is expected to consist of some 60 volumes. These will be grouped into eight divisions, as follows:

Division   I — Electromagnetic Separation Project
Division   II — Gaseous Diffusion Project
Division   III — Special Separations Project
Division   IV — Plutonium Project
Division   V — Los Alamos Project
Division   VI — University of Rochester Project
Division   VII — Materials Procurement Project
Division VIII — Manhattan Project

Soon after the close of the war the Manhattan Project was able to give its attention to the preparation of a complete record of the research work accomplished under Project contracts. Writing programs were authorized at all laboratories, with the object of obtaining complete coverage of Project results. Each major installation was requested to designate one or more representatives to make up a committee, which was first called the Manhattan Project Editorial Advisory Board, and later, after the sponsorship of the Series was assumed by the Atomic Energy Commission, the Project Editorial Advisory Board. This group made plans to coordinate the writing programs at all the installations, and acted as an advisory group in all matters affecting the Project-wide writing program. Its last meeting was held on Feb. 9, 1948, when it recommended the publisher for the Series.

The names of the Board members and of the installations which they represented are given below.

Atomic Energy Commission
    Public and Technical Information
      Service   Alberto F. Thompson

    Technical Information Branch,   Brewer F. Boardman
      Oak Ridge Extension

    Office of New York Operations   Charles Slesser, J. H. Hayner,
                                     W. M. Hearon *

Brookhaven National Laboratory   Richard W. Dodson

Carbide & Carbon Chemicals   R. B. Korsmeyer, W. L. Harwell,
  Corporation (K-25)   D. E. Hull, Ezra Staple

Carbide & Carbon Chemicals   Russell Baldock
  Corporation (Y-12) †

Clinton Laboratories ‡   J. R. Coe

General Electric Company, Hanford T. W. Hauff

General Electric Company,   John P. Howe
  Knolls Atomic Power Laboratory

Kellex Corporation   John F. Hogerton, Jerome Simson,
                                   M. Benedict

Los Alamos   R. R. Davis, Ralph Carlisle Smith

National Bureau of Standards   C. J. Rodden

Plutonium Project
  Argonne National Laboratory   R. S. Mulliken, H. D. Young

  Iowa State College   F. H. Spedding

  Medical Group   R. E. Zirkle

SAM Laboratories §   G. M. Murphy

Stone & Webster Engineering   B. W. Whitehurst
  Corporation

University of California   R. K. Wakerling, A. Guthrie

University of Rochester   D. R. Charles, M. J. Wantman

---

* Represented Madison Square Area of the Manhattan District.
  † The Y-12 plant at Oak Ridge was operated by Tennessee Eastman Corporation until May 4, 1947, at which time operations were taken over by Carbide & Carbon Chemicals Corporation.
  ‡ Clinton Laboratories was the former name of the Oak Ridge National Laboratory.
  § SAM (Substitute Alloy Materials) was the code name for the laboratories operated by Columbia University in New York under the direction of Dr. H. C. Urey, where much of the experimental work on isotope separation was done. On Feb. 1, 1945, the administration of these laboratories became the responsibility of Carbide & Carbon Chemicals Corporation. Research in progress there was transferred to the K-25 plant at Oak Ridge in June, 1946, and the New York laboratories were then closed.

Many difficulties were encountered in preparing a unified account of Atomic Energy Project work. For example, the Project Editorial Advisory Board was the first committee ever organized with representatives from every major installation of the Atomic Energy Project. Compartmentation for security was so rigorous during the war that it had been considered necessary to allow a certain amount of duplication of effort rather than to permit unrestricted circulation of research information between certain installations. As a result, the writing programs of different installations inevitably overlap markedly in many scientific fields. The Editorial Advisory Board has exerted itself to reduce duplication in so far as possible and to eliminate discrepancies in factual data included in the volumes of the NNES. In particular, unified Project-wide volumes have been prepared on Uranium Chemistry and on the Analysis of Project Materials. Nevertheless, the reader will find many instances of differences in results or conclusions on similar subject matter prepared by different authors. This has not seemed wholly undesirable for several reasons. First of all, such divergencies are not unnatural and stimulate investigation. Second, promptness of publication has seemed more important than the removal of all discrepancies. Finally, many Project scientists completed their contributions some time ago and have become engrossed in other activities so that their time has not been available for a detailed review of their work in relation to similar work done at other installations.

The completion of the various individual volumes of the Series has also been beset with difficulties. Many of the key authors and editors have had important responsibilities in planning the future of atomic energy research. Under these circumstances, the completion of this technical series has been delayed longer than its editors wished. The volumes are being released in their present form in the interest of presenting the material as promptly as possible to those who can make use of it.

The Editorial Advisory Board

The Manhattan Project Technical Section of the National Nuclear Energy Series is intended to be a comprehensive account of the scientific and technical achievements of the United States program for the development of atomic energy. It is not intended to be a detailed documentary record of the making of any inventions that happen to be mentioned in it. Therefore, the dates used in the Series should be regarded as a general temporal frame of reference, rather than as establishing dates of conception of inventions, of their reduction to practice, or of occasions of first use. While a reasonable effort has been made to assign credit fairly in the NNES volumes, this may, in many cases, be given to a group identified by the name of its leader rather than to an individual who was an actual inventor.

LOS ALAMOS PROJECT FOREWORD

The volumes comprising the Los Alamos Division of the National Nuclear Energy Series represent only a fraction of the total documentation of the activities of the Los Alamos Scientific Laboratory since its establishment early in 1943. They were prepared originally as part of the Los Alamos Technical Series, a group of books intended as a comprehensive survey of the accomplishments of the Atomic Bomb Project. However, the necessary restrictions imposed on the dissemination of technical information affecting the nation's security have permitted the inclusion in the National Nuclear Energy Series of only that portion of the Los Alamos work which does not deal specifically with the nuclear weapon program.

Most of the volumes of the Los Alamos Technical Series were prepared late in 1945 and early in 1946, and because of the impossibility at that time of predicting the precise nature of a declassification policy that had not yet been formulated, they were written primarily as laboratory manuals intended for use by authorized staff members of the Laboratory and the Manhattan Project, rather than as books that might conceivably be made available to the general public at some unknown time in an obscure future. Despite the fact that a considerable portion of the work contained information of quite general scientific interest and had no obviously close connection with the design and construction of weapons, it has been a difficult, tedious, and unfinished task to extract such material from the existing volumes in order to create books of a publishable nature. In most cases, the Technical Series volumes were so written that the separation of unclassified from classified information requires a major rewriting and editing program, which is even further complicated because a number of the original authors and editors are no longer directly associated with the program of the Atomic Energy Commission.

Only one of the original volumes was written in such a manner that a substantial proportion might be declassified with minor deletions and revision. It bore the title "Experimental Techniques," and was divided into three main parts, each of which seemed of sufficient length to justify being made into a separate volume for inclusion in the National Nuclear Energy Series. These were (1) "Electronics" by William C. Elmore and Matthew Sands, (2) "Ionization Chambers and Counters" by Bruno B. Rossi and Hans H. Staub, and (3)

"Miscellaneous Physical and Chemical Techniques" by Alvin C. Graves et al. These now will appear as the first published volumes of the Los Alamos part of the National Nuclear Energy Series. Darol K. Froman, one of the originators of the Los Alamos Technical Series and editor of the original volume on "Experimental Techniques," has served as volume editor for each of these three divisional books.

Robert R. Davis
Ralph Carlisle Smith

June, 1949

PREFACE TO THE "EXPERIMENTAL TECHNIQUES"
VOLUMES OF DIVISION V

In the late summer of 1945 it appeared likely that many of the electronic circuits and experimental techniques that were employed in what is now known as the Los Alamos Scientific Laboratory would be of appreciable value to the scientific world outside the Los Alamos Laboratory. Moreover, it was already apparent that many of the physicists, chemists, and engineers most prolific in devising circuits and techniques would not remain indefinitely with the Laboratory. Thus, for the sake of the history of accomplishment in the Laboratory, the inheritors of the physical plant, and the general scientific community, it became necessary to record in intelligible form some of the practices that were found most useful.

After much discussion it was decided that the only feasible approach to this problem must be made with the purely utilitarian objective of producing a laboratory manual. We decided to write down how to do things we knew how to do. In the great majority of these cases the "know how" was the result of experimentation and thought by many members of the laboratory staff, and very frequently fundamental ingredients were imported from the vast fields of common scientific knowledge, from other laboratories associated with the Manhattan Engineer District, and from other wartime projects. In particular, a large number of the electronic circuits involve fundamental elements or ideas derived from the work carried on at the Radiation Laboratory at Massachusetts Institute of Technology. During the war years much of the work of the Laboratory was either described sketchily in local reports or not described at all. Under these conditions it was apparent that proper credit for the development of circuits or techniques could not be given to individuals or even to groups. Yet it was felt that the value of a systematic recording would outweigh any demerit arising from an unorthodox omission of references. The work is not written completely without references but, in general, references are given only when it is thought that they would be of distinct aid to the reader. These are our excuses and apologies for omission of recognition to the hundreds of investigators whose work made these volumes possible.

Preparation for the writing was begun by circularizing the Laboratory for topics that should be included and indexing the topics. About this time the plan of writing the Los Alamos Technical Series was given considerable momentum, and the present work naturally became part of that series. The magnitude of the job became apparent at about the same time, and the authors of the various chapters were persuaded to undertake the task. In each case an author was selected for his intimate knowledge of the material and of the accomplishments of the Laboratory in the field. In every case at least some of the developments described are attributable directly to the authors. Little attempt has been made to make the various chapters uniform in mode of presentation since the clarity might have been impaired by altering the presentation of the authors.

We wish to express our appreciation for the efforts of the Laboratory's Declassification Section and Patent Group in expediting the release of the information in the present volumes on "Experimental Techniques." Since many of the developments appeared in writing for the first time in the manuscripts of these volumes, the job of tracing a device or part back to its inventor and writing adequate patent applications was a very major undertaking. Obviously the work could not be released until it was carefully reviewed to protect the interests of the U.S. Government.

The preparation of these volumes of Division V of the Manhattan Project Technical Section was encouraged in every possible way by the administration of the Laboratory under the direction first of J Robert Oppenheimer and second of Norris E. Bradbury.

The work on "Experimental Techniques" is divided into three volumes by subject matter and for ease in binding. It may be that many readers will want only one volume, and for this reason some items are duplicated in different volumes. Also, an attempt has been made to keep cross-references to a minimum.

It is our earnest hope that these volumes will be found of practical value to experimentalists, particularly nuclear physicists, in spite of the fact that many of the techniques and circuits are now well known and some are even obsolescent.

Darol Froman
Los Alamos Scientific Laboratory

June, 1949

AUTHORS' PREFACE

The Electronics Group, a subdivision of the Los Alamos Laboratory, was responsible for the design of electronic instruments for the research program of the Laboratory. During the period from 1943 to 1945 this group devised several hundred circuits for specific requirements of other research groups. In August, 1945, Dr. Darol K. Froman invited the authors, who were members of the Electronics Group through most of its existence, to write a report of the work that had been done by the Laboratory in electronic instrumentation.

The first step in the preparation of this account was the selecting of circuits that appeared to be worth describing. At the time of the writing there were more than seven hundred diagrams of circuits in the files of the Electronics Group and many diagrams of circuits in the Laboratory devised by other groups. Circuits chosen for inclusion in this volume were judged on the basis of their general usefulness as proved at the Laboratory, and of their probable usefulness in other laboratories. Some special-purpose circuits were chosen which have no general utility but which illustrate some particular method or technique. For reasons of security no circuits having a special application to weapon technology were included.

The collection of diagrams, a few reports, the two years of experience that the authors had in the Electronics Group, and the counsel of other staff members constituted the raw materials for this book. The circuits selected are arranged in five general categories, and these form the basis of Chapters 3 to 7. Certain "circuit elements," or parts of a complete circuit such as amplifier stages or blocking oscillators, are used repeatedly in the design of the complete circuits described. The elements most often used are presented separately in Chapter 2, and the circuits of later chapters are described in terms of these elements. Chapter 2 by itself should prove useful to those who desire to acquire a background of information for use in designing electronic circuits for special applications. Chapter 1, "Circuit Components and Construction Practice," deals briefly with the properties of such circuit components as resistors and capacitors, and with such problems as the physical layout of circuits. It gives a far from exhaustive account of these particular topics, since no systematic testing or selection of electronic components was undertaken at the Laboratory.

The task of writing this account was essentially completed by July, 1946. Since no new material has been added since that time, a number of the circuits are already obsolescent. It is hoped, however, that at least some of the material is of more than historical interest.

The circuits described in this book were designed by many individuals and often by groups of individuals in collaboration. It appeared impossible to trace the origin and to give credit to the source of each idea in every circuit. It would be unjust to attribute any single circuit to the individual who was responsible for the final design of the circuit. Accordingly no attempt is made in this volume to attach names to specific circuits. Several of the more important circuits have been described in the journals since this account was written. For the development of many of the circuits and the writing of this volume we owe much to Darol K. Froman and William A. Higinbotham, who were successively Group Leaders of the Electronics Group; and to Robert F. Bacher, of whose Division the Electronics Group was a part. The authors are indebted to the many unnamed members of the Electronics Group and of the Laboratory who made numerous contributions to the design, construction, and testing of the circuits described here.

William C. Elmore
Matthew Sands

July, 1949

CONTENTS

CHAPTER 7

Chapter 1

CIRCUIT COMPONENTS AND CONSTRUCTION PRACTICE

By William C. Elmore

1. INTRODUCTION

The first part of this chapter is devoted to a brief discussion of components that have been found suitable for constructing the various electronic circuits described in later chapters. It is not intended to make an exhaustive treatment of circuit components here, nor to present information of the sort readily available in standard hand-books or the catalogues of manufacturers. The second part of the chapter will be devoted to a description of a number of different methods that have been used at Los Alamos for the mechanical construction of electronic circuits. It is felt that a discussion of these two matters will be useful to anyone wishing to build electronic apparatus for research purposes. The discussion forms a necessary supplement to the circuits presented in later chapters, since emphasis there has been placed mainly on the function of circuits and on how this function is accomplished by combinations of various circuit elements. Other than indicating the values, and possibly the type of components to be used, a circuit diagram in itself usually contains little information of the sort required by a technician. The present discussion is an attempt to supply some of the necessary background material that will later be assumed to be part of the reader's knowledge.

2. CIRCUIT COMPONENTS

The term "circuit component" is used to distinguish the elementary parts with which an electronic circuit is constructed: a resistor, a capacitor, a transformer, etc. The term "circuit element" will later be used to signify combinations of circuit components that together

1

have certain desirable properties. A complete circuit can be considered as a combination of circuit elements. This manner of subdividing an electronic circuit will be found to simplify any discussion of it. In the following sections the most common circuit components will be discussed, partly for the purpose of indicating what has become standard practice at Los Alamos and partly for the purpose of aiding the reader to interpret circuit diagrams presented later.

2.1 <u>Resistors</u>. A variety of different types of resistors are required in the construction of electronic instruments. When stability in value is required, it is desirable to use wire-wound resistors, which normally have a lower temperature coefficient than carbon or metalized resistors. Wire-wound resistors are also substantially free from "aging," which may occur in the case of resistors of other types.

When wire-wound resistors occur in the circuits described later, the designation "WW" is written following the wattage rating. Similarly, where a carbon-composition or metalized resistor is specifically called for, the designation "C" is used. If it is important that a particular resistor be substantially free from parasitic inductance, the symbol "NI" (noninductive) is used. Where, for stability, it is desirable to employ a noninductive wire-wound resistor, types 5NI and 10NI, made by the Sprague Products Company, have been found suitable. The symbol "BW," which is used occasionally, refers to an inductive wire-wound type of resistor made by the International Resistance Company (IRC).* When the symbol "WW" is found, ordinarily an IRC resistor of type WW4, or one of comparable rating, has been used in the circuit.

In certain cases the parasitic inductance afforded by an inductively wound resistor is used to shunt-compensate a circuit element (see Chap. 2, Sec. 2.3). Where this feature is important the symbol "IND" is written following the resistor designation.

Resistors are commonly available in the following wattage ratings: ½, 1, 2, 5, 10, and 20 watts. Although resistors having lower and higher ratings than these values can be obtained, this range of values will be found sufficient to meet most needs. It has been a customary precaution to specify a power rating at least twice the computed power dissipation expected in a resistor. In some cases where high-value resistors are employed, it is important to observe the voltage

---

*Throughout this volume, wherever there are references to components made by certain manufacturers, it is to be understood that similar components of other manufacturers can be substituted.

rating specified by the manufacturer of the resistor (usually 350 volts for the ½-watt rating, and 500 volts for the 1- and 2-watt ratings).

Two systems of resistor values are in current use: the old standard system and the preferred, or logarithmic, system. In addition, resistors of the types most used are available with several tolerance

Table 1.1—Preferred Values of Resistance (One Decade)

5 (Gold)	10 (Silver)	20 (No color)	5 (Gold)	10 (Silver)	20 (No color)
10	10	10	33	33	33
11			36		
12	12		39	39	
13			43		
15	15	15	47	47	47
16			51		
18	18		56	56	
20			62		
22	22	22	68	68	68
24			75		
27	27		82	82	
30			91		
			100	100	100

ratings, such as 20, 10, and 5 per cent. Unless otherwise specified, a tolerance rating of 10 per cent will be assumed for all resistor values specified in the circuits of this volume. It will be noticed that resistor values called for in some circuits have been chosen from the old standard system. This came about as the result of a transition from the old system to the new during the progress of the project. There is no doubt that the logarithmic system is far superior to the older system, and it is unfortunate that the obvious advantages of the latter system were not realized at an earlier time. The essential features of the preferred system of resistor values are shown in Table 1.1.

Variable resistors, or potentiometers, are made either in a wire-wound or in a carbon type. If a precision wire-wound potentiometer is called for in subsequent diagrams, the designation "G.R." (General Radio) is used. Where the simple designation "WW" is found, a Mallory potentiometer type MP can be used in the circuit. The symbol "C" stands for a carbon-type potentiometer, such as that made by the Allen-Bradley Company. The noninductive feature of this type of potentiometer is often of importance. Normally a minimum rating of 2 watts has been specified, even when only a fraction of a watt is being dissipated. This has been done to simplify the number and variety of components called for in the circuits.

2.2 Capacitors. Fixed capacitors of at least four types are commonly used in the construction of the electronic circuits discussed in this volume. They include mica, ceramic, paper, and electrolytic capacitors. In most instances the type of capacitor that can be used for a particular function in a circuit is clearly defined by the well-known properties of the capacitors involved. The following discussion will serve simply to indicate in a general way what has become customary practice in cases where a certain option exists. In the circuit diagrams included in later chapters, the notation "M" denotes an ordinary mica capacitor, "SM" a silver mica capacitor, "P" a paper capacitor, "OIL" an oil-impregnated capacitor, and "A" an air capacitor. The word "ceramic" denotes a capacitor having a ceramic dielectric. An electrolytic capacitor is indicated by having its polarity shown.

It has been customary to employ a mica capacitor when a value of capacitance of 0.01 μf or less is required. In many applications, however, mica and paper capacitors can be used interchangeably. In positions where signals having high-frequency components are involved, there seems to be some reason for employing mica capacitors. Not only are mica capacitors more compact than the paper variety, but their parasitic inductance is somewhat lower on account of shorter leads.

The practice of connecting two or more capacitors in parallel is found occasionally to lead to trouble. The difficulty, of course, arises in the series resonant circuit that is produced. If fast transients are likely to be encountered in a circuit, a transient oscillation may be excited in the resonant element and appear superposed on the signal being generated or transmitted by the circuit.

Little use has been made of fixed ceramic capacitors, although in most instances this type of capacitor can be used interchangeably with low-valued mica or paper capacitors. It is worth noting that ceramic capacitors having a variety of positive and negative temperature coefficients are available. Few applications, however, have been made of this feature.

Wax-impregnated or oil-impregnated paper capacitors have normally been used in cases where a capacitance greater than 0.01 μf is required, and where the leakage existing in an electrolytic capacitor would be troublesome. A paper capacitor completely encased in a tight metal container has been used where adverse conditions of temperature and humidity are likely to be encountered. If the stray capacitance of such a component must be kept at a minimum, it can be mounted on insulating posts.

Electrolytic capacitors have been normally employed only for by-passing or decoupling the d-c voltage supplied to various points in a circuit and for filtering the output voltage of a power supply. It has been customary to use an electrolytic capacitor rated at 450 volts for voltages no higher than 300 volts. When this is done, the number of failures due to breakdown are found to be very small. Electrolytic capacitors having an octal plug for a base are available. This type of construction has been found to be particularly suitable for laboratory apparatus to be used over a period of time, since it simplifies the task of servicing the apparatus.

The variable capacitors that have been found to be of greatest use are of the ceramic trimmer capacitor type, although in occasional circuits a variable air capacitor is required. The stability of a variable ceramic capacitor is much greater than that of a capacitor of the compression mica type, whose use has been avoided.

2.3 Inductors. The inductors, or chokes, used in filters for a power supply have been chosen from any of the standard lines of chokes available commercially and require no particular comment here. Small radio-frequency chokes are found to have a number of uncommon uses, especially in the construction of delay lines (see Chap. 2, Sec. 2.4). Inductors for compensating or "peaking" unfed-back amplifiers have been constructed by rewinding the components employed for this purpose in commercial oscillographs. These inductors are permeability-tuned, and they enable the amplifier to be adjusted for good transient response to a step-function test signal. When an inductor having a fixed inductance of a few microhenrys is needed, a convenient winding form is afforded by a high-value resistor of the ½-, 1-, or 2-watt size, depending on the inductance required. This type of construction has been used occasionally for constructing inductors for compensating an amplifier.

2.4 Transformers. A transformer for the power supply of an average electronic circuit of the sort described in later chapters can be selected from the standard lines of transformers manufactured for use in radios, audio-frequency systems, etc. Most transformers of this type will ordinarily not have as many heater windings as required, and it is often necessary to use one or more additional heater transformers. In circuits where a 300-volt stabilized supply is called for, the transformer should have a center-tapped secondary supplying at least 800 volts between the two ends of the winding. In view of the somewhat optimistic power ratings that are given by some manufacturers for their transformers, it has been customary to choose a transformer having a current rating perhaps 30 per cent higher than the current required by the circuit with which it will be used. It is possible that the discrepancy between the rating quoted by the manufacturer and the observed performance lies in the customary use of an input capacitor for the filter. A capacitive input to the filter results in an inefficient loading of the transformer, but it is often necessary to obtain a sufficiently high voltage.

Table 1.2 — Some Blocking-oscillator Transformers

		Turns	
Manufacturer	Part no.	Leg 1	Leg 2
Westinghouse	145 EW	150-150-150	
	132 AW	32-32-32	
	132 BW	32-32-32-10	
	132 DW	32-32-32	
	132 DW2	20-20-20	
	134 BW	70-140	70-140
Utah	0A15	80-80	80-80
	0A18	50-50-50	50-50-50
General Electric	68G813	37-74	74-111
	68G709	150-150	150-150

Blocking-oscillator transformers have been used extensively where fast signals must be generated. A list of the blocking-oscillator transformers that have been employed in trigger-circuit applications is included in Table 1.2.

2.5 Vacuum Tubes. The vacuum tubes employed in electronic measuring apparatus are generally of the small receiving-tube variety. Table 1.3 gives a list of types of tubes that have proved to be most useful, together with certain operating data that are difficult to keep in mind. For characteristic curves and other operating data it is necessary to refer to a standard tube manual, such as the "RCA Tube Handbook," Vols. I-IV, Radio Corporation of America, Harrison, N. J.

Although a tube manual is found to constitute an indispensable aid in designing electronic equipment, it is well for the designer to become thoroughly familiar with the most important properties of a limited number of tubes, such as those listed in Table 1.3. If this is done, then other tubes for which an occasional use may be found can be quickly catalogued, using the known characteristics of tubes from the list as a basis for comparison. In addition to the tubes listed in the table, it is necessary, of course, to become familiar with several rectifier tubes, such as the 5V4, 5U4-G, 5R4-GY, and 6X5, and with the series of voltage-regulator tubes.

In many electronic circuits used for making measurements, an ordinary vacuum tube is employed in an unconventional manner, and a tube manual is found to offer little design information other than giving values of maximum power, maximum voltages, and the like.

Table 1.3 — Some Commonly Used Tubes

Type	Heater, amp	Plate Max. volts	Plate Max. watts	Screen Max. volts	Screen Max. watts	μ	g_m, μmhos	r_p, ohms
6AL5	0.30	(420-volt peak inverse; 9-ma peak current)						
6H6	0.30	(420-volt peak inverse; 8-ma peak current)						
6J6	0.45	300	1.5			30	4,000	7,500
6N7	0.80	300	5.5			35	1,500	23,000
6SF5	0.30	300				100	1,200	83,000
6SL7	0.30	250	1.0			70	1,600	44,000
6SN7	0.60	300	2.5			20	3,000	6,700
6AC7	0.45	300	3.02	150	0.38		9,000	$\approx 10^6$
6AG7	0.65	300	9.0	300	1.5		11,000	0.13×10^6
6AK5	0.175	180	1.7	140	0.5		5,000	0.34×10^6
6AS6	0.175	180	1.7	140	0.75		3,200	0.15×10^6
6L6	0.9	360	19.0	270	2.5		6,000	22,500
6SG7	0.3	300	3.0	200	0.6		4,000	$\approx 10^6$
6SH7	0.3	300	3.0	150	0.7		4,500	$\approx 0.5 \times 10^6$
6SJ7	0.3	300	2.5	125	0.3		1,600	$\approx 10^6$
6SK7	0.3	300	4.0	125	0.4		2,000	$\approx 0.8 \times 10^6$
6V6	0.45	315	12.0	285	2.0		4,000	50,000
6Y6	1.25	200	12.5	135	1.75		7,000	10,000
807	0.9	750	30.0	300	3.5		6,000	25,000
6L7	0.3	300	1.5	100	1.0			
6SA7	0.3	300	1.0	100	1.0			
2D21	0.6	650	(1,300-volt peak inverse; 500-ma peak cathode current)					
884	0.6	300	(300-ma peak cathode current)					
2050	0.6	650	(1,300-volt peak inverse; 1-amp peak cathode current)					

An example is afforded by a blocking oscillator where a peak cathode current of several hundred milliamperes may be drawn for a fraction of 1 μsec. During this time the grid will be driven perhaps 100 volts positive with respect to the cathode. Tube life does not seem to be impaired very much by this mode of operation, but at present it is necessary to acquire information of this kind mostly by experience.

Another type of useful information not found in tube manuals is illustrated by the curves given in Fig. 1.1 for the voltage-current characteristics of several diodes or of multielectrode tubes connected as diodes. These curves, for instance, are necessary for predicting the performance of a diode clamp of the sort discussed in Chap. 2,

Sec. 5.1 Characteristic curves of tubes used in various other un-conventional ways are of interest, and it is ordinarily necessary to determine them by actual measurement. It is estimated that in per-haps half of the applications described in this volume, a vacuum tube is used where the operating conditions are unusual, and design must proceed by an empirical method guided by previous experience.

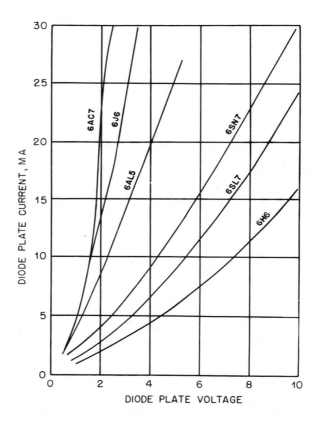

Fig. 1.1 — Voltage-current characteristics of several diodes.

2.6 Cables and Cable Connectors. In most experimental setups where electronic equipment is employed, the problem arises of con-veying fast electrical signals or pulses from one piece of equipment to another. Ordinarily the signal connection will be single-sided, i.e., the signal will exist between some point in the circuit and ground. In such cases it has been customary to employ a coaxial cable to make the connection between circuits in separate chassis. If the length of cable used is short, i.e., if the length is less than approximately $3 \times 10^7 T_R$ meters where T_R is the rise time of the signal in seconds,[*] then the cable can be considered primarily as a capacitive load on the source of signals. In an application of this sort it is important to employ a coaxial cable having the lowest possible capacitance per unit length. If, however, the cable must be long, i.e., greater than about $3 \times 10^7 T_R$ meters, it may be necessary to terminate the cable by a resistance equal to its characteristic impedance, in order to avoid troublesome reflections. In such cases it is usually advantageous to employ coaxial cable having as high a characteristic impedance as possible.

There are several types of coaxial cable commercially available, including the so-called "microphone" type (rubber dielectric), Amphenol-beaded coaxial cable, and Army-Navy coaxial cable (stabilized-polyethylene dielectric). Little use is ever found for cable of the microphone type, on account of its large capacitance per unit length and poor transmission characteristics at high frequencies. The Amphenol-beaded cable can be obtained with a capacitance as low as 5.8 $\mu\mu f/ft$ (characteristic impedance 195 ohms). The chief disadvantage of beaded cable lies in its poor mechanical properties. It is found to break readily, and it requires considerable skill and patience to make a good join to a coaxial-cable connector. The coaxial cable having a polyethylene dielectric has been found to be most suitable for general laboratory use. In Table 1.4 are listed some useful types of coaxial cable, together with their most important properties.

Cable connectors to fit the various cables listed in Table 1.4 can be obtained commercially. The newer types of connectors developed specifically for use with the Army-Navy type of coaxial cable represent a considerable improvement in design over the older types of microphone-cable connectors, which, however, continue to be popular for certain applications.

When it is necessary to run power leads from one chassis to another, the most satisfactory power connector is of the Army-Navy type, of which a large variety of different styles are available. These connectors are normally used with flexible conduit, which requires special tools for permanently attaching ferrules to the ends of the conduit. An example of a cable of this type is afforded by the Model 100 preamplifier cable (see Fig. 3.14).

---

[*] This condition is approximately equivalent to the usual condition for sinusoidal oscillations that the cable length be less than one-eighth wavelength.

Table 1.4 — Some Useful Types of Coaxial Cables

Type	No. of conductors	Wire size	No. of shields and braids	Over-all diameter, in.	Nominal impedance, ohms	Nominal capacitance, μμf/ft	Maximum operating volts (rms)	Description
Army-Navy coaxial cable (dielectric material: stabilized polyethylene, protective covering, vinyl)								
RG-7/U*	1	No. 19 AWG solid copper	1	0.370	95	12.5	1,000	Low capacitance video and IF cable
RG-8/U	1	7/No. 21 AWG copper	1	0.405	52	29	4,000	General-purpose medium size
RG-9/U*	1	7/No. 21 AWG sil ctd copper	2	0.420	51	29	4,000	Double-shielded low level
RG-11/U*	1	7/No. 26 AWG	1	0.405	75	20	3,500	Medium-size video, flexible
RG-13/U	1	7/No. 26 AWG copper	2	0.420	74	20	4,000	Double-shielded IF cable
RG-14/U	1	No. 10 AWG solid copper	2	0.545	52	29	5,500	General-purpose power cable, semiflexible
RG-21/U	1	No. 16 AWG resistance	2	0.332	53	29	2,700	Attenuating cable, low-temperature coefficient of attenuator
RG-22/U*	2	7/No. 26 AWG copper	1	0.405	95	17	1,000	Small twin conductor
RG-29/U*	1	No. 20 AWG copper	1	0.179	51	30	1,900	Small size video cable for equipment wiring
RG-54/U*	1	7/.0152 in. plain copper	1	0.250	58	27	3,000	Special design G.E. delay cable
RG-34/U	1	7/No. 21 AWG copper	1	0.625	72	21	6,500	Designed for specific equipment
RG-57/U	2	7/No. 21 AWG copper	1	0.617	95	17	300	Large twin conductor
RG-62/U*	1	No. 22 AWG copperweld	1	0.242	93	13.5	750	Low capacitance video and IF cable
RG-63/U*	1	No. 22 AWG copperweld	1	0.40	125	10		
RG-65/U	1	No. 32 AWG helix	1	0.405	950	44	3,000	High-impedance video; helical inner conductor
Amphenol coaxial cable (mica-filled bakelite beads; maximum temperature 285°F)								
76-22T	1	No. 22 AWG copperweld	1	0.275	115	12.0		
76-26T	1	No. 26 AWG copper	1	0.275	137	9.8		
76-30T	1	No. 30 AWG copper	1	0.275	160	8.0		
72-30T	1	No. 30 AWG copper	1	0.385	195	5.8		

*Cables most commonly used.

3. CONSTRUCTION PRACTICES

There exist several well-defined styles of construction that can be adopted for electronic apparatus. There are also many unorthodox styles, which are occasionally chosen to suit the requirements of unusual applications. It is found that electronic circuits that can be considered as standard laboratory items, such as amplifiers, counters, etc., are best built in units suitable for mounting in a standard relay rack. Various ways of constructing electronic units for this type of mounting will be illustrated later in the present section. Laboratory test apparatus that must be readily portable is best built in a metal cabinet, of which several standard types are available. Pulse generators, vacuum-tube voltmeters, and similar pieces of test equipment are ordinarily constructed in this manner. Before illustrating typical styles of construction, several practices regarding the mounting of parts, the wiring of circuits, etc., will be described.

Except in special cases where the presence of high voltages has dictated otherwise, electronic circuits have been constructed on metal chassis. Ordinarily the chassis serves as a partial shield, reducing interaction between portions of a circuit as well as constituting the local ground for the circuit. In circuit diagrams appearing later, a heavy line has been drawn to indicate the supply bus that has the potential of the metal chassis. It should be emphasized, however, that it is normally not considered good practice to employ the chassis as a common connection for all leads at ground potential. If signals having high-frequency components exist in the circuit or if the circuit is sensitive to low-level hum pickup, there may be trouble if the chassis is used as the ground bus. Where it appears satisfactory to employ the chassis in this way, the practice of soldering leads to the metal chassis should be adopted. To avoid 60-cycles-per-second currents in the chassis, it is often wise to distribute heater power using twisted leads, and to ground one side of the heater supply at only one point of the chassis.

The construction of pulse amplifiers whose frequency-response characteristic may extend well into the megacycle range requires special comment. Although published descriptions of pulse amplifiers often call for separate shielding of individual stages (to avoid interaction between stages), this practice is found to be not at all necessary if proper care is taken in the layout and in the wiring of the amplifier. The customary manner of wiring a pulse amplifier having a rise time of 0.1 μsec, i.e., an upper half-power frequency of about 3.5 megacycles per second, is illustrated in Fig. 1.2, which shows a photo-

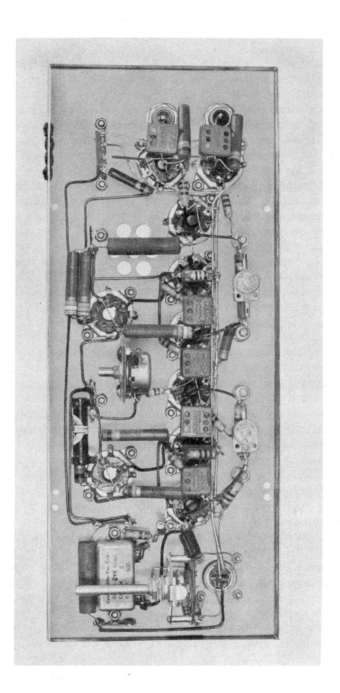

Fig. 1.2 — Style of wiring for a wide-band pulse amplifier.

graph of the subchassis of a Model 500 amplifier (see Chap. 3, Sec. 7.2). In an amplifier of this type, octal sockets that possess a grounding ring containing four soldering lugs are employed. To ensure a reliable low-impedance connection between the individual grounding rings, a heavy lead is run along one side of the row of tube sockets and securely soldered to each grounding ring. The ground leads of the electrolytic capacitors used for by-passing screen- and plate-supply voltages are brought to the appropriate sockets and soldered to one of the lugs there. It should be evident from Fig. 1.2 that the tube sockets have been carefully oriented to result in the shortest possible path between the plate of one tube and the grid of the next. All signal-carrying leads, in fact, are made as short as possible, and parts are arranged to keep parasitic capacitances at a minimum. The RC networks used for feedback are securely mounted on insulating posts to avoid any possible changes in parasitic capacitance caused by vibration. One of the heater leads is run at ground potential and connected to pin 7 of each tube. The other heater lead is connected to pin 2, which is shielded by pins 1 and 3, both of which are at ground potential (except in the case of the stages serving as cathode followers). No difficulty has ever been experienced from interactions between parts of a pulse amplifier that has been constructed in this manner. A similar type of construction has been adopted for all the pulse and transient amplifiers described in Chap. 3. The use of a separate brass amplifier subchassis has been adopted to simplify the problem of wiring and to enable a single power-supply model* to serve for a variety of amplifiers. The subchassis can be mounted rigidly, or with rubber grommets to serve as shock mounts, in a window $4\frac{1}{2}$ by 14 in. cut in the top of the 13- by 17-in. metal chassis used for the power supply.

Other electronic circuits—for example, an electronic counter— require somewhat less care in layout. For this type of circuit either point-to-point wiring or, less commonly, wiring with resistor mounting strips has been employed. The appearance of a typical circuit wired point to point is illustrated in Fig. 1.3, whereas Fig. 1.4 shows a typical circuit in which resistor mounting strips are used in the wiring. It is felt that the latter type of construction is best suited to circuits constructed in considerable quantities, and only to circuits where it is not important to minimize parasitic capacitance.

A somewhat unusual case of construction is illustrated by the r-f high-voltage supply for a Geiger-Mueller counter (see Chap. 7, Sec. 6), shown in Fig. 1.5. Here it was desired to obtain a completely

---

*The Model 50 power supply, described in Chap. 7, Sec. 4.1.

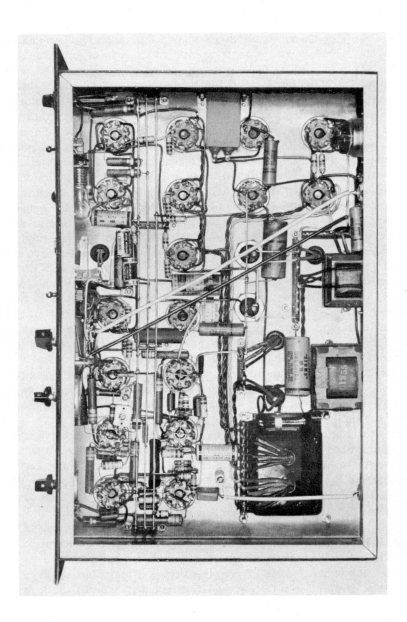

Fig. 1.3 — Appearance of a circuit with point-to-point wiring.

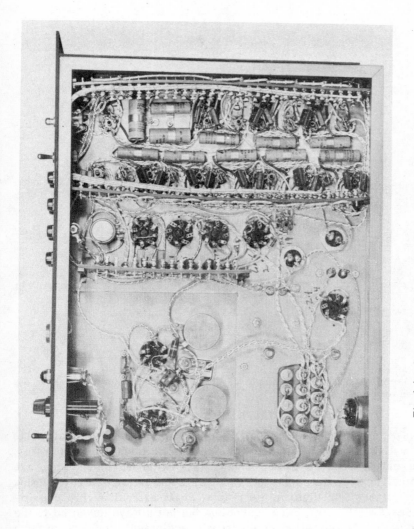

Fig. 1.4 — Appearance of a circuit with resistor mounting strips.

shielded, compact unit with short leads connecting the stepup transformer to the type 8016 rectifier tube. All connections are made to
an octal plug located at the center of the bottom of the shield can.

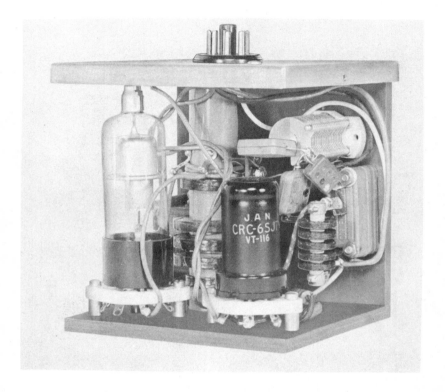

Fig. 1.5—Appearance of an r-f supply for Geiger-Mueller counters. The shield box
has been removed.

It is perhaps worth noting that a considerable variety of small parts
are available to facilitate the construction of electronic apparatus.
Some parts, such as cable connectors, switches, fuses, etc., are
practically essential, whereas others, such as resistor mounting
strips, standoff insulators, tie points, shaft extensions for potentiometers, switches, etc., are convenient but not always essential to the
construction or operation of electronic equipment. The use of such
parts, however, considerably speeds the construction of apparatus,
and in most cases can be justified because of the more reliable unit
obtained.

3.1 Types of Construction. The most common type of construction suitable for a complete electronic circuit, including the power supply, is illustrated in Fig. 1.6. Tubes, transformers, and other components requiring mechanical support are mounted on a metal chassis

Fig. 1.6—An example of standard panel-and-chassis construction.

17 in. long. The width of the chassis is chosen to accommodate the components used in the circuit, but it is rarely more than 13 in. The depth of the chassis is ordinarily chosen to be 3 in. If it is desired to mount certain parts below the top of the chassis, such as a potentiometer having a 3-in. diameter, it may be necessary to use a deeper chassis.

A variety of suitable metal chassis are available in standard sizes, either with or without a removable top. A removable-top chassis has been found convenient to use, since the punching of holes for sockets, windows for transformers, etc., is somewhat simplified, as is the wiring of most of the circuit. Standard front panels are 19 in. long and are available in a range of heights varying in increments of 1.75 in. Standard sizes for side brackets are also readily available. Knobs and dials for switches, potentiometers, etc., as well as meters, coaxial connectors, terminals, etc., can be mounted either on the front panel or, with the exception of meters, on the back edge of the chassis.

Experience with many circuits constructed in the manner illustrated in Fig. 1.6 has shown that this type of construction has several drawbacks. Perhaps the greatest trouble lies in the difficulty of testing or servicing a unit when it is mounted in a relay rack along with associated equipment. To reach the wiring inside the chassis, it is necessary to remove the unit from the relay rack. If the operation of the circuit is intimately tied in with that of other circuits, servicing may have to be done by placing the unit on a table next to the relay rack and reconnecting all cables leading to these circuits. This procedure is evidently inconvenient. It can be avoided only by adopting some style of construction that provides ready access to the wiring while the unit is in the relay rack.

Another trouble with the standard type of construction is the inefficient cooling that results when a number of units are mounted one above the other in a rack. Cooling takes place by the flow of air by convection — an efficient process only when the air has a reasonably unobstructed vertical channel in which to move. Since much of the heat is generated in vacuum tubes and in power transformers, efficient cooling favors the mounting of these parts on a vertical, instead of horizontal, surface, thus permitting the flow of air past them. When this mode of construction is not employed, it is often necessary to install fans or blowers to provide adequate cooling of the equipment.

The inconvenience of removing, exchanging, or regrouping units in a relay rack can be lessened by welding narrow lengths of angle iron to the inside surfaces of the vertical pieces of channel iron that form the sides of the rack. If this is done, then each unit becomes, in effect, a drawer in a simple but sturdy framework.

When it is desirable to retain the advantages of the relay-rack style of construction, and at the same time to provide better access to important parts of a circuit, the type of construction shown in Fig. 1.7 can be adopted. Here two metal chassis are bolted together at right angles in the form of an L. A narrow panel is permanently mounted, as shown in the illustration, to supply panel space for controls. Since the panel is too narrow to support the unit, supporting brackets must be provided in the relay rack. The upper portion of the vertical chassis can be covered by a panel, if desired, when the unit is mounted in a rack. This type of construction is convenient for circuits having many vacuum tubes, since a greater area and volume are available for components. The power supply, which usually requires little attention, can be constructed on the horizontal chassis, leaving the vertical chassis for the portion of the circuit likely to require servicing. A row of large holes punched where the two chassis come together makes it possible to carry out wiring in a convenient manner.

Fig. 1.7 — An example of a modified panel-and-chassis construction.

Still another way of constructing units to be mounted in a relay rack is illustrated in Fig. 1.8. Either of two methods can be adopted to make possible the removal of part of the front panel for servicing the unit while it is located in a rack. If the unit is not very large, the front panel can be divided into three parts by two vertical saw cuts, and the two end pieces securely bolted to the chassis. One or both of the end pieces of the panel can be made wide enough to accommodate the necessary controls and connectors. The middle piece is free to be removed at any time, thus providing ready access to the wiring.

In the case of a larger unit, the front panel can be divided by a horizontal cut; or two separate panels can be used, the narrower panel serving to hold the unit in a relay rack.

Construction of the type illustrated in Fig. 1.8 favors efficient cooling, since air can flow with little resistance past all units mounted

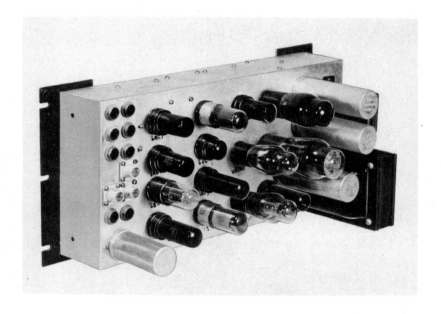

Fig. 1.8 — An example of construction with a vertical chassis.

in a vertical relay rack. Its only obvious disadvantage is the somewhat greater relay-rack area required for a given circuit. A minor disadvantage results when it is desired to use circuits constructed in this way with circuits constructed in the standard way. It will also be found that greater care must be exercised in arranging the components in the circuit, since the positions where switches, potentiometers, etc., can be placed are restricted by the space available on the permanent portion of the front panel.

A special style of construction, illustrated in Fig. 1.9, has been used for cathode-ray oscillographs that are meant to be mounted in a relay rack. The two side brackets of rectangular shape are made by welding together pieces of ¾-in. angle iron. The cover for the portion of the circuit located at the rear of the unit is a standard chassis with windows cut to expose small panels holding the necessary cable connectors. The portion of the circuit contained in the metal box is an r-f high-voltage supply providing accelerating voltages for the cathode-ray tube (see Chap. 7, Sec. 6). There is room to construct an amplifier, such as the Model 1000 transient amplifier (see Chap. 3, Sec. 8.2), on the rear panel next to the socket for the cathode-ray tube.

Fig. 1.9—Style of construction suitable for an oscillograph.

The method of mounting the high-voltage bleeder with the focus and intensity controls (near the front panel) is clearly shown. The meter on the front panel serves to indicate the accelerating voltage.

Certain circuits possessing many components—such as a ten-channel differential-amplitude discriminator (see Chap. 4, Sec. 2.5)—have been constructed as a single unit in a relay rack. An example of this style of construction is shown in Fig. 1.10. To facilitate wiring, each portion of the circuit has been built on specially constructed chassis, which are nothing more than shallow channels folded from galvanized sheet iron. The height of each chassis can be chosen to suit space requirements, and the length need not be standard (i.e., 19 in.) since it is a simple matter to weld together a sturdy frame in which to mount the assemblage of individual chassis. This style of construction not only provides good cooling but permits ready access to all points in the circuit while it is in operation. The open type of construction used does not afford protection against the accumulation

Fig. 1.10—Open-rack style of construction.

of dust or against mechanical damage to the circuit. In the case of permanent equipment, the entire rack could be mounted in a cabinet provided with removable front and rear panels and with ventilating slits at top and bottom.

Fig. 1.11 — A style of construction suitable for portable equipment.

A final example of construction practice is given in Fig. 1.11, which illustrates one style of building electronic equipment for portable use. The device pictured is a Model 100 pulse generator (see Chap. 6, Sec. 3.1). Equipment used at a variety of places is best constructed in this manner. Although a variety of standard boxes and cabinets for use in this type of construction are available, in particular cases it has been found worth while to design cabinets to suit particular requirements. Many examples of good styles of construction are provided by commercial electronic equipment and need not be described here.

4. THE ELECTRONICS LABORATORY

Design, construction, and testing of electronic devices are greatly facilitated by having a suitable laboratory workbench equipped with certain useful test equipment. In the present section a typical setup will be described, together with certain laboratory procedures that have proved valuable.

Work with electronic circuits of the sort described in this volume is a constantly changing procedure. Often the design of a new circuit is completed in a few days, and it is rare that more than a few weeks need be devoted to the design of the most complicated circuit. On

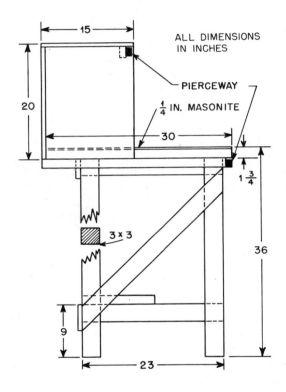

Fig. 1.12—End view of bench.

account of the nature of experimental work in electronics, it is necessary not only to have adequate working space available but also to have close at hand test equipment of several types. It will be found that a flat working space, such as that provided by a simple bench or table, is inadequate. A style of bench that has been widely used at Los Alamos and has proved to be very convenient is illustrated in Fig. 1.12. Test equipment of a permanent nature can be placed on the upper shelf, where it is immediately available but out of the way. To provide the many outlets for power required by equipment, it is convenient to run strips of Pierceway* along the complete length of both the edges of the main bench and the edge of the upper shelf. Workbenches having the cross section that is illustrated in Fig. 1.12 have been constructed either as long benches (6 to 12 ft) or as square consoles in which a person is surrounded by working space on three sides.

The test equipment required for experimental work on circuits to be described later can be divided roughly into two categories: that which is absolutely essential and that which is very convenient but not necessarily essential. The first category includes a cathode-ray oscillograph; a laboratory sweep circuit; a high-impedance, general-purpose test meter for measuring voltages, resistances, and possibly currents; a source of pulses that can be delayed with respect to the start of the oscillograph sweep; a pulse generator for testing amplifiers; and a power supply furnishing both positive and negative voltages. In the second category can be placed a multiple-trigger generator; various sinusoidal oscillators; a Q meter; a high-impedance, vacuum-tube voltmeter; a sweep-speed calibrator; a circular-sweep oscillograph for time calibrations; etc. Some of the test equipment can be obtained commercially, and some must be specially constructed. A description of several devices often needed for testing and calibrating electronic equipment is given in Chap. 6.

After the design of a new circuit has progressed beyond the stage where tentative values for all components have been assigned, it is often expedient to study the behavior of the circuit experimentally, prior to its construction as a finished unit. The circuit, or important parts of it, is put together in a rough fashion to enable tests to be made and to crystallize the final design. A particularly satisfactory method of constructing the circuit for tests of this sort is to employ what may be termed a "universal breadboard," whose nature may be best understood by reference to Fig. 1.13.

The breadboard consists of a metal chassis containing two or three rows of tube sockets mounted upside down, with one or two rows of bare, heavy bus wires traversing the length of the chassis between the rows of sockets. These wires are used to distribute plate-, bias-, and heater-supply voltages, and to afford convenient places for attaching circuit components. The voltages can be obtained from the bench

---

*A product of the Pierce Laboratory, Inc., Summit, N. J.

power supply by means of a cable-and-plug arrangement. A number of holes punched here and there in the chassis can be used for mounting potentiometers, switches, and brackets to hold other components that may be required. If component parts are conveniently at hand, it is possible to solder together a fairly complicated circuit in an hour

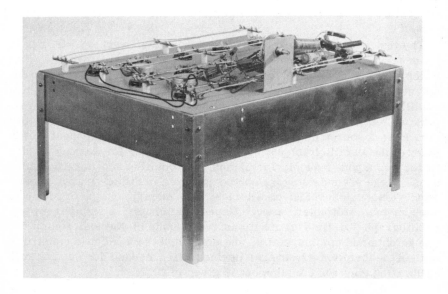

Fig. 1.13 — A convenient construction for investigating new circuits.

or two, leaving all leads on resistors, capacitors, etc., at their full length. After completing tests on the circuit, the breadboard can be cleared for future use in a few minutes by tipping it sideways and touching a hot soldering iron to each connection. The heater leads to each socket are usually left in place to speed the wiring of a future circuit. The breadboard technique described represents a considerable improvement over older procedures that have been popular. Its description here is justified in view of the rapidity with which experimental results can be obtained.

Chapter 2

CIRCUIT ELEMENTS

By William C. Elmore and Matthew Sands

1. INTRODUCTION

The primary purpose of this chapter is to describe the different elements that constitute the complete circuits described in later chapters. This mode of presentation has been selected both to save space and to aid the reader in obtaining a clearer notion of the design and operation of the complete circuits. When these circuits are discussed, constant reference will be made to the basic circuit elements described in this chapter.

It is the experience of the members of the Los Alamos electronics group that the design of a complicated electronic circuit proceeds first with the drawing of a block diagram of circuit elements, each of which must perform a simple function, and then with the designing of the individual elements. The skill of the designer lies not only in his ability to choose the simplest over-all pattern of circuit operation, but also in his ability to design the individual elements in such a way that they will reliably perform the task assigned them. Both these skills require a practical familiarity with as many circuit elements as possible, and it is only rarely that an essentially new circuit element will be invented to perform a given task.

The circuit elements described in this chapter do not by any means exhaust the list of known useful elements, but an attempt has been made to select those most commonly found in electronic circuits devised for research in nuclear physics and for the studying and recording of fast electrical transients. In discussing these circuit elements, it is assumed that the reader has a general familiarity with textbook electronics and circuit analysis. For this reason a discussion of the general operation of a given element is often omitted, so that emphasis can be placed on the more subtle points of design as well as on the general properties of the element affecting its use in combination with other elements.

It has been found convenient to divide circuit elements into four
categories: linear passive elements, linear electronic elements,
trigger circuits, and nonlinear electronic elements. The amount of
space devoted to each category reflects in part the variety of that

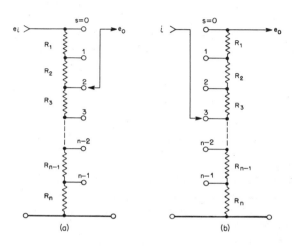

Fig. 2.1—Simple resistance attenuators.

type of element in common use and in part the amount of discussion
found necessary to supplement existing accounts of the subject. If an
adequate discussion of a particular element is readily available in
standard textbooks and handbooks, the discussion here has been restricted to as brief an account as is consistent with continuity in
presentation. No attempt is made to attribute the origin of any electronic element, or of any idea, to a particular person. Indeed, it
would be difficult to do so, since the origin of the vast majority of the
elements has merged into a heritage of electronic techniques which
exist for the most part in the minds of designers, and which have
become divorced from their original source. Particular mention,
however, should be made of the Radiation Laboratory of the Massachusetts Institute of Technology, which constituted a fertile source of
circuit information during the development of many of the circuits
described in this volume.

2. LINEAR PASSIVE ELEMENTS

2.1 Resistance Networks. We shall consider in detail only one
type of resistance network—a type that is much used for attenuating
signals in wide-band amplifiers or for attenuating signals from a
standard pulse generator. Since for these applications an attenuator

must pass frequencies well into the megacycle range, it is evident that parasitic capacitances must be kept at a minimum, and noninductive resistors may have to be used as components in its construction.

The attenuator consists of the simple voltage divider shown in Fig. 2.1(a). Usually resistances are so chosen that each successive position of the switch reduces the signal by some definite fraction ρ.* To aid in designing such an attenuator of total resistance R, the following relations may be used:

$$
\left.
\begin{aligned}
R_1 &= R(1 - \rho) \\
R_s &= R_1 \rho^{s-1} = R_{s-1}\rho \qquad (s = 1, 2, \ldots, n-1) \\
R_n &= R\rho^{n-1} = \frac{R_{n-1}\rho}{1 - \rho}
\end{aligned}
\right\}
\qquad (1)
$$

An attenuator of this type is often made the load of a cathode follower or used as the termination of a coaxial cable connecting two separate electronic circuits. Some examples of its use will be found among the amplifier circuits in Chap. 3. Where the attenuator must pass signals having a rise time of about 0.1 μsec, the parasitic capacitances in the attenuator and in the circuit following the attenuator usually require that R be 2,000 ohms or less.

In certain applications the input signal to the attenuator comes from what is essentially a constant-current generator having an extremely high impedance—e.g., from the plate circuit of a pentode. If it is desired that the attenuator always present a constant output impedance, then it may be connected as indicated in Fig. 2.1(b). The design equations (Eq. 1) also hold for this mode of connection.

A simple resistance attenuator of the type described is not very satisfactory for reducing the amplitude of a very fast pulse by a large factor and simultaneously preserving the shape of the pulse. Parasitic capacitances in the attenuator, as well as parasitic inductances of the resistors and connecting leads, tend to increase the rise time of the pulse and to superpose small oscillations on it. For big reductions in signal level, a relatively low-impedance, ladder-type attenuator can be used, or the resistance attenuator can be capacitively compensated, as discussed in the next section.

---

* The use of the language of decibels has been deliberately avoided in writing this book. Two reasons are advanced for this decision. In the first place, most physicists, especially nuclear physicists, do not think in terms of decibels. In the second place, the magnitude of signals encountered in the application of electronic techniques to nuclear measurements is most naturally expressed in terms of microvolts, millivolts, volts, etc., and not in terms of power levels.

2.2 Resistance-Capacitance Networks. The voltage divider, Fig.
2.2, is frequency-independent when $R_1C_1 = R_2C_2$, and so may be used
as the basis of a signal attenuator of the type just discussed. It is
most often used where a single step of attenuation is required, such
as 10 to 1, or 100 to 1. Ordinarily the larger capacitance C_2 is fixed
in value and so chosen that the smaller capacitance C_1 can be a small
ceramic trimmer capacitor whose value is adjusted empirically to
give a frequency-independent voltage division. The best value for C_1
can be determined by observing the effect of its setting on the transmission of a step pulse of short rise time. If C_1 is too large, the output pulse will have an overshoot, whereas if C_1 is too small the rise
time of the output pulse will be increased. Capacitance compensation
permits the use of high resistances in the attenuator, and therefore
such an attenuator is suitable for applications where a low-impedance
attenuator cannot be used.

Let us next consider the properties of some other RC elements,
starting with the simple network represented in Fig. 2.3(a). This
element is often used in electronic circuits to pass a signal between
two points differing in d-c level. The value of the time constant RC
can be so chosen that a signal of a given duration is transmitted
practically undistorted or is distorted in a manner that may be loosely
described as "differentiation."*

To illustrate the properties of this network for transmitting pulses,
several figures have been prepared. In each case the curve drawn in
a heavy line represents the input pulse. In Fig. 2.3(b) the input pulse
is a unit step signal having an infinitely fast rise, and the output pulse
is the exponentially decaying voltage exp $(-t/\tau)$, where τ = RC. In
Fig. 2.3(c) the input pulse is a step signal of linear rise requiring
unit time, and the output pulse is represented analytically by

$$e_0 = \tau \, (1 - e^{-t/\tau})$$

holding for unit time, followed by an exponentially decaying voltage
having a time constant τ. Values of τ in the figure are expressed in
units of the total time required for the linear rise.† In Fig. 2.3(d) the
input pulse is a signal rising exponentially to its final value, and the
output pulse is the difference between two exponentially decaying
voltages.

---

*For a discussion of differentiating and integrating circuits see O.S. Puckle, "Time
Bases," Appendix IV, John Wiley & Sons, Inc., New York, 1943.

† The total time required for the linear rise is not necessarily the so-called "rise
time" of the pulse. See Chap. 3, Sec. 4.1, for a discussion of rise time. According to
the definition, Eq. 11, Chap. 3, the rise time is $\sqrt{\pi/6}$ = 0.716.

$$e_0 = \frac{\tau}{\tau - 1} \, (e^{-t/\tau} - e^{-t})$$

where times are measured in units of the time constant of the input signal. The loss in pulse height for small values of τ is especially to

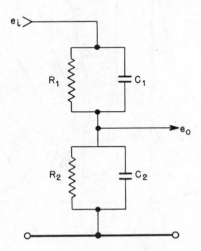

Fig. 2.2 — Resistance-capacitance voltage divider.

be noted in Figs. 2.3(c) and (d). It will be shown in Chap. 3, Sec. 6, that the loss in pulse height affects the signal-to-noise ratio of pulse amplifiers.

The transmission characteristics of this element for sinusoidal signals of frequency f may be expressed

$$\frac{e_0}{e_i} = \frac{F}{\sqrt{1 + F^2}} \, e^{j \, \tan^{-1}(1/F)} = g(F) \, e^{j\phi(F)}$$

where $F = 2\pi fRC$. The amplitude and phase relations are shown graphically in Fig. 2.4. The phase of the output voltage always leads that of the input voltage by the angle ϕ.

The two RC networks shown in Figs. 2.5(a) and (b) are completely equivalent as regards output signal if $i_i = e_i/R$. Element (a) usually occurs in an electronic circuit by virtue of the parasitic circuit capacitance C occurring across the resistance R. Either element can be used for the purpose of "integrating" a signal, provided the time

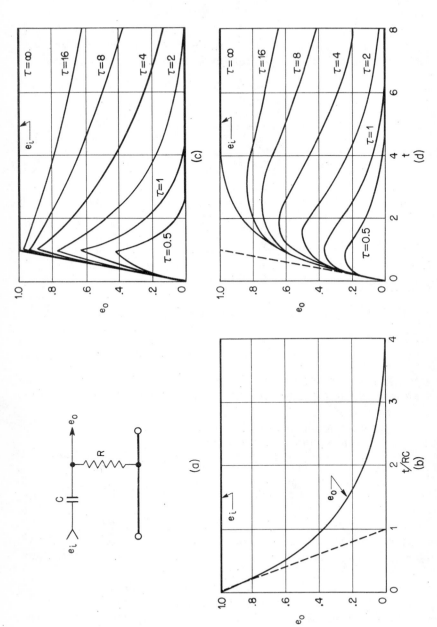

Fig. 2.3 — RC-coupling element and some typical transient-response curves.

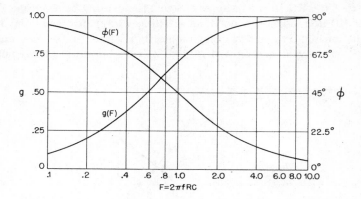

Fig. 2.4—Transmission characteristics of RC-differentiating element.

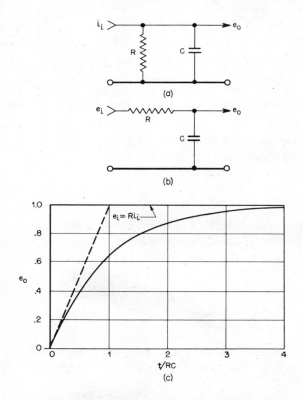

Fig. 2.5—Two equivalent RC elements and their transient response to a unit step signal.

constant τ = RC is much longer than the duration of the signal.* Element (b) is most often used as a filter, either for reducing the amplitude of high frequency components in a signal or for decoupling the supply voltage of one part of a circuit from the main power supply.

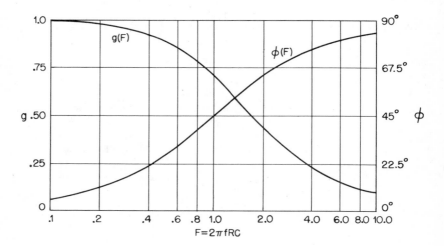

Fig. 2.6—Transmission characteristics of an RC-integrating element.

If a unit step signal is applied to an element of this type, the output voltage rises exponentially to its final value according to

$$e_0 = 1 - e^{-t/\tau}$$

as depicted in Fig. 2.5(c). The first part of the rise is linear and therefore represents an accurate integral of the input signal.

The transmission characteristics of this element for sinusoidal voltages are given by

$$\frac{e_0}{e_i} = \frac{1}{\sqrt{1 + F^2}} \; e^{-j \tan^{-1}F} = g(F) \, e^{-j\phi(F)}$$

where F = 2πfRC. This relation is shown graphically in Fig. 2.6. The phase of the output voltage always lags behind that of the input voltage by the angle ϕ.

*Puckle, loc. cit.

2.3   Resistance-Capacitance-Inductance Networks. Let us first consider the RCL network shown in Fig. 2.7(a). The addition of the inductance L to the RC element Fig. 2.3(a) reduces the time required for the output signal to approach zero following the application of an input step-voltage signal. Only the case for $L = \frac{1}{4} R^2C$ will be considered, for if L is larger than this critical value the output signal will oscillate following the application of a fast input signal. Smaller values of L than the critical value are of less interest and will not be considered here. In Fig. 2.7(b) is shown the output signal obtained with a step signal applied to the input. In Fig. 2.7(c) the input signal is a step signal having a linear rise, and in Fig. 2.7(d) a step signal having an exponential rise. The response curves for these cases should be compared with the corresponding curves for which $L = 0$, previously given in Figs. 2.3(b), (c), and (d). This particular element is of some interest, since it can be used in a pulse amplifier for shaping pulses from an electrical detector, as described in Chap. 3, Sec. 3.

Next let us consider the RCL network shown in Fig. 2.8. This element is of importance in the shunt compensation of amplifiers. It has the complex impedance

$$\frac{e_0}{i_i} = Z = \frac{R + pL}{1 + pRC + p^2LC}$$

where $p = j\omega$. If we write $L = \alpha R^2C$ and $F = 2\pi fRC$, then

$$Z = Rg(F)\ e^{j\phi}$$

where
$$g(F) = \sqrt{\frac{1 + \alpha^2\ F^2}{(1 - \alpha\ F^2)^2 + F^2}} \tag{2}$$

$$\tan\phi = F(1 - \alpha + \alpha^2\ F^2)$$

The function $g(F)$, which approaches unity for small values of F, expresses the dependence on frequency of the absolute value of the impedance Z. The amplitude and the phase relations are shown graphically in Fig. 2.9 for $\alpha = 0,\ 0.25,\ (\sqrt{2} - 1)$, and 0.6.

The transient response of this element to a unit step of current is shown in Fig. 2.10. Although a value of $\alpha = \sqrt{2} - 1$ gives the broadest flat-frequency response, there is an appreciable oscillation in the transient response for this case. For no overshoot in the transient response, $\alpha \leq 0.25$. A further discussion of some properties of this element appears in Chap. 3, Sec. 4.

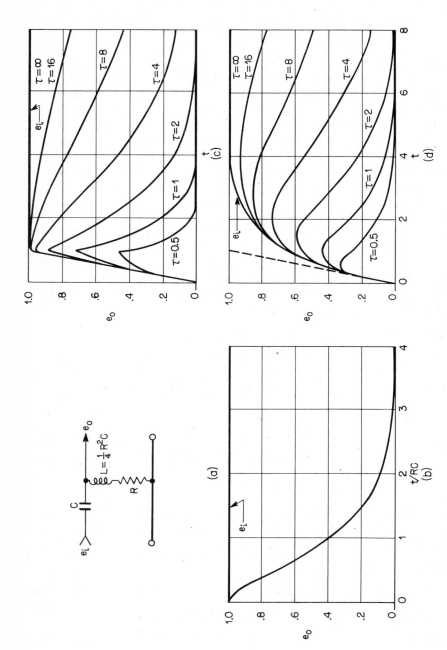

Fig. 2.7 — RCL-coupling element and some typical transient-response curves.

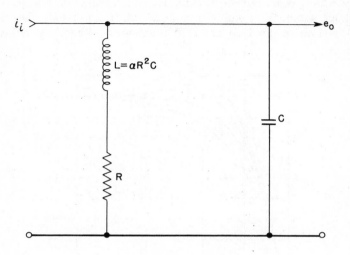

Fig. 2.8 — Shunt-compensated RC element.

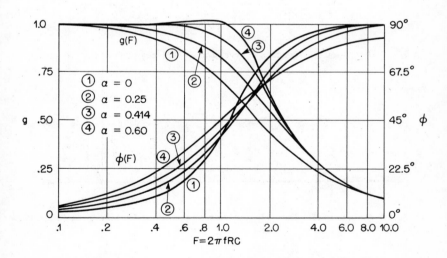

Fig. 2.9 — Driving-point impedance of a shunt-compensated RC element.

2.4 Delay Lines. An ideal delay line is a four-terminal passive element which, when correctly terminated, transmits a sinusoidal signal without attenuation but with a phase shift $\phi = 2\pi f T_D$, where T_D is the delay time of the line and f is frequency. Practical delay lines

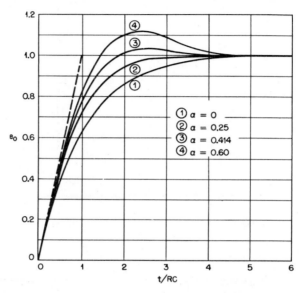

Fig. 2.10 — Transient-response curves for a shunt-compensated RC element.

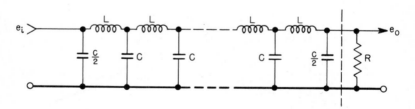

Fig. 2.11 — A simple delay line. The resistor R constitutes the terminating impedance of the line.

always attenuate the transmitted signal somewhat, the attenuation increasing rapidly with frequency above a critical frequency. Moreover, in the frequency range where enhanced attenuation sets in, the phase shift is no longer a linear function of frequency. A delay line is therefore characterized by a certain useful bandwidth. If a step voltage of infinitely fast rise is applied at one end of the line, the output signal will have a finite rise time T_R, and possibly will have transient oscillations superposed on it. For many purposes the figure of merit of a delay line can be expressed by the ratio T_D/T_R. Practical high-fidelity delay lines can be built with a figure of merit in excess of 10.

Most delay lines are based on some form of low-pass, ladder-type filter, one form of which is indicated in Fig. 2.11. The nominal characteristic impedance of this filter is

$$Z_c = \sqrt{L/C} \tag{3}$$

the delay for n sections is

$$T_D \doteq n \sqrt{LC} \tag{4}$$

and the upper cutoff frequency is

$$f_c = \frac{1}{\pi \sqrt{LC}} \tag{5}$$

Since a numerical computation of the rise time of a ladder-type delay line is extremely tedious, measurements have been made to determine an empirical relation that can be used for design purposes. These measurements show that in the range of from 3 to 30 sections the rise time (time for delayed signal to rise from 10 to 90 per cent of its final value, in response to a step input signal) is represented very well by

$$T_R \approx 1.1 n^{\frac{1}{3}} \sqrt{LC} \tag{6}$$

Excessive distortion of a transmitted pulse will occur if the pulse contains essential frequency components higher than about one-half the cutoff frequency. Although for high-fidelity applications it is possible to design an elaborate corrective network for a lumped-parameter delay line, it has been found simpler to construct "smooth" delay lines in which the series inductances L and the shunting capacitances C in Fig. 2.11 are replaced by an almost continuous distribution of inductance and capacitance. Smooth delay lines are briefly discussed later in the present section.

The simple delay line shown in Fig. 2.11 can be used for delaying pulses to serve as delayed triggers for various electronic devices. For applications discussed in this book, the total time of delay lies in the microsecond range, usually less than 10 μsec. The sections of the line are often connected to a selector switch, so that a series of pulses delayed in small equal steps are available. Since a lumped-parameter delay line is constructed of standard components, the exact values of the characteristic impedance and of the delay per section are chosen so as to suit the availability of parts.

A delay line for trigger applications can be designed as follows: The desired rise time and total delay are used in Eqs. 4 and 6 to determine the approximate number of sections, and therefore the delay per section. If the number of sections required is excessive, the rise time will have to be sacrificed, and the delayed pulse later sharpened by some means. After a value for the delay per section, $\sqrt{LC}$, has been decided on, a value of $Z_c = \sqrt{L/C}$ is tentatively selected. Values of Z_c from a few hundred to a few thousand ohms are reasonable, the higher resistances being most suitable for pulses having a long rise time. The values of L and C are then computed, and an adjustment is made so that they agree with values of standard components. The value of C should always be somewhat larger than parasitic capacitances in the circuit, i.e., $C \geq 20$ $\mu\mu$f. Part or all of the capacitance of the first and the last capacitor of the line can be the parasitic capacitance of attached electronic devices. As a simple example of design, suppose a delay line of about 0.5 μsec rise time is required, having a total delay of 2 μsec. The delay per section can be taken as 0.2 μsec, so that a total of 10 sections is needed. Equation 6 indicates that the rise time will then be 0.47 μsec. We now have LC = 4×10^{-14} sec^2. If $Z_c = 1,000$ ohms, then $L/C = 10^6$ ohms^2, giving L = 200 μh and C = 200 $\mu\mu$f. To obtain inductances that are approximately 200 μh, individual sections of a small 3-section 1-mh r-f choke can be used. The small mutual inductance between sections is not particularly harmful.

Smooth delay lines may be made by winding a long slender solenoid of insulated wire, to which is attached a number of circumferentially disposed conducting strips separated from the solenoid by a thin layer of dielectric material. These strips are connected in parallel, forming the common input and output terminal of the line and affording a certain capacitance C_1 per unit length to the underlying turns of the solenoid. If L_1 is the inductance per unit length of the solenoid, then the delay per unit length will be

$$T_{D1} = \sqrt{L_1 C_1}$$

and the nominal characteristic impedance is

$$Z_c = \sqrt{L_1/C_1}$$

It is relatively easy to construct very satisfactory delay lines of this sort, especially if a very short delay (≤ 0.5 μsec) is required and if the characteristic impedance is kept low (100 ohms or less). However, for high-fidelity applications requiring longer delays it is usually more satisfactory to employ one of the commercially built lines. A discussion of the theory and construction of high-fidelity delay lines of certain types is contained in recent publications of the Radiation Laboratory of the Massachusetts Institute of Technology. Table 2.1 contains a list of some useful commercially built delay lines, with their nominal delay, bandwidth, and characteristic imped-ance.

Table 2.1 — Some Commercial Delay Lines

Make	Number	Nominal impedance, ohms	Nominal delay time, μsec	Nominal bandwidth, megacycles/sec	Rise time, measured, μsec	D-c resistance, measured, ohms
W.E.	D168435	555	0.5	9.5	0.075	26.8
W.E.	D168705	460	$\begin{bmatrix} 2.2 \\ 2.0 \\ 1.8 \end{bmatrix}$	5.5	$\begin{cases} 0.22 \\ 0.18 \\ 0.16 \end{cases}$	97.3
W.E.	D163169	650	4.5	8.0	0.10	317.0
Sickles	K52J851	500	0.5		0.12	20.0
Sickles	12647	350	1.2	~5.0	0.05	29.3
Sickles	12799A	600	5.0		0.17	140.0
G.E.*		1,000	0.7 μsec per ft		0.06 μsec per 2.7 ft	167.0 ohms per ft

* Continuous delay line.

Included in Table 2.1 are the measured values of rise time and of the d-c resistance of each delay line. Rise times have been deter-mined by using a mercury switch to produce an input-voltage step function and simultaneously to initiate a fast calibrated sweep of an oscillograph. The values quoted are for the time of rise from 10 to 90 per cent of the delayed step wave. The transient response of none of the lines tested is free from small damped oscillations.

In certain pulse-forming applications, a smooth delay line is used as a two-terminal device, with the far end either shorted or open-circuited. In this case there is no need for the line to be unbalanced or single-sided, since a balanced line will do just as well. A smooth, balanced line can be made by winding two solenoids, one on top of the other, with perhaps a thin layer of a suitable dielectric material be-tween the two windings. Viewed from an end, one solenoid must be wound clockwise, the other counterclockwise. For a given delay time and characteristic impedance, a balanced line of this sort will have about half the d-c resistance of a similar single-sided line. This result derives from the fact that the total inductance per unit length of the double-layer line is nearly four times that of a single-layer line on account of mutual inductance between the two windings.

Occasionally a continuously variable range of delayed pulses is required in timing applications where the total range of delay amounts to only a few microseconds. For this type of application, steps of equal delay can be obtained from a lumped-parameter delay line and

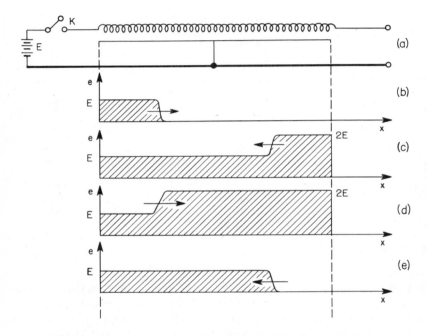

Fig. 2.12 — Propagation and reflection properties of an ideal delay line.

a continuously variable delay line constructed to interpolate between the adjacent steps. A continuously variable delay line is obtained by baring the wires along one side of a smooth delay line and mounting a sliding contactor that can move along the bared side of the solenoid. Alternatively, it is also possible to rewind a General Radio–type wire-wound potentiometer with enameled copper wire and to attach some conducting strips around the outside of the winding to give a distributed capacitance. The edge of the winding where the movable contact arm normally makes connection is made bare with some fine emery cloth. Variable delay lines of this sort have to be calibrated, and their characteristic impedance has to be determined empirically.

Some Application of Delay Lines. Besides the obvious application for delaying signals, delay lines can be used as elements in pulse-forming circuits. To understand these applications it is necessary to consider the propagation of steep wave fronts on an unterminated delay line.

Let us first consider the case where the receiving end of the line is open-circuited and a key and a resistanceless battery are connected to the sending end, as indicated in Fig. 2.12(a). For purposes of illustration we assume the line to be lossless and of infinite bandwidth. On closing the key at time $t = 0$, a step wave of amplitude $+E$ travels toward the open-circuited end, where it is reflected without inversion at $t = T_D$. When the reflected wave reaches the sending end, at $t = 2T_D$, the entire line is charged to potential $+2E$. The sending end is effectively short-circuited through the battery, so that the reflection of the step wave there occurs with inversion, causing a step wave of amplitude $-E$ to start toward the open end. This wave reaches the open end at $t = 3T_D$ and reflects without inversion. On its return to the sending end at $t = 4T_D$, it has completely wiped off the remaining potential left by earlier excursions of the wave, and the cycle commences once again. The various stages in the progress of the wave are shown in Figs. 2.12(b), (c), (d), and (e). In a practical case the wave suffers attenuation as it progresses, and the steep front tends to spread out into a more gradual rise. The corresponding behavior for the case in which the receiving end is short-circuited can be readily visualized. If the line is terminated by a resistance R greater (or less) than the characteristic impedance Z_c of the line, a reflection occurs without inversion (or with inversion), but the reflected wave is reduced in amplitude by an amount given by the coefficient of reflection $(Z_c - R)/(Z_c + R)$. Any terminating impedance other than a pure resistance distorts the reflected wave.

Rectangular pulses can be generated by discharging a charged open-circuited line through its characteristic impedance. One type of circuit used for this purpose is shown in Fig. 2.13(a).

The operation of this circuit can be understood by reference to Figs. 2.13(b), (c), and (d). The resistor R serves only to charge the line between successive pulses and is usually greater than 500,000 ohms, so that the thyratron will extinguish readily. It plays no part during the formation of a pulse. Let us then suppose that in the equivalent circuit (b) the key K is closed at $t = 0$, i.e., the thyratron fires at this instant. This closure connects the resistance $R_K = Z_c$ across the end of the line, so the voltage there drops to $E/2$,[*] since the line

---

[*] For simplicity in describing the behavior of the circuit, the voltage drop E_1 across the thyratron is neglected.

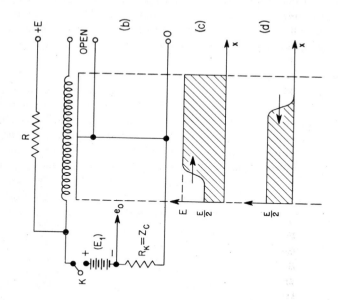

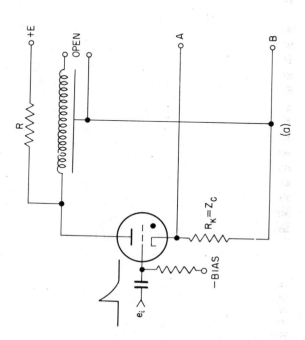

Fig. 2.13—Circuit using a delay line for generating rectangular pulses.

itself momentarily presents its true characteristic impedance Z_c. A wave starts down the line as shown in (c), is reflected without inversion at the far end at time $t = T_D$, and then travels back, completing the discharge of the line at $t = 2T_D$. When the reflected wave reaches the input end, the voltage drops to zero. The absence of voltage extinguishes the thyratron in the actual circuit, and the line then recharges through R, getting ready for another cycle of operation.

If point B in the circuit is grounded, a rectangular positive pulse of amplitude $E/2$ and duration $2T_D$ can be taken from point A. If A is grounded, then a similar negative pulse appears at B. The thyratron is normally biased off, and so requires a positive trigger pulse applied to its grid in order that it may fire and generate an output pulse.

3. LINEAR ELECTRONIC ELEMENTS

In discussing linear electronic circuit elements, it is assumed that the reader is familiar with the characteristic curves of vacuum tubes and with the general methods of choosing suitable operating points, constructing load lines, and obtaining bias voltages.* A familiarity with the equivalent circuits of vacuum tubes is also required in order to derive many of the quantitative relations that are given. It is felt that a detailed derivation of these relations would detract from the presentation, besides requiring too much space.

3.1 <u>Single Triode and Pentode Voltage-amplifier Stages</u>. We shall consider first the simple triode amplifier, as shown in Fig. 2.14(a). The complex gain A of such a stage is

$$A = - \frac{\mu Z_L}{Z_L + r_p + (\mu + 1) Z_K} \tag{7}$$

where the effect of the cathode impedance Z_K on the gain is included. This type of amplifier is used only occasionally at frequencies higher than those in the audio-frequency band, chiefly on account of the low input impedance arising from the Miller effect, i.e., the multiplication of the grid-plate capacitance C_{gp} by the factor $(1 - A)$.

Since pentodes have a very low grid-plate capacitance, the amplifier shown in Fig. 2.14(b) has greater applicability in wide-band amplifiers. Its gain is

$$A = - \frac{g_m Z_L}{1 + g_K Z_K} \tag{8}$$

---

* "RCA Tube Handbook," Vols. I to IV, and F. E. Terman, "Radio Engineers' Handbook," McGraw-Hill Book Company, Inc., New York, 1943, are particularly helpful.

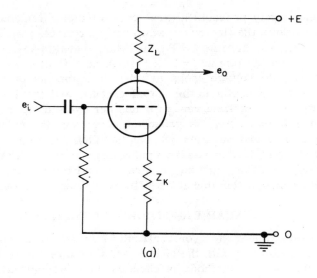

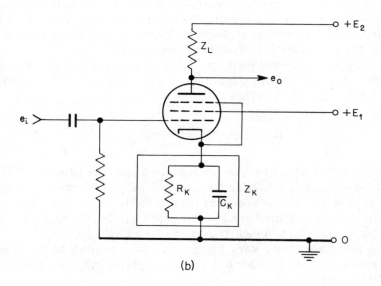

Fig. 2.14—Single-tube amplifiers.

where the usual approximations based on the fact that $\mu \gg 1$ and $r_p \gg |Z_L|$ have been made. Equation 8 also contains approximations made necessary by the change in screen-cathode potential. The grid-cathode transconductance g_K is given by the approximate expression

$$g_K \approx g_m (1 + I_{g2}/I_p) \tag{9}$$

where I_{g2} and I_p are the average screen and plate currents, respectively.

The plate-load impedance Z_L in any voltage-amplifier stage contains a parallel parasitic capacitance C_L to ground, consisting of the sum of the output capacitance of the tube, the wiring capacitance, and the input capacitance of the succeeding electronic stage or device. By inserting a small inductance in series with the plate-load resistor R_L, the deleterious effect of this parasitic capacitance at high frequencies can be reduced somewhat. This method, known as "shunt compensation," is discussed in Sec. 2.3 of this chapter and also in Chap. 3, Sec. 4. Where greater bandwidth than that obtained with shunt compensation is required, at the cost of greater complexity, a four-terminal interstage network may be used. Such networks are often designed to achieve maximum bandwidth without regard to good transient behavior. Since no four-terminal interstage networks have been used in the circuits described in later chapters, they will not be discussed here.

A few practical suggestions regarding the design of voltage-amplifier stages follow:

Triode or pentode audio-frequency stages can be based on the resistance-coupled amplifier charts in the "RCA Tube Handbook." For pulse amplifiers, or other special-purpose amplifiers, the operating condition recommended for particular tubes can usually be followed. When attempting to achieve a maximum gain-bandwidth product (which is proportional to g_m/C, where g_m is the tube transconductance and C is the sum of input and output capacitances of the tube), the listed tube dissipation sets the maximum g_m that can be obtained. Maximum screen dissipation is often reached before the plate is overloaded. The following types of tubes have been found most useful in wide-band amplifiers: 6AC7, 6AK5, 6SH7, 6SJ7, 6V6, 6Y6, 6AG7, 6L6, 807, 829B. The 6AG7 and the beam-power tetrodes are used in output stages where the ratio $I_{p_{max}}/C_{out}$ must be kept as large as possible.

Use of Feedback with Single Stages. Negative-current or voltage feedback can be used with either the single-triode or the single-pentode amplifier to improve linearity for large signals, to increase stability in gain against variations in tube parameters, or to modify the frequency response of the amplifier.

Negative-current feedback results if the cathode resistor in Fig. 2.14(a) or (b) is not by-passed, except by a small trimming capacitor which serves to partially compensate the high frequency loading of the parasitic capacitance in the plate circuit. For a pentode stage, where this type of feedback is often used, the mid-band gain is approximately

$$A = -\frac{g_m R_L}{1 + g_K R_K} \qquad (10)$$

The optimum value of the compensating capacitance across the cathode resistor is ordinarily determined empirically. For no overshoot on a fast step wave, the time constant $R_K C_K$ of the cathode load

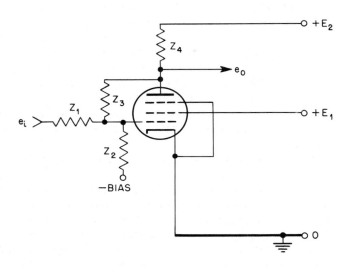

Fig. 2.15 — Single-stage, voltage-fed-back amplifier. Each impedance Z_i represents a resistor R_i and a capacitor C_i in parallel.

should be made precisely equal to the time constant $R_L C_L$ of the plate load. When the two time constants are equal, the high-frequency response will be that of an amplifier with no feedback but with a plate-load resistor that would give the same net gain. In other words, padding the cathode resistor with a small capacitor cannot increase the rise time of the amplifier for an assigned stage gain. The negative feedback, of course, will increase the stability and the linearity of the amplifier for large signals.* In low-level stages, the unby-

---

*See Sec. 3.8 of this chapter ior a discussion of certain limitations common to all feedback amplifiers used for large fast signals.

passed cathode resistor may increase hum pickup from the heater. A special case of negative current feedback with triodes is that in which $R_L = R_K$. This case will be discussed under phase inverters (see Sec. 3.2 of this chapter).

A second type of single-stage feedback amplifier in common use is illustrated in Fig. 2.15. Each impedance Z_i represents a resistance R_i in parallel with a capacitance C_i. Here the input signal, at any convenient d-c level, and the output signal are combined through a Y network to drive the grid at the center of the Y. The complete gain formula for such a voltage-fed-back stage is

$$A = -\frac{Z_3}{Z_1} \frac{1 - \dfrac{1}{g_m Z_3}}{1 + \dfrac{1}{g_m}\left[\dfrac{1}{Z_t} + \left(1 + \dfrac{Z_3}{Z_t}\right)\left(\dfrac{1}{Z_1} + \dfrac{1}{Z_2}\right)\right]} \qquad (11)$$

where $Z_t = r_p Z_4/(r_p + Z_4)$. The other symbols are shown in Fig. 2.15. When the tube is a pentode, the terms involving g_m can be made small compared with unity, so that the mid-band gain is very nearly R_3/R_1. By adjusting the capacitor C_1, the stage can be compensated for optimum high-frequency response. If the stage is to be used only for amplifying narrow pulses, the resistors R_1 and R_3 can be omitted, so that the gain is set primarily by the ratio C_1/C_3. In this case it is convenient to use cathode bias with the resistance R_2 returned to ground. When the tube is a triode, the complete expression, Eq. 11, must be used for computing the gain, since the terms involving g_m may contribute as much as 30 per cent to its value.

The exact expression for the complex output impedance Z_0 of the voltage feedback amplifier is given by

$$\frac{1}{Z_0} = \frac{1}{Z_t} + \frac{Z_1 + Z_2}{Z_1 Z_2 + Z_1 Z_3 + Z_2 Z_3}\left(1 + g_m \frac{Z_1 Z_2}{Z_1 + Z_2}\right) \qquad (12)$$

The output impedance at mid-band frequencies consists of the resistance

$$R_0 = \frac{1}{g_m}\left[1 + \frac{R_3}{R_1}\left(1 + \frac{R_1}{R_2}\right)\right] \qquad (13)$$

in parallel with the resistor network and the plate resistance r_p. Hence, when $R_2 \gg R_1$ and the ideal gain R_3/R_1 is unity, the output impedance is essentially $2/g_m$, i.e., twice that of the cathode follower. (See Sec. 3.4 of this chapter.) The input impedance of the amplifier is approximately Z_1, the magnitude of which may limit the usefulness of the amplifier for pulses of short rise time.

When the amplifier gain is made exactly -1 and the amplifier is biased to deliver a large negative output, it is suited to inverting a saw-tooth waveform for the purpose of driving, in a push-pull operation, the sweep of an oscillograph. Since the amplifier in the form shown in Fig. 2.15 is direct-coupled, it will invert very slow saw-toothed signals, as well as signals lasting only a few microseconds. When it is used for large fast signals, there is a possibility that grid current may be drawn or that the tube current may be cut off (see Sec. 3.8 of this chapter).

3.2 <u>Phase Inverters</u>. The term "phase inverter" is here used to specify a circuit element that will deliver a push-pull, or balanced, voltage output (i.e., separate output voltages, one of which is the negative of the other) linearly related to a single-sided, or unbalanced, input. One form of phase inverter suitable for wide-band application is shown in Fig. 2.16(a). The mid-band gain is

$$A = \frac{2\mu R}{R(\mu + 2) + r_p} = \frac{2}{1 + \dfrac{2}{\mu} + \dfrac{1}{g_m R}} \tag{14}$$

The output voltage is balanced, since the plate and cathode load resistors are equal and identical currents flow through them. The gain is always less than 2, but when $1/g_m R \ll 1$ it depends only slightly on tube parameters. This inverter is particularly useful at low and moderate voltage levels in systems where stability and linearity of response are important. In applications where fast transients are being inverted, it is necessary to ensure a proper balance between the capacitive loads across the plate and cathode resistors. An approximate balance is attained when $C_K = C_L + 2C_{pg}$. Thus when the phase inverter is driving two identical loads, such as two succeeding amplifier stages, exact capacitive balance ordinarily requires trimming the cathode resistor with a small capacitor, the adjustment of which is best done empirically, using square test waves. The output impedance between cathode and ground is much less than that between plate and ground, so the inverter is not very useful in applications where unbalanced load conditions may be expected.

Another type of phase inverter, also suitable for wide-band applications, is indicated in Fig. 2.16(b). Here inversion takes place in the common cathode resistor R_K, and for balanced output the two plate-load resistors must differ somewhat in resistance. A simple

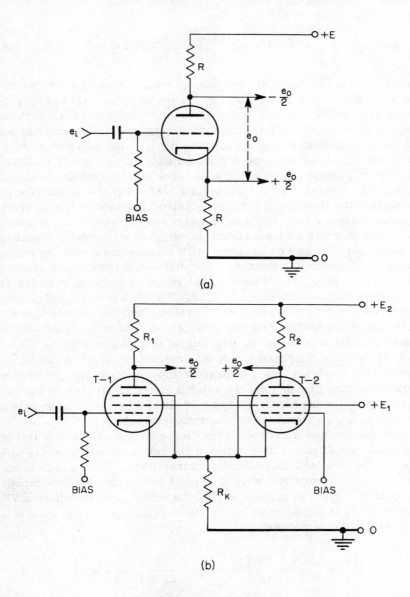

Fig. 2.16—Phase inverters.

analysis shows that they should be related as follows:

$$\frac{1}{R_2}\left[r_p + \frac{g_K}{g_m}(1 + \mu)R_K\right] + 1 = \frac{g_K}{g_m}(1 + \mu)\frac{R_K}{R_1} \tag{15}$$

where, in case the tubes are triodes, $g_K = g_m$.* When the two-plate-load resistances are related by Eq. 15, the over-all gain is approximately that which one tube of the inverter would have if its cathode resistor were completely by-passed. The gain of the inverter is not stabilized by feedback, and so depends directly on tube parameters. The linearity of the inverter for moderately large signals is better than that of a single amplifier stage because even harmonic distortion is reduced. Values for the plate-load resistors are ordinarily so chosen that the inverter will have a desired bandwidth or rise time. Its high-frequency response can be improved by shunt compensation. When response at high frequencies is unimportant, greater linearity for large signals can be obtained with triodes than with pentodes, since it is possible with triodes to use plate-load resistances greater than the tube plate resistances. The common cathode resistor is ordinarily chosen to make $R_K g_K \geqq 10$. The choice of its value also depends on the available plate-supply voltage and the desired operating points of the tubes. The common cathode phase inverter can be asymmetrically biased for use with pulses of a single polarity.

3.3 <u>Difference Amplifiers</u>. A difference amplifier is a circuit element that combines two independent input-voltage signals to give an output signal that is linearly related to the difference of the two input signals. Of the numerous types of difference amplifiers, only a few used in d-c applications will be discussed here.

The most obvious difference amplifier consists of a single triode or pentode amplifying stage in which the two input voltages are applied to the grid and the cathode, respectively. Such a difference amplifier is only effective when the signal comes from a low-impedance source — e.g., in certain voltage-regulator circuits where a VR tube furnishes a comparison voltage to the cathode. In the case of a triode stage, the output voltage is

$$e_o = -\frac{(2\mu + 1)R_L}{2(r_p + R_L)}\left[(e_1 - e_2) - \frac{1}{2\mu + 1}(e_1 + e_2)\right] \tag{16}$$

where e_1 and e_2 are the voltage signals applied to the grid and cathode, respectively, and R_L is the plate-load resistance. The same relation

*See O. S. Puckle, op. cit., p.119.

will hold for a pentode stage, provided the screen potential is kept constant with respect to the cathode. If the screen potential is held fixed with respect to ground, then

$$e_0 = -\frac{(2\mu_{gp} + \mu_{sp} + 1)\,R_L}{2(r_p + R_L)}\left[(e_1 - e_2) - \frac{\mu_{sp} + 1}{2\mu_{gp} + \mu_{sp} + 1}\,(e_1 + e_2)\right] \quad (17)$$

where μ_{gp} is the usual grid-to-plate amplification factor and μ_{sp} is the screen-to-plate factor.

A more complicated difference amplifier is shown in Fig. 2.17. Here two triodes have their common cathodes supplied by a constant-current device, such as is described in Sec. 3.7 of this chapter. Since

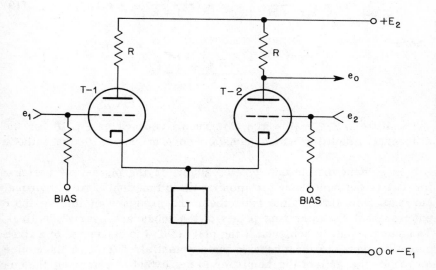

Fig. 2.17 — Difference amplifier.

the sum of the two tube currents is a constant, a signal applied to the grid of one tube will always produce equal and opposite current changes in the two tubes. If the tubes are matched and operating in the linear portion of their characteristics, the output voltage will be

$$e_0 = \frac{\mu R}{2(r_p + R)}\,(e_1 - e_2) \quad (18)$$

Under these conditions the same signal applied to both grids results in no output signal. Furthermore, if the tubes are sufficiently alike, changes in the grid-cathode contact difference of potential, as produced by heater-supply fluctuations, produce no voltage output.

The double high-mu triodes 6SL7 and 6SU7 are often used in this type of difference amplifier and in the modification to be described next.

For many purposes a sufficiently good difference amplifier results if the constant-current device in the cathode circuit of Fig. 2.17 is replaced by a resistance R_K. The value of R_K should be as high as is consistent with the available power-supply voltage and with the tube currents necessary to ensure a sufficiently large range of linear operation. For matched triodes, the output voltage is given by

$$e_o = \frac{\mu R}{2(r_p + R)} \left[(e_1 - e_2) - \frac{a}{1 + a} (e_1 + e_2) \right] \tag{19}$$

where

$$a = \frac{R + r_p}{2(\mu + 1) R_K}$$

When $2(\mu + 1) R_K \gg (R + r_p)$, this result reduces to Eq. 18 for the difference amplifier with a constant-current device in the cathode circuit.

It is evident that in this type of amplifier the plate-load resistor for T-1 is not necessary for the circuit to function. Providing equal currents flow through the two tubes, the presence of this resistor ensures that the operating points of the tubes are nearly identical. The same result is achieved if the plate of T-1 is connected to a fixed potential equal to the average plate potential of T-2. This device increases the gain of the amplifier to the extent of removing the coefficient 2 from the resistance R in the denominator of Eq. 18 and of producing a comparable change in Eq. 19.

A vacuum-tube voltmeter is obtained if a milliammeter is connected between the plates of the two triodes in the difference amplifier. The grid of the second tube is then returned to a suitable bias voltage, which can serve as a zero adjustment. The meter current is given by

$$i_M = \frac{\mu (e_1 - e_2)}{R_M + r_p \left(2 + \frac{R_M}{R} \right)} \tag{20}$$

where R_M is the meter resistance and the two triodes are assumed

identical. The meter current is independent of R_K, whose value therefore can be chosen to suit the bias requirements. When $R_M \ll 2r_p$,

$$i_M \approx \frac{g_m}{2}\,(e_1 - e_2) \tag{21}$$

Evidently $g_m/2$ is the maximum possible transfer admittance from
the grids to the meter. For a 6SN7 double triode, a meter current of
about 1 ma can be obtained for a grid change of 1 volt.

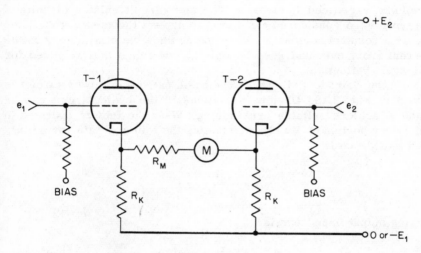

Fig. 2.18—Vacuum-tube voltmeter.

The balanced nature of the circuit gives considerable stability
against zero drift caused by changes in supply voltage. If high resistances ($> 10^5$ ohms) are used in the input grid circuit for the purpose
of measuring small direct currents, the zero balance is likely to shift
slightly when resistors are switched. This effect is caused by small
grid currents. It can be minimized by switching like resistors in the
grids of both tubes.

Another type of balanced difference amplifier for driving a milliammeter is shown in Fig. 2.18. This circuit consists essentially of
two cathode followers (see Sec. 3.4 of this chapter) with the meter
connected between the two cathodes. The meter current is given by

$$i_M = \frac{e_1 - e_2}{R_M \left(1 + \dfrac{1}{\mu}\right) + \dfrac{1}{g_m}\left(2 + \dfrac{R_M}{R_K}\right)} \tag{22}$$

To the extent that R_M is the dominating term in the denominator of Eq. 22, the meter current is independent of tube constants. This possibility of inverse-feedback stabilization constitutes the chief attraction of the circuit. When $R_M \ll 2/g_m$, a condition more difficult to satisfy than $R_M \ll 2r_p$, the maximum transfer admittance is $g_m/2$, which is the same value as obtained by connecting the meter between the plates of the double-triode difference amplifier. Hence, when it is necessary to have great meter sensitivity, the circuit first described should be used, whereas, when stability is at a premium, sensitivity should be sacrificed in favor of the other circuit. Meter circuits of the types here considered can serve to protect the meter from damage as a result of accidental overloading, since the maximum possible current from overload need be only a few times that required for full-scale deflection.

3.4 The Cathode Follower. The basic cathode-follower circuit is shown in Fig. 2.19. Obvious variations in the basic circuit can be made to achieve suitable grid biasing. When the tube is operated in the linear portion of its characteristic, the follower gain for infinite load impedance is

$$A = \frac{\mu}{\mu + 1} \approx 1 \tag{23}$$

and the output impedance is

$$Z_o = \frac{r_p}{\mu + 1} \approx \frac{1}{g_m} \tag{24}$$

The gain for a finite load can readily be computed using these relations. An important feature of the cathode-follower amplifier is its high input impedance, since any impedance between the grid and the cathode, such as that arising from the grid-cathode capacitance, is increased by the factor $1/(1 - A)$. The cathode-follower stage finds its chief application as an impedance-matching device, particularly in cases where fast signals must be faithfully transmitted through coaxial cable from one device to another.

The cathode-follower amplifier is particularly suited for use as an output stage in pulse amplifiers where the output pulse may be a large positive signal of short rise time. As an example of this use, consider a cathode-follower circuit consisting of a triode-connected 6AC7 tube having 200 volts on its plate and drawing initially only a few milliamperes. In response to a positive signal applied to its grid, the tube can deliver, without drawing grid current, an additional 50 ma to the cathode load. Hence, if this load is a resistance of 5,000 ohms in parallel with a parasitic capacitance of 100 $\mu\mu$f, the output pulse can rise initially at the rate of about 500 volts per microsecond, i.e., 50 volts in 0.1 μsec. During the rapid rise in voltage, the current delivered to the capacitive load is large compared with that

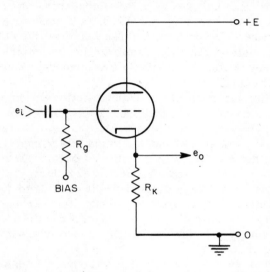

Fig. 2.19 — Cathode follower.

furnished the resistive load. Indeed, the transient behavior is essentially that of a generator of internal impedance $1/g_m$ driving the load R_K, C_K. However, if the input pulse should subsequently return to zero in a very short time, the tube current is cut off and the transmitted pulse will initially fall according to V_K exp $(-t/R_K C_K)$, where V_K is the voltage across R_K at the start of the rapid return of the input signal to zero. When the cathode potential has decreased to such a value that tube current is again flowing, restoring the transconductance of the tube to normal, the shape of the pulse will again be governed by the transient behavior of a generator of internal impedance $1/g_m$ driving the load R_K, C_K. The lengthening of the tail of a pulse of this sort is often of little consequence since the fast rise and the height of the pulse are faithfully transmitted. Indeed, a second, similar, pulse, occurring immediately after the first one, is correctly transmitted as to height, and it is often necessary to make sure only that the drop in voltage between the two pulses is sufficient to permit the recording equipment to distinguish their identity.

It is evident that a cathode-follower output stage is expensive in tube current if it must be capable of delivering large negative pulses of short rise time. For this reason it is worth while to avoid the necessity for output pulses of this character. In some cases the voltage-fed-back gain-of-minus-one amplifier, described in Sec. 3.1 of this chapter, may be used as a low-impedance output stage where fast negative pulses are involved. Such an output stage is not economical, of course, for delivering large fast positive pulses. In certain respects, this particular amplifier is the complement of the cathode-follower stage. Its relatively low input impedance constitutes its chief disadvantage.

An interesting variation of the cathode-follower amplifier results if the tube is connected as a pentode. This connection is ordinarily made in the following way: Screen-bias voltage is furnished by a suitable dropping resistor connected to the power supply. The screen is then tied to the cathode by a suitable capacitor. The pentode connection results in a lower input capacitance; in fact, the grid lead can be shielded and the shield connected to the cathode to further reduce the input capacitance. The pentode cathode follower has a gain more nearly unity than the gain of a triode stage, since the value of μ is so large. It is not so satisfactory as the triode cathode follower for handling large signals.

3.5 Two- and Three-stage Feedback Loops. In designing multistage wide-band amplifiers stabilized by feedback, it is advantageous to use feedback over several stages in order to realize the full benefits of this type of circuit. The basic circuit element in such an amplifier consists of the several amplifying stages and the associated feedback network that together constitute a feedback loop. Two types of feedback loops have been found useful in high-gain wide-band amplifiers having rise times in the range 0.5 to 0.05 μsec. These circuit elements will be described in the present section, and their use in complete amplifiers will be treated in Chap. 3. An exact circuit analysis for the transient behavior of the two feedback loops is so involved that the design of these elements has depended primarily upon cut-and-try methods.

The feedback loop shown in Fig. 2.20(a) is the more conventional of the two circuit elements to be discussed. Here feedback is accomplished by the network between the plate of the second tube and the cathode of the first. The mid-band gain of such a loop is given by

$$A = \frac{A_\infty}{1 + \dfrac{1}{\mu_1} + \dfrac{1}{G}\left[A_\infty + \dfrac{R_F}{R_t} + R_2\left(\dfrac{1}{R_K} + \dfrac{1}{R_t}\right)\right]} \tag{25}$$

and the mid-band output impedance by

$$R_o = \frac{\dfrac{R_2}{G}\left(A_\infty + \dfrac{R_F}{R_t}\right)}{1 + \dfrac{1}{\mu_1} + \dfrac{1}{G}\left[A_\infty + \dfrac{R_F}{R_t} + R_2\left(\dfrac{1}{R_K} + \dfrac{1}{R_t}\right)\right]} \tag{26}$$

where

$$A_\infty \equiv (R_F + R_K)/R_K$$

$$G \equiv g_{m1}R_1 g_{m2}R_2$$

$$R_t \equiv r_t/(1 + \mu_t)$$

$$\mu_1 \equiv -\left(\frac{\partial E_{screen}}{\partial E_{grid}}\right)_{E_p,\ I_p}$$

The significance of all the symbols in these equations is obvious with the possible exception of R_t and μ_1. The resistance R_t would be the output resistance of T-1 between cathode and ground, if it were connected as a triode. The quantities r_t and μ_t are the triode plate resistance and amplification factor, respectively. The amplification factor μ_1 of the pentode T-1 is very nearly equal to its triode amplification factor μ_t and therefore will have a value in the range 20 to 35 depending on the type of tube used. In a practical amplifier the actual gain will be several per cent smaller than the "ideal" gain A_∞. Equation 25 is useful in estimating the relative importance of the various circuit parameters. The mid-band output resistance will ordinarily have a value of a few hundred ohms or less.

When the feedback loop of Fig. 2.20(a) is used at high frequencies, several design problems are encountered in regard to the feedback path that exists between points differing considerably in d-c level. Either unduly large values of R_F and R_K must be used to avoid excessive direct currents, or else an unduly large blocking capacitor must be used in the feedback path. In either case trouble is experienced with stray capacitances to ground or to other parts of the circuit. For instance, a parasitic capacitance of 2 $\mu\mu$f has a reactance of about 30,000 ohms at 3 megacycles per second, so that the character of the feedback at high frequencies may be markedly altered when R_F has a resistance of this order of magnitude. In practice it is desirable to keep the value of R_F sufficiently low so that a small trimmer C_F [see Fig. 2.20(a)] across R_F is needed, in addition to the parasitic capacitance of R_F, to compensate the loop for no transient overshoot on a fast test pulse. A value of R_F as large as 22,000 ohms

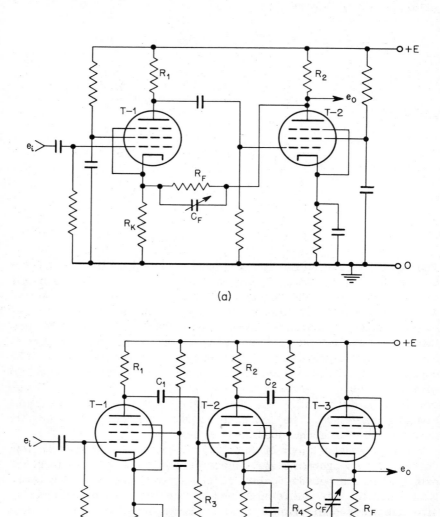

Fig. 2.20 — Feedback loops.

has been used successfully in this type of loop where the upper half-power frequency is around 6 megacycles per second. In such an amplifier it is necessary to mount all components securely to avoid variations in parasitic capacitances once the loop has been adjusted for good transient response.

If a blocking capacitor is used in the feedback path, it should have a small reactance at 60 cycles per second compared with R_K. Otherwise hum and microphonics will not be fed back. The physically large capacitor required is ordinarily undesirable on account of its excessive capacitance to ground.

The plate-to-cathode type of feedback loop has been used chiefly as a low-gain high-level amplifier for driving the deflecting plates of a cathode-ray tube. When used for large signals, as in this instance, the plate-load resistor R_2 of the second stage should be shunt-compensated by using a wire-wound resistor (10- or 20-watt size) having a parasitic inductance somewhat larger than that required for critical damping. The shunt compensation so afforded will aid the amplifier in delivering fast transients of considerable magnitude without the grid of the second tube being overdriven.

The second type of feedback loop to be described is shown in Fig. 2.20(b). It consists essentially of two amplifying stages preceding a cathode follower, a fraction of whose output voltage is fed back to the cathode of the first tube. On account of the similarity of this feedback loop to the one just discussed, the mid-band gain and output impedance are given by Eqs. 25 and 26, respectively, where now

$$G \equiv \frac{\mu_3}{1 + \mu_3} \ g_{m1}R_1g_{m2}R_2$$

and where R_2, occurring in Eqs. 25 and 26, must be replaced by $R_c = r_{p\,3}/(1 + \mu_3)$, the cathode-follower output impedance of T-3. As in the case of the other feedback loop, a typical amplifier made with high-transconductance pentodes will have a gain that is several per cent less than A_∞. Its mid-band output impedance, however, will be somewhat less than 10 ohms.

The addition of the cathode follower to the feedback loop not only results in a low mid-band output impedance, but affords certain conveniences in the design of the circuit. Feedback occurs between points whose d-c level can be chosen to suit the requirements of the direct-coupled feedback network. The feedback resistances R_F and R_K can thus have relatively low values. Often R_K can be chosen to give the correct bias for T-1. For instance, if T-1 is a 6AC7, R_K can be 75 to 100 ohms; thus, for a loop gain of 100, R_F is 7,500 to 10,000 ohms. For no transient overshoot on a fast step wave, the trimmer C_F across R_F will need to be set at a few micromicrofarads. Such a feedback loop will have a rise time of perhaps 0.06 μsec,* corresponding to an upper half-power frequency of about 5 megacycles per second.

The high-frequency response of the amplifier can be decreased by increasing the value of C_F. This method of reducing the width of the pass band tends to increase the stability of the amplifier rise time, since the shape of the high-frequency cutoff is determined primarily by a property of the feedback path and not by the shape of the unfed-back gain-frequency curve. It is undesirable to limit bandwidth by deliberately introducing additional parasitic capacitance in the amplifier portion of the loop.

When using tubes recommended for video amplifiers, the plate-load resistances should ordinarily lie in the range 5,000 to 25,000 ohms, the values chosen depending upon the available plate-supply voltage and on the tube plate currents. Necessary decoupling between feedback loops to avoid motorboating will lower the available plate-supply voltage for all but the output loop. It is not necessary to decouple the three tubes within a loop. In fact, it is often convenient to use common screen bias for the first two amplifying stages.

In a feedback loop having two RC grid couplings affecting the low-frequency response, phase shifts may cause a peaking of the response at low frequencies. To avoid this difficulty, the two time constants should differ by a sufficiently large factor, whose value depends on the amount of feedback. Often it is possible to arrange the operating points of T-2 and T-3 so that the plate of T-2 can be direct-coupled to the grid of T-3. This device lowers the parasitic capacitance of the interstage coupling besides preventing trouble at low frequencies.

The unfed-back gain G in a typical feedback loop may have a value of 10,000. For a loop gain of 100, the approximate feedback factor will be as large as 50. It will not be 100 on account of the additional terms in the denominator of Eq. 25. These terms are neglected in the usual elementary account of feedback amplifiers. A feedback factor of this magnitude will reduce to negligible proportions the major ills that plague unfed-back wide-band amplifiers, namely, nonlinearity for high-level output signals and lack of gain stability.

When a feedback loop is compensated for no overshoot on a fast transient, its upper half-power frequency will be approximately the same as that which an unfed-back amplifier would have if the same number of tubes were used and the plate-load resistors were reduced

---

* Rise time is defined in Chap. 3, Sec. 4.1.

to make the unfed-back gain identical to the gain of the feedback loop. The lower half-power frequency of a feedback loop will be reduced below that characterizing the amplifier without feedback by a factor approximately equal to the feedback factor. For this reason the lower half-power frequency of a wide-band feedback loop employing an interstage coupling having a time constant as small as $RC = 2 \times 10^{-4}$ sec ($C = 0.001$ μf and $R = 200,000$ ohms) will be a few cycles per second.

No attempt has been made to devise wide-band feedback loops using more than two amplifying stages (or two amplifying stages plus a cathode follower) since the excessive phase shift occurring at high frequencies will be likely to cause oscillations. The feedback loops that have been described appear to fill the most immediate needs for wide-band, stabilized amplifiers required in nuclear physics investigations and in the study of fast electrical transients.

In using three-tube feedback loops, there are several precautions to be observed. If the cathode follower furnishing output voltage is loaded by a capacitance, the phase shift occurring in the cathode follower may be sufficient to alter the high-frequency response of the loop, even to the point of causing oscillations. In other words, at high frequencies the output impedance has an inductive component and a negative real part. For this reason any load on the loop must be primarily resistive. In the case of low-level signals, for instance, a properly terminated coaxial cable is satisfactory, but not one that is unterminated, even though it be only a few feet long. Trouble may also be experienced with parasitic oscillations in the first tube of the loop. Such oscillations can be prevented by a suppressor resistance of perhaps 50 ohms, placed in series with the input grid.

3.6 <u>Linear Oscillators</u>. The linear oscillators discussed in the present section have been found to be useful elements in designing timing circuits and special circuits that require a constant-frequency source having either a greater stability or a better waveform than is obtainable with a simple relaxation oscillator. In timing applications there is often little need for an oscillator whose stability is better than 0.1 per cent, since other quantities measured in the experiment are usually in error to a much greater extent than this amount. The important considerations affecting the choice of an oscillator circuit element are simplicity, reliability, and compactness. Where oscillators having a calibrated, continuously variable frequency output are required, it is usually most satisfactory to employ a commercially built instrument. For this reason the oscillators considered here are meant to be used at a single frequency, or at several definite frequencies that can be selected by a simple switching operation. The circuits described include an RC oscillator, some LC oscillators, a pulsed LC oscillator, and several crystal oscillators.

(a) <u>An RC Oscillator</u>. The RC-oscillator circuit shown in Fig. 2.21 is of the type that is used in several commercial variable-frequency generators.* It consists essentially of an amplifier whose gain is

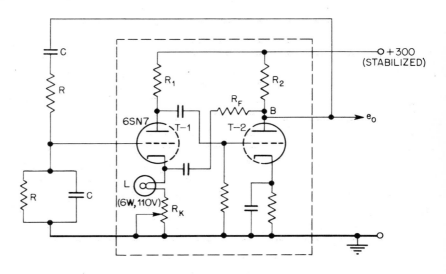

Fig. 2.21 —Simple RC oscillator.

determined by an inverse feedback network, and of an RC network that affords a regenerative feedback path between the output and input terminals of the amplifier. The phase of the regeneratively fed-back voltage depends on frequency. If the amplifier has no phase shift at the frequency of oscillation, the condition for oscillation is

$$G = 3 \tag{27}$$

where G is the gain of the amplifier between input and output terminals. The frequency of oscillation is

$$f = \frac{1}{2\pi RC} \tag{28}$$

For good frequency stability and good output waveform, the gain must be kept exactly 3 and the output signal limited in amplitude to where

---

*See F. E. Terman et al., Proc. I.R.E., 27:649 (1939).

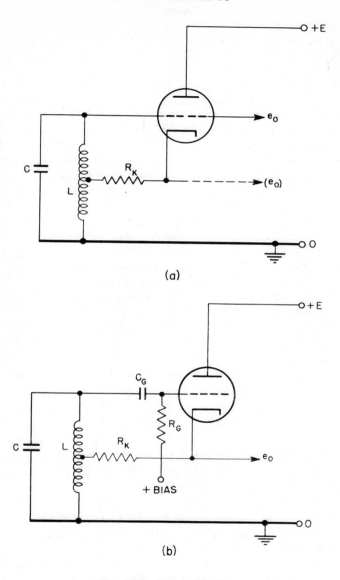

Fig. 2.22 — LC oscillators.

T-2 is operating over a linear portion of its characteristic. The tungsten lamp L in the feedback network of the amplifier automatically ensures these conditions, for if the amplifier gain increases, tending to make the amplitude of oscillation build up, the lamp increases its resistance and, through greater inverse feedback, restores the gain of the amplifier to exactly 3. To aid in establishing a suitable operating condition for T-2, the variable resistance R_K can be placed in series with the lamp. If appreciable amounts of power are to be drawn from the oscillator, an additional amplifying stage must be added to the circuit shown.

The design of an oscillator of this sort proceeds in a straightforward manner. Where possible, low temperature coefficient components should be used in the RC network and the value of C kept large compared with the input capacitance of the amplifier. The amplifier required for the circuit is evidently of the type described in the previous section. The particular amplifier shown in Fig. 2.21 is about the simplest one that can be built. It is suitable for use up to frequencies where an appreciable phase shift in the amplifier begins to set in (i.e., about 100 kc/sec). Greater frequency stability can of course be obtained with an amplifier based on pentodes instead of triodes. The circuit shown, however, can be used in applications where there is a need for a simple oscillator at audio frequencies having good waveform but not exceptional frequency stability.

(b) LC Oscillators. The basic LC-oscillator circuit to be considered here is shown in Fig. 2.22(a). It is a variety of the well-known Hartley circuit. The resistance R_K in the cathode lead serves the dual purpose of furnishing bias and affording negative-current feedback. At the resonant frequency, $f = 1/(2\pi \sqrt{LC})$, the capacitor-coil combination has the parallel impedance $R_p = \omega L Q = \omega^2 L^2/R_s$, where $Q \equiv \omega L/R_s$ and R_s is the series resistance of the coil. The approximate condition for oscillation can be shown to be

$$\tfrac{1}{4} R_p = R_K + 1/g_m \approx R_K \qquad (29)$$

When R_K has the value indicated by Eq. 29, the tube will not be severely overdriven, and the frequency of oscillation will tend to be independent of changes in tube characteristics. At frequencies where the reactance of parasitic capacitances is small, it is convenient to make part of R_K adjustable. A very stable oscillator at audio frequencies and at low radio frequencies results if R_K consists principally of a low-wattage 110-volt tungsten lamp and if the circuit is so designed that the lamp stabilizes the amplitude of oscillation as in the RC-oscillator circuit, enabling the tube to operate Class A.

The output signal from an oscillator of this type can be taken from the grid or from the cathode, or the oscillator tube can be made a pentode and the signal taken from the plate circuit. The latter circuit is termed an "electron-coupled oscillator" and does not require a buffer stage to isolate it from other circuits with which it is being used. When the signal is taken from the cathode, a better waveform can be obtained by biasing the grid positive — for instance, by the method shown in Fig. 2.22(b).

In certain timing applications it is necessary to have a pulsed oscillator, i.e., an oscillator that can be turned on at a definite time by means of a trigger pulse. One of the simplest circuits of this sort is shown in Fig. 2.23(a). The original trigger is used to initiate, in another circuit element (not shown), the negative pulse, or "gate" e_i.[*] This gate cuts off the steady current I flowing through tube T-1 and the inductance L, so that the voltage across the coil and capacitor immediately begins to oscillate sinusoidally with amplitude $V_m = I\omega L$. If the resistance R_K in the cathode of tube T-2 is chosen correctly, then T-2 will serve to maintain the amplitude of oscillation constant for the duration of the negative gate. As soon as current is again drawn by tube T-1, thus loading the resonant LC circuit by the cathode-to-ground output resistance of T-1, the amplitude of oscillation quickly dies to zero.

In designing a pulsed oscillator of this sort, it is necessary to choose values of I and of L such that a reasonable amplitude of oscillation, $V_m = I\omega L$, can be obtained. The value of V_m evidently determines the minimum amplitude that the negative gate can have, for tube T-1 must remain nonconducting when its cathode is at $- V_m$ volts below ground potential. Furthermore, it is evident that the rise time of the leading edge of the gate should be short compared with one period of oscillation. The resistance R_L in the plate of T-1 serves to control the magnitude of the current through the inductance. Its value must not be made so low that the maximum allowable plate dissipation of the tube is exceeded.

Pulsed oscillators based on the circuit shown in Fig. 2.23(a) can be built to run at frequencies as high as 2 megacycles per second, but for pulsed operation in the range of a few megacycles it is better to rearrange the biases in the circuit so that the clamping tube T-1 can be replaced by a pentode clamp (see Sec. 4.1 of this chapter). The parasitic capacitance across the resonant circuit is thereby reduced. Moreover, the task of cutting off the current through the inductance in a time short compared with one period of oscillation is considerably simplified. The basic circuit element of this type is indicated in Fig. 2.23(b). The output signal from such an oscillator may require some amplification before it is large enough for practical use.

---

[*] The univibrator (see Sec. 4.2 of this chapter) is ordinarily used for generating the negative gate.

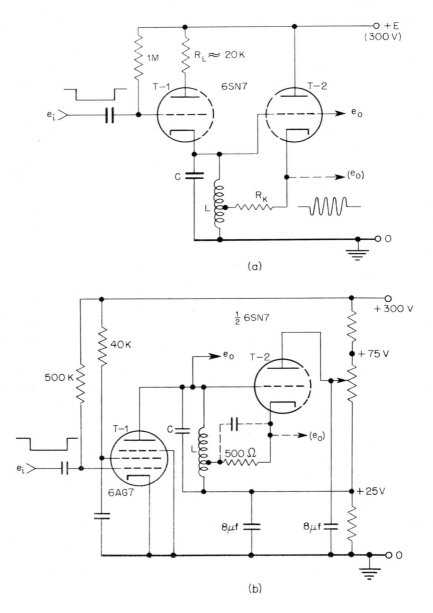

Fig. 2.23 — Pulsed LC oscillators.

(c) Crystal Oscillators. It is often convenient in designing timing and calibrating equipment to use an oscillator whose frequency-determining element is a piezoelectric crystal instead of an LC circuit. As compared with other types of oscillators, a crystal oscillator is less subject to frequency drift, and its frequency ordinarily does not need to be measured, since the factory calibration of the crystal is sufficiently accurate. Moreover, such an oscillator requires but little space, and no great care need be exercised in its construction to ensure adequate frequency stability. The chief precaution to be observed in designing a simple crystal oscillator is to avoid over-excitation of the crystal. Overexcitation, which is particularly easy in the case of crystals whose resonent frequency lies below 1 mega-cycle per second, may lead to the destruction of the crystal. The crystal current should preferably be kept considerably less than the maximum value recommended by the manufacturer of the crystal.

If a choice of several different fundamental frequencies must be available in a given circuit, it is convenient to have plug-in oscillator units. For general timing applications, crystals of frequencies 100, 200, 500, 1,000, and 2,000 kc/sec are useful. Circuits suitable for crystals of these frequencies are shown in Fig. 2.24. Each circuit, including the crystal, can be built into a shield having a five-prong plug for its base.* The oscillator tube consists of one-half of a 6SN7, whose other half may either be used as a cathode-follower buffer stage, or be used elsewhere in the circuit. It should be pointed out that the circuits shown in Fig. 2.24 are not suitable for use in constructing a secondary frequency standard, where a much greater frequency stability is required than in the timing of laboratory experiments. Moreover, in applications where an appreciable amount of power must come from the oscillator, the oscillator circuit should be based on a pentode or beam-power tube.

In certain timing applications it is necessary to convert the sinusoidal signal from a crystal oscillator into a series of narrow voltage pulses. Although this may be done by passing the sinusoidal signal through some form of distorting amplifier, it is more economical to generate the voltage pulses directly from the current pulses that occur when an oscillator is running Class C. A suitable circuit for use at 1 megacycle per second is shown in Fig. 2.25. With this circuit, positive pulses can be obtained that are more or less triangular in shape, about 40 volts high, and perhaps 0.25 μsec wide at their

---

* The National Radio Products PB-10-5, 5-prong base and shield, has been found suitable.

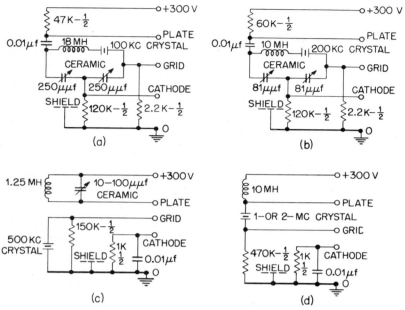

Fig. 2.24 — Crystal oscillators.

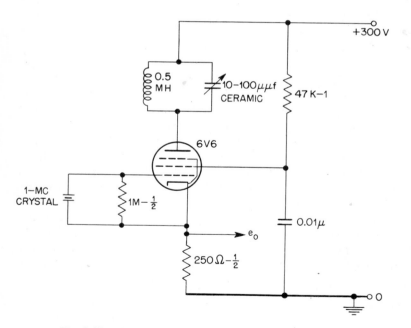

Fig. 2.25 — Crystal oscillator for delivering voltage pulses.

base. Parasitic capacitance across the output must, of course, be kept at a minimum. This method of obtaining narrow pulses can be applied to any oscillator that is operating Class C. It has been used successfully with an LC oscillator having a frequency of 1,000 cycles per second.

3.7 Constant-current Devices. A constant-current device is a two-terminal circuit element that can furnish a steady current independent of voltage changes in the circuit branch in which it is placed. Most practical devices of this sort fail to meet the strict requirements of the definition, and so correspond to a high resistance R_s in parallel with an ideal constant-current source I or in series with a constant-voltage source $E_s = R_s I$. Moreover, practical devices can function only over a limited range of voltage variations between their terminals.

The most common constant-current device consists of a pentode connected as shown in Fig. 2.26(a). The manner of biasing the control grid and the screen grid in an actual circuit depends on the available fixed-supply voltages. The resistance R_s that can be realized with this circuit is at most only a few times the plate resistance r_p of the pentode. Although increasing the cathode resistance R_K results in a value of R_s somewhat higher than r_p, the chief function of R_K is to stabilize the constant current against changes in pentode characteristics. The relation $E \approx (I + I_{screen})R_K$ gives the approximate grid bias. The screen bias voltage must be chosen high enough to avoid danger of the tube's drawing grid current. A very high value of bias is undesirable, since the plate resistance decreases once the plate potential is less than that of the screen. This effect tends to limit the operating range over which the plate potential may vary.

In applications requiring constant currents of the order of 1 ma or less, a high-mu triode with degeneration in the cathode circuit, as shown in Fig. 2.26(b), makes an excellent constant-current device. Values of R_s that can be obtained are given by

$$R_s = r_p + (\mu + 1)R_K \tag{30}$$

As an example consider a 6SF5 triode with $\mu = 100$. If $E_g = 100$ volts and $I = 0.5$ ma, then $R_K \approx 2 \times 10^5$ ohms, and $R_s \approx 20$ megohms.

An altogether different type of constant-current device can be used for charging a capacitor in order to realize a linearly increasing voltage. The basic circuit of this type is shown in Fig. 2.27(a). The "constant current" exists in the resistance R as soon as the switch K is opened, and persists until the cathode follower overloads, or until the switch is closed. As soon as the switch is closed, the circuit recovers to its initial state in a time dependent on the capacitor C_1 recovering its charge. In most applications the switch K is a pentode clamp (see Sec. 4.1 of this chapter).

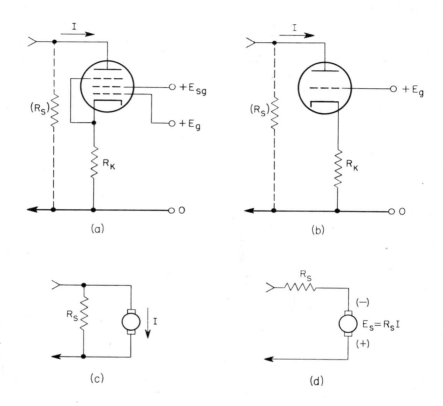

Fig. 2.26 — Constant-current devices. Equivalent circuits are shown in (c) and (d).

The detailed operation of the circuit proceeds as follows: When K is opened, the current $I_0 = E_2/R$ flows into the capacitor C, whose potential difference V_c thereby starts to increase linearly. The voltage V_c is applied to the grid of the cathode-follower tube, whose output $A V_c$ is fed back through a large blocking capacitor C_1 to point P at the far end of the resistor furnishing current to C. The diode allows the potential of point P to rise above the supply voltage E_2. If the gain A of the follower were unity and if no potential drop were to occur across C_1, then the potential difference across R would be

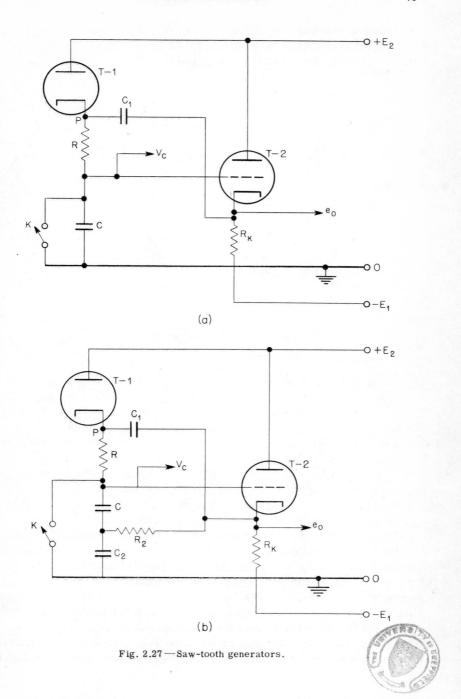

Fig. 2.27 — Saw-tooth generators.

maintained constant, resulting in a constant current I_o flowing into C.
Taking into account a value of A less than unity and a changing potential across C_1, the current flowing into C becomes

$$I = I_o - \frac{V_c}{FR} \qquad (31)$$

where

$$F = \frac{1}{1 + \dfrac{C}{C_1} - A} \qquad (32)$$

Equation 31 indicates that the current source has an effective resistance $R_S = RF$ in parallel with it. The charging of the capacitor C
therefore proceeds according to

$$V_c = FE_2 \left[1 - \exp\left(-t/FRC\right)\right]$$

$$= E_2(t/RC) \left[1 - (1/2F)(t/RC) + \ldots\right] \qquad (33)$$

Inspection of this result indicates that when $V_c \approx \frac{1}{2} E_2$, at time $t = \frac{1}{2}$
RC, the departure from a true linear increase in 25/F per cent. Since
it is not difficult to obtain values of F in the range 10 to 25, the resulting waveform is sufficiently linear for many purposes.

The particular type of constant-current, capacitor-charging device
just described is usually termed a "saw-tooth generator." It finds
its chief application in circuits for generating sweep voltages for
cathode-ray tubes and in circuits for producing relatively long time
delays between an input and an output pulse. In the latter application
it is often desirable to improve the linearity of the device over that
indicated by Eq. 33. This can be accomplished by employing the network R_2, C_2 as indicated in Fig. 2.27(b). The addition of this network
affects the voltage V_c in the following way: On opening the switch K,
V_c increases as the result of (1) the current I, which charges the two
capacitors in series, and (2) the current I_2, which charges only capacitor C_2. Now the current I decreases as V_c increases, as indicated by
Eq. 33. The current I_2, however, increases with increasing V_c. By
properly choosing the value of the time constant $R_2 C_2$, it is possible
to make the term in t^2 vanish in the power-series expansion for V_c.

An analysis of the circuit indicates that the proper relationship is

$$R_2 = R \frac{C}{C_2} \frac{A - C/(C + C_2)}{1 + C/C_1 - A + (1 - A)(C/C_2)} \tag{34}$$

where A is the gain of the cathode follower with all resistive loads taken into account. Usually the capacitor C_2 is chosen to have several times (perhaps 10 times) the capacitance of C, so that the resistance R_2 will have the order of magnitude of R. With the above restriction on R_2C_2, the series expansion for the voltage V_c becomes

$$V_c = \frac{E_2}{R} \left(\frac{1}{C} + \frac{1}{C_2}\right) t \left[1 - \frac{(1 - A)}{6RR_2C_2} \left(\frac{1}{C} + \frac{1}{C_1}\right) t^2 + \cdots\right] \tag{35}$$

As an example of the degree of linearity that can be obtained, let $A = 0.90$, $C/C_1 = 0.01$, and $C/C_2 = 0.2$. Then the computed departure from linearity for $V_c = \frac{1}{2} E_2$ amounts to approximately 0.05 per cent.

3.8 **Some Properties of Feedback Circuits.** A number of the linear circuit elements already described have employed inverse feedback in some form. Since elementary as well as advanced treatments of feedback amplifiers are readily available,* it has been assumed that the reader is acquainted with the method and with its important advantages. In most of the circuit elements considered here, feedback is used primarily to improve the stability of gain and to increase the linearity of response of high-level stages, and at the same time to maintain a desirable high-frequency response characteristic. In this connection it seems fairly certain that the two- and three-stage feedback loops discussed in Sec. 3.5 of this chapter do not represent the optimum design for obtaining the fastest possible monotonic transient rise for a given gain. Little attention has been given by designers of feedback amplifiers to this problem, which differs from the more usual problem of obtaining the maximum gain-bandwidth product without regard to good transient behavior of the amplifier.

When a feedback circuit is used for high-level operation, some care in design must be exercised; otherwise the grid of one of the stages will be overdriven, causing the circuit to block. There is a possibility

---

*For elementary accounts see H. J. Reich, "Theory and Applications of Electron Tubes," Secs. 7 to 24, McGraw-Hill Book Company, Inc., New York, 1944; and F. E. Terman, op. cit., Sec. 5. For an advanced treatment, see H. W. Bode, "Network Analysis and Feedback Amplifier Design," D. Van Nostrand Company, Inc., New York, 1945.

that this can occur if the maximum possible grid swing is greater than either the grid bias in the case of positive signals, or the voltage required for cutoff in the case of negative signals. In the normal operation of the circuit, feedback prevents the tube from being overdriven. However, there is a time delay between the application of a signal and the compensating voltage signal returning through the feedback path, and in this short time interval the tube may be overdriven. Evidently this difficulty will occur only if the input signal has an extremely rapid rise.

In estimating the possibility that a particular tube will be overdriven, it is necessary to know the greatest magnitude and the minimum time of rise of any signal that can conceivably occur at the grid of the tube. Often the minimum rise time is set by preceding low-level stages and therefore can be computed with sufficient accuracy. Although the magnitude of the grid-to-cathode signal can usually be estimated for legitimate signals of given rise time, difficulty is sometimes experienced with very large signals picked up inadvertently just before the proper signal occurs. In applications where this can happen, it may be advisable not to use a feedback amplifier. However, if such an amplifier seems called for, on account of its greater gain stability or its greater linearity of response it may be possible to employ diodes, such as types 6AL5 or 6H6, to limit the magnitude of the signal reaching the output stages of the amplifier where overloading will first occur. An alternate scheme involves direct-coupling of the output stages, so that grid-current flow will not cause the amplifier to block. After a feedback amplifier intended for wide-band application has been designed and constructed, its overload characteristics should be investigated, using test signals similar to the signals for which it has been designed. Suitable pulse generators and other test equipment are described in Chap. 6.

The input and the output impedance of an amplifier are normally altered by the presence of a feedback network. This property of a feedback circuit is well exemplified by the cathode follower, which has been discussed in Sec. 3.4 of this chapter. It can be used in various ways to obtain a large (or small) effective value of some circuit parameter other than resistance, such as capacitance. As an illustration, consider the circuit elements shown in Figs. 2.28(a) and (b). If $|G|$ is the magnitude of the mid-band gain of the amplifier, the effective input capacitance for a range of frequencies will be $(1 + |G|)C$. This method of obtaining a large effective capacitance is occasionally useful where the physical size or the electrical quality of a very large capacitor is objectionable.

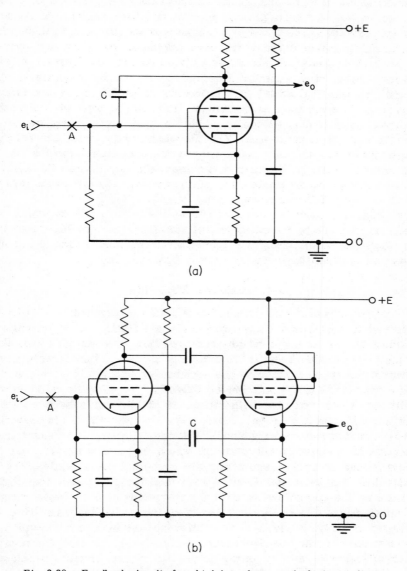

(a)

(b)

Fig. 2.28 — Feedback circuits for obtaining a large equivalent capacitance.

A circuit element of the type described can be used as the basis for an electronic integrating circuit. In this case a resistance R is placed in series with the input grid (at point A in either circuit). If the amplifier is suitably designed, the output voltage signal e_o will be proportional to the integral of the input signal to within an accuracy of 1 per cent or better. It should be pointed out that an alternative form of integrating circuit can be based on the simple RC integrating element shown in Fig. 2.5(b). The output signal will then require amplification. The chief disadvantage of this simple type of integrating circuit rests in the difficulty of obtaining a high-quality capacitor having a large capacitance. If in an integrating circuit the relative positions of R and C are interchanged, the circuit becomes a differentiating circuit. In the case of the feedback amplifiers of Fig. 2.28, some revision of the biasing is required before either can be used as the basis of a differentiating circuit.

A trigger circuit is here defined as a circuit element which can exist in only one or the other of two stable or quasi-stable states and in which the transition from one state to the other takes place in a more or less discontinuous or irreversible manner.

4. TRIGGER CIRCUITS

Trigger circuits find an application in the production of certain desired discontinuous or impulsive signals having some prescribed periodicity, or having a definite time relation with signals from other circuit elements. Trigger circuits can be placed in three general classifications according to the number of absolutely stable states they possess: (1) "relaxation oscillators," or circuits with no absolutely stable state but with two quasi-stable states between which the circuit continually oscillates; (2) circuits with a single stable state in which they remain until a suitable trigger pulse causes them to pass to a quasi-stable state in which they remain for a certain time before returning spontaneously to their original state; (3) circuits that can be made to pass back and forth between two stable states by the application of suitable triggering signals (usually two). A brief discussion of several useful examples of the three types of trigger circuits is given in the following sections. No attempt has been made to make the discussions complete or rigorous, but particular attention is paid to those properties of the circuits which are important for understanding the design of electronic equipment discussed in later chapters, and to those properties which it is believed are not adequately covered or stressed in existing literature or which may not be obvious to one who is first trying to use these circuits.

More detailed discussions of the operation of several circuits of this type, as well as much useful background material, will be found in "Time Bases," by O. S. Puckle, and in recent publications of the Radiation Laboratory of the Massachusetts Institute of Technology.

4.1 <u>Relaxation Oscillators.</u> The relaxation oscillator is a convenient source of relatively large impulsive signals. It may be used either free-running or synchronized with some other periodic signal to serve as a source of signals of a desired form or of a frequency that is a subharmonic of the frequency of the driving source (frequency divider). Since the operation of a relaxation oscillator depends, in part, upon the property of thermionic emission, the frequency of oscillation is not so stable as that of a linear (sinusoidal) oscillator. Relaxation oscillators to be considered here are the thyratron oscillator, the multivibrator, and the free-running blocking oscillator.

(a) <u>The Thyratron Oscillator.</u> An example of a thyratron-oscillator circuit and the voltage waveforms associated with it is shown in Fig. 2.29. For the indicated supply voltages, the period of oscillation is determined by the resistance R_1 and the capacitance $C_1 + C_2$ and is nearly $R_1(C_1 + C_2)$. In the particular circuit shown, the frequency can be varied from 100 to 300 cycles per second. When a wide range of frequencies is desired, various values of C_1 can be selected by means of a multiple-position switch. If successive values of capacitance are related by powers of 3, a range of frequencies continuously adjustable from 1 to 10,000 cycles per second can be obtained conveniently.

The fixed portion of R_1 must be large enough that the maximum charging current through it will not maintain a discharge in the tube. Its minimum value depends on the values of other circuit components and usually cannot be less than 50,000 ohms. Because of parasitic leakage resistance to ground, the maximum value of R_1 is usually limited to 10 megohms. The resistances R_2 and R_3 serve to limit the maximum grid and plate currents to safe values.

Triode thyratrons are almost universally used in relaxation oscillator circuits. Tetrodes can be used, but because of the steepness of their anode-voltage firing characteristic their operation is not reliable, resulting in an unstable frequency.

The output signal from a thyratron oscillator may be taken from the anode or cathode circuit. If the imperfect saw-tooth wave that appears at the plate is to be used to drive a high-impedance circuit, the components C_2 and R_4 can be omitted. It is more often desired to obtain a low-impedance positive signal of short duration. The "signal output" connection indicated in Fig. 2.29(a) provides such a voltage

80 ELECTRONICS

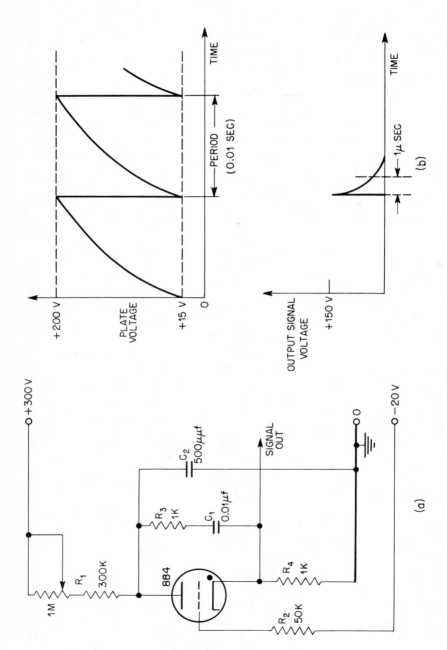

Fig. 2.29 — A thyratron oscillator.

pulse, whose form is shown in Fig. 2.29(b). The lower side of C_1 is connected to the cathode rather than to ground, so that the duration of the exponential tail of the pulse is determined only by the time constant $R_4 C_2$ and does not vary with changes in frequency. The value of R_4 is not critical since it affects the amplitude of the output signal only in a secondary manner. Values commonly used for R_4 range from 100 to 10,000 ohms. When the signal is taken from the circuit in the manner shown, the frequency of oscillation does not depend upon the impedance of the load. The capacitive reactance of the load, however, must be kept small compared with that of C_2 if the pulse amplitude is not to be decreased.

The thyratron oscillator is the relaxation oscillator most commonly used in the equipment discussed in this book. The output signal, which is often used for triggering other circuit elements, has a fast rise and comes from a relatively low-impedance source. The frequency of the oscillator is readily variable over a wide range and can be conveniently synchronized with a standard-frequency source. The circuit itself requires few components and is reliable in operation. Care must be taken when using the circuit in combination with other elements to prevent the current surges, which occur when the tube fires, from inducing transient electromotive forces in near-by circuits. It is usually sufficient to keep all leads short, but in some cases it may be necessary to increase the value of R_3 or to shield the circuit from its neighbors.

(b) The Multivibrator. The multivibrator is occasionally used as a relaxation oscillator when its characteristic rectangular output waveform is desired, and when an output pulse of somewhat slower rise is satisfactory. It is useful where similar pulses of opposite sign, occurring at the same time or at different times, are desired. The frequency of its oscillation cannot be varied conveniently. The circuit and waveforms of a symmetrical multivibrator are shown in Fig. 2.30. The rise times of the steep parts of the waveforms are about 2 to 5 μsec. Since a multivibrator is essentially a wide-band amplifier with the input coupled to the output, the same considerations affecting the design of wide-band amplifiers are applicable here, and presumably multivibrators can be made with rise times of the order of 0.1 μsec. However, such multivibrators would require a large expenditure of power and necessitate the use of two pentodes, so that their general use could not be justified economically.

The frequency of a symmetric multivibrator is determined primarily by R_1 and C_1 and is inversely proportional to the product of the two if R_2 is much smaller than R_1. Frequencies from 10 to 100,000 cycles per second can be secured conveniently. When large coupling capacitors (C_1) or small anode loads (R_2) are employed, it may be necessary to insert a series resistance, 50,000 ohms or more, in the

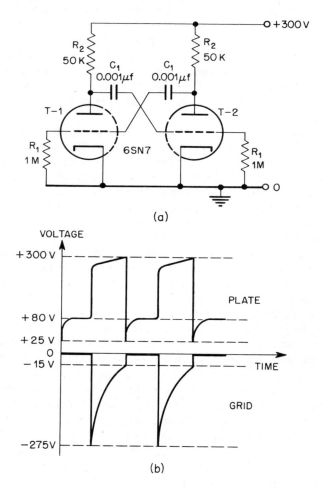

Fig. 2.30 — Multivibrator.

anode-grid circuits to prevent excessive grid current from flowing each time a capacitor is being charged. This resistor can be shunted with a small capacitor (20 $\mu\mu$f) if it is desired to maintain a short rise time.

Asymmetric multivibrators are convenient for special applications. Their frequency, which is a complicated function of the circuit parameters, is not very stable if the half periods of the two stable states differ by more than a factor of 10. The same considerations as for the symmetric case apply to the rise time of output signals.

(c) The Blocking Oscillator. The free-running blocking oscillator is most useful for frequencies above the range that can be handled conveniently by the thyratron oscillator or the multivibrator. The blocking oscillator has been used successfully for frequencies from 1 kc/sec to more than 1 megacycle per second. It can provide, at low impedance, sharp pulses of either sign, and its frequency can be varied and controlled easily. The circuit of a typical free-running blocking oscillator is shown in Fig. 2.31. The transformer L can be one of several types designed specifically for this application. Although it is possible to use a pentode in the circuit, a triode that can supply a large peak current is almost universally employed. The frequency of a blocking oscillator is determined in part by the type of transformer and tube used, and in part by the values of C_1 and R_3.* For a given setup it varies approximately linearly with the resistance R_3, whose value may range from several thousand ohms to several megohms. Varying the capacitance C_1 will change the frequency of oscillation, but for satisfactory operation a value must be chosen to suit the particular transformer used. This value will usually lie between one hundred and a few thousand micromicrofarads. Output pulses 75 volts high can be obtained as indicated in Fig. 2.31. The positive and negative signals are identical except for sign (plus or minus) and d-c level. Output signals can also be taken from a suitable point on the transformer or from a tertiary winding. Unless the ratio of primary turns to tertiary turns is small, either of the last-mentioned methods yields a high output impedance.

Any of the relaxation oscillators described can be synchronized with a primary periodic-voltage source whose frequency is slightly higher than the natural frequency of the oscillator or is a multiple of its natural frequency. The synchronization is accomplished by injecting, at a proper point in the oscillator, triggers of a suitable nature (the requirements are usually critical) from the primary source. Frequency dividers of this type will operate successfully with dividing ratios as high as 10 per stage, and several such stages can be

---

* For operation at high frequencies it may be desirable to return the resistor R_3 to the plate supply bus instead of to ground.

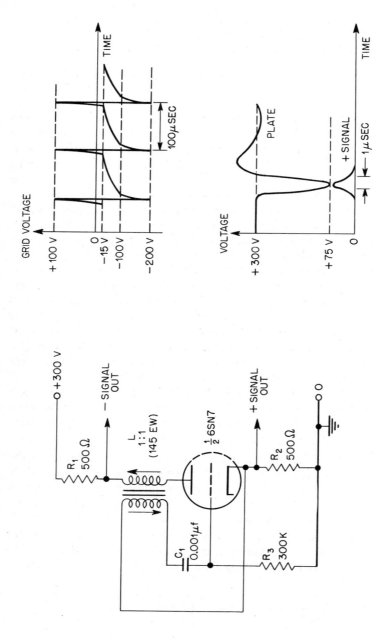

Fig. 2.31 — Free-running blocking oscillator.

used. Thyratron oscillators are suitable for dividing frequencies below 10 kc/sec, and blocking oscillators for higher frequencies. Methods of injecting synchronizing signals are discussed in Sec. 4.4 of this chapter, under "Methods of Triggering."

4.2 Trigger Circuits with One Stable State. The second class of trigger circuits to be considered is the type that has one absolutely stable state and one quasi-stable state. Under the influence of an applied trigger, the circuit can be made to pass from the first state to the second. It then returns to the original state after a time that is determined by circuit parameters. This type of circuit is useful for obtaining voltage pulses of standard shape and magnitude, in response to triggers that may occur intermittently and may be of varying or undesirable shape and magnitude. Another important application is in the producing of a pulse that is delayed with respect to the applied trigger by a time determined by the duration of the quasi-stable state. The three simple forms of circuits in common use are the biased thyratron, the univibrator, and the biased blocking oscillator.

(a) Thyratron Circuits. Thyratron circuits of the types in Fig. 2.32 have a stable state in which the tube is nonconducting. When the thyratron is fired by the application of a trigger, the circuit passes into a quasi-stable state in which the tube is conducting. After a time that depends only on circuit parameters, the tube is extinguished and the circuit returns to its original state. A biased thyratron circuit is used for obtaining large fast uniform output signals in response to small input triggers that may occur irregularly spaced in time and may have undesirable pulse shapes.

The circuit of Fig. 2.32(a) is like the thyratron oscillator discussed in the preceding section. Its output is similar in shape to that of the oscillator but is somewhat larger, since the condenser C_1 gets fully charged to the supply voltage before the tube is fired. The circuit shown in Fig. 2.32(b) is similar in operation except that the shunt capacitance of the delay line, D.L., gets discharged through the tube and the resistance R_3 at a uniform rate. If R_3 is equal to the characteristic impedance of the delay line, the output signal will be a negative rectangular pulse whose height is one-half the supply voltage and whose width is twice the delay time of the line.*

For the most satisfactory operation of biased thyratron circuits, the triggering signals should be large, have a short rise time, and be of short duration. If the trigger is 50 volts or larger and rises in less

---

* Delay lines and their use in circuits of this type are discussed in more detail in Sec. 2.4 of this chapter.

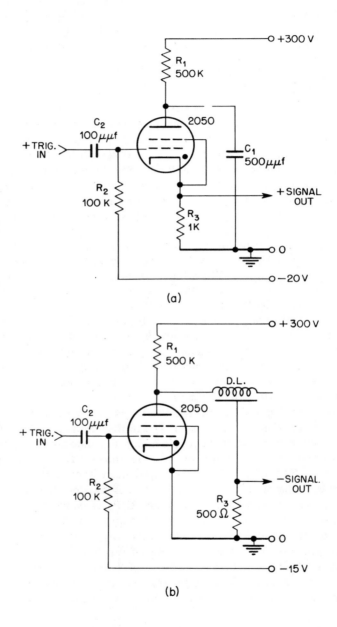

Fig. 2.32 — Biased-thyratron circuits.

than 0.1 μsec, the delay in the appearance of the output signal will be less than 0.1 μsec. The duration of the trigger ordinarily should be no longer than 10 μsec. Triggers shorter than this will have no effect on the recovery time of the circuit, but if they come from a low impedance source and if C_2 is larger than necessary, some of the input signal will appear in the output, and excessive grid currents may be drawn. In such cases it is advisable to insert some resistance — 10,000 ohms or more — in series with the input-signal lead.

The circuits in Fig. 2.32 will operate satisfactorily with a wide range of values for R_1 and C_1 (or the shunt capacitance of the delay line). Minimum and maximum values for the resistance R_1 are set by the same considerations as for the corresponding resistance in the thyratron oscillator circuit. The value of C_1 is usually determined by the shape or magnitude desired of the output signal. It must not be so small that the thyratron will not extinguish. The minimum value depends on the values of R_1 and R_3, and is usually somewhat less than 100 $\mu\mu$f. If uniform output signals are desired, it is important that the time constant R_1C_1 be less than one-third of the minimum time separation between any two input triggers. This ensures that C_1 will become completely charged during each cycle of operation. Because of the relatively long deionization time of the thyratron, the recovery time usually cannot be made less than 500 μsec. Gas tetrodes are almost exclusively chosen for this application because of their sensitive firing characteristic and their fast response time. Triodes are sometimes used, especially if it is desired to decrease the recovery time, which with triodes can be made as short as 25 μsec.

(b) <u>The Univibrator</u>. The delay multivibrator, or so-called "univibrator," is an important modification of the multivibrator. It is a circuit element that finds many applications in the design of special electronic devices. Its utility comes from the fact that the duration of its quasi-stable state is easily controlled over wide limits, and the fact that there are points in the circuit where the potentials are steady except during a transition between states. These properties make it particularly suitable as a "delay circuit," i.e., one in which an output signal is produced at some controllable time after the occurrence of an initial trigger. It is also useful as a source of rectangular voltage pulses, or "gating signals."

A typical univibrator circuit diagram is shown in Fig. 2.33(a). Since there are many suitable methods of applying a trigger to such a circuit, these methods will be discussed in a separate section (Sec. 4.4 of this chapter), and no means of triggering has been provided in Fig. 2.33. Furthermore, no output-signal lead is shown, since the output can be taken from any one of several points in the

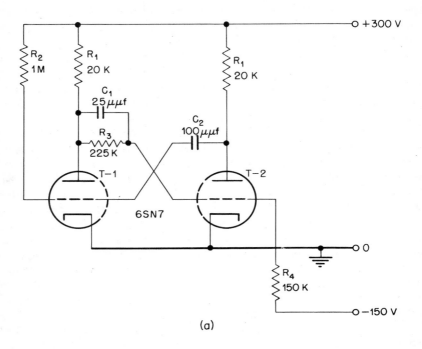

(a)

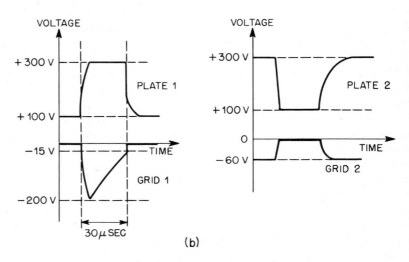

(b)

Fig. 2.33 — Univibrators.

circuit, according to the type of signal desired. The circuit shown in Fig. 2.33 resides in a stable state when the grid of the tube T-1 is at ground potential and draws grid current sufficient to maintain the supply voltage drop across the resistor R_2. Under these conditions the tube T-1 has a plate current of 10 ma, and its plate rests at +100 volts. Because of the voltage-divider action of the resistors R_3 and R_4, the grid of the tube T-2 is at -55 volts, cutting off the current through the tube. The anode of T-2 is therefore at the positive supply voltage, and the capacitor C_2 is charged to +300 volts. Under these conditions tube T-2 has zero transconductance, and the state of the circuit is completely stable. If, by some triggering mechanism, the grid of T-2 is brought to within 15 volts of ground, the circuit becomes regenerative and quickly transfers to a new state that is only temporarily stable. In this state the grid of T-2 is at ground, its anode is at +100 volts, and tube T-1 is cut off. After an interval of time during which the capacitor C_2 discharges through R_2, the grid of T-1 reaches a potential within 15 volts of ground. The circuit therefore is again regenerative and will transfer to its original stable state. The length of time spent by the circuit in its quasi-stable state is called the delay time.

Waveforms at four points in the circuit are shown in Fig. 2.33(b). It is evident from the waveform at the plate of T-2 (plate 2) that the transfer from the stable state to the quasi-stable state takes place very rapidly (about 2 μsec for the circuit shown). The transfer to the stable state takes place equally rapidly, but the circuit is not completely restored to its original condition for a somewhat longer "recovery time." This is due to the fact that the capacitor C_2, which discharges through R_2 during the quasi-stable state, must recharge through R_1 by means of current flowing to the grid of T-1. The time required for this recharging operation sets a lower limit to the time that must elapse between the completion of one operation and the beginning of the next if the delay times are to be equal for both operations. The sloping waveform of the signal on the grid of T-1 during the quasi-stable state is part of an exponential curve that is proceeding toward +300 volts with a time constant of R_2C_2. The square waves at the plate of T-1 and at the grid of T-2 are of shapes suitable for use as gating pulses. When differentiated by means of an RC-coupling network having a short time constant, they provide delayed pulses for triggering other circuits.

The circuit of a univibrator may be varied in several ways to suit different applications. The following considerations affect the choice of circuit components and the exact arrangement of the circuit.

The duration of the quasi-stable state is determined by the resistance R_2 and the capacitance C_2. It is proportional to the product R_2C_2, and for the circuit of Fig. 2.33 it is approximately $\frac{1}{3} R_2C_2$. Either or both of these components may be made variable. An upper limit to the value of R_2 is set by the presence of circuit-leakage resistance. The circuit, however, may tend to become unstable for other reasons if resistances greater than 10 megohms are used. With some sacrifice in the stability of the delay time, longer times can be secured with lower resistances by connecting R_2 from the grid of T-1 to ground instead of to the positive supply bus. In this case the delay time is more nearly $2R_2C_2$ for the circuit of Fig. 2.33. The capacitance C_2 should be not less than 20 $\mu\mu$f. Smaller values are undesirable on account of parasitic circuit capacitances that affect the voltage division at the grid of T-1 and therefore impair the operation of the circuit. Values of C_2 as large as several microfarads can be used, but with values so large the recovery time (time for the complete transition between quasi-stable and stable states) will be inconveniently long. In fact, it may be necessary with large capacitances to insert a resistance of 100,000 ohms or more in series with C_2 and the grid of T-1 in order that excessive grid currents shall not be drawn while C_2 is charging.

The speed with which a change of state occurs in a univibrator is determined both by the bandwidth of the amplifiers of which the circuit may be considered as being constructed and by the gain around the regenerative loop. This applies only when the input trigger is sufficient merely to initiate the regenerative action. In certain cases the trigger may be so violent that it completely dominates the transfer action, in which case the change of state may occur much faster. For normal triggers, the bandwidth and gain considerations that apply to wide-band amplifiers also apply here. In addition to affecting the gain and bandwidth considerations, the value of the anode-load resistor R_1 of the tube T-2 also affects the recovery time of the circuit. In some cases the anode-load resistors of the two tubes differ in value. The purpose of the condenser C_1 is to improve the high-frequency response of the voltage divider R_3,R_4, whose response would otherwise be hurt by parasitic circuit capacitances.

The values of the resistances R_3 and R_4 are chosen subject to a compromise between two desirable conditions. For maximum stability of the normal state and of the delay time, it is desirable that a small amount of grid current be drawn when the grid of T-2 is at ground, and furthermore that, when tube T-1 is conducting, the grid of T-2 should be as far as possible below the cutoff voltage of the tube. Values of R_3 and R_4 are usually adopted that will set the grid voltage

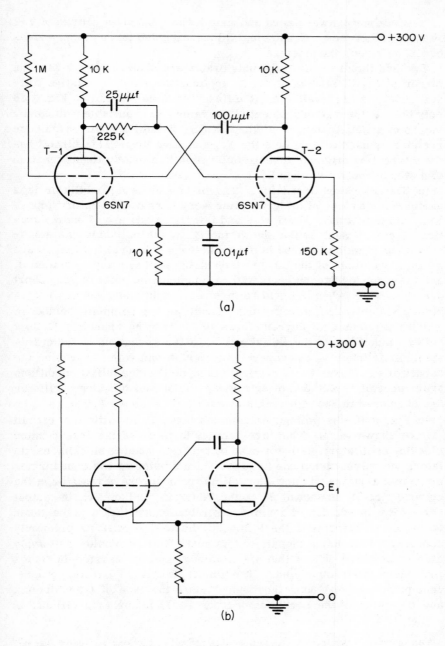

Fig. 2.34 — Univibrators.

of T-2 midway between zero and cutoff when the plate voltage of T-1
is midway between the extreme values expected for nominal values
of all the circuit parameters.

Two additional forms of the univibrator are shown in Fig. 2.34. The
circuit of Fig. 2.34(a) is useful in applications where a negative voltage supply is not available. It differs from the circuit of Fig. 2.33
only in that the cathode potential is raised to a suitable voltage by
means of a self-biasing resistor. In Fig. 2.34(b) a common cathode
resistor is used to complete the regenerative loop. This circuit has
the interesting property that the delay time is a nearly linear function
of a steady control voltage E_1.

(c) The Blocking Oscillator. The biased blocking oscillator is a
useful circuit element for generating very narrow pulses, or "pips,"
i.e., pulses that have short rise and fall times and are of short duration. A circuit such as that shown in Fig. 2.35(a) is stable in a quiescent state in which the tube is biased below cutoff and all voltages are
steady. The plate of the tube is then at the positive supply potential,
and the cathode at ground potential. A quasi-stable state of very short
duration exists when the grid voltage is brought above cutoff. In this
state a violent oscillation results, usually of one complete period, in
which sufficient grid current flows to charge the capacitor C_1 to a
voltage much below the initial value. After cessation of the quasi-
stable state there is a recovery time during which the charge on the
capacitor C_1 returns to its original value, so that the initial conditions
again prevail.* Methods of triggering the biased blocking oscillator
are discussed in Sec. 4.4 of this chapter.

In Fig. 2.35 the voltage waveforms associated with the circuit
(a) are shown in (b). They are similar to those of the free-running
blocking oscillator. As in the case of the free-running blocking oscillator, the output signal can be taken from a point on the transformer
or from a tertiary winding, as well as from across a resistor in the
cathode circuit, as shown. Since the "current" pulse, i.e., the output
across R_2, is usually of a more desirable shape than a pulse taken
from the transformer, the following discussion will be primarily
concerned with output signals of this sort. The discussion will apply
also to negative pulses that are obtained if R_2 is inserted in series
with the positive supply bus. The amplitude and the duration of current pulses depend upon the type of tube, the type of transformer,
and the value of the series impedance R_3, C_1 in the grid circuit. If

---

* An analysis of the transient conditions that prevail in blocking oscillators can be
found in publications of the Radiation Laboratory of the Massachusetts Institute of
Technology.

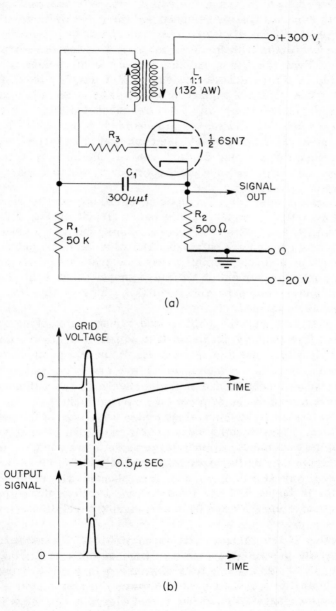

Fig. 2.35 — Biased blocking oscillator.

triangular-shaped pulses are desired, R_3 is made zero and C_1 is chosen to suit the transformer used and the pulse width desired. Suitable values of C_1 usually lie between 100 and 5,000 $\mu\mu f$. Two types of blocking oscillator transformers made by Westinghouse are in common use. Type 145 EW is suitable for producing pulses from 1 to 5 μsec wide, and type 132 AW for pulses of 1 μsec or less. It is possible to produce pulses as narrow as 0.1 μsec by using a type 132 DW or 132 DW2 transformer with a triode-connected 6AC7. It is necessary, when fast, narrow pulses are desired, to ensure that the triggering pulse itself has a short rise time and is as large as possible. Pulses much longer than 5 μsec can be obtained by using transformers other than the ones mentioned, or by winding more turns on the 145 EW core.

Rectangular pulses from a blocking oscillator can be secured in a number of ways by modifying the basic circuit of Fig. 2.35. If the resistance R_3 is made a few hundred ohms, current pulses roughly rectangular in shape are obtained. The width of these pulses is still determined as before. A small inductance inserted in series with R_3 gives some improvement in the pulse shape. Also, it is possible to get rectangular pulses by replacing C_1 by a delay line that is open-circuited at its far end.

For most purposes the 6SN7 triode is used in blocking oscillator circuits. If extremely large or fast output signals are desired, a 6AC7 or a 6AG7 connected as a triode, or the two sections of a 6SN7 connected in parallel, can be used. These tubes, as well as a 6V6 or a 6L6 triode-connected, are suitable when high repetition rates are encountered, making the average tube current high.

The resistance R_2 is determined by the amplitude of the output signal desired. For values below 500 ohms the signal is nearly proportional to the resistance. If much larger values are used, the operation of the circuit may be impaired. Occasionally the value of R_2 is made very large, say 10,000 ohms, and it is shunted with a large capacitance, for instance, 0.01 μf. Under these conditions the output signal is a vertical step, followed by a part having a relatively long exponential decay.

The value of the resistance R_1 is not critical. Its maximum value is set by the permissible recovery time of the circuit; that is, the capacitor C_1 should become fully discharged through R_1 between successive operations of the circuit. A lower limit on the value of R_1 is set by the fact that its impedance must be large compared with that of C_1 at the natural frequency of oscillation during the operating state. With oscillators delivering very narrow pips, values as low as a few thousand ohms have been used successfully. It should be remembered that the effective value of R_1 includes the internal resistance of the negative bias supply to which it is connected. On account of grid current, the average resistance presented by the circuit to the bias supply is negative; that is, the circuit furnishes current to the supply instead of taking current from it. Under these conditions of Class C bias, a very convenient bias source is a cathode follower.

Since instantaneous currents of the order of 1 amp may be drawn during the transient state of a blocking oscillator, it is necessary that suitable precautions be taken to prevent the oscillator from interacting with neighboring circuits. This entails the use of short connecting leads and the introduction of a simple RC decoupling filter between the oscillator and the positive supply bus. If the signal is taken from the cathode circuit or from the transformer, 5,000 ohms and 0.01 μf constitute a satisfactory filter. If the signal is taken from across a resistor in series with the positive supply bus, a capacitance of 0.1 μf or larger may be necessary to avoid an undesirable tail on the output signal.

4.3 Trigger Circuits with Two Stable States. Two classes of trigger circuits having two stable states are of interest. The first class contains circuits that have an indefinite "memory," i.e., they possess two discrete, absolutely stable states, and can be transferred from one state to the other by suitable triggering pulses. They have the important property that, when all connections to other elements have their normal potentials, they can exist indefinitely in either of two states depending upon a previous sequence of events. A circuit of this sort is an indispensable part of certain types of computing or tallying circuits, and is also extremely useful in many other complex circuit combinations. The second class of circuits includes trigger circuits that exist in either of two stable states, depending on the instantaneous value of an external control voltage.* This type of circuit should perhaps not be termed a "trigger circuit" at all, but the designation does conform strictly to the definition of trigger circuit made previously. It should be made clear that the transition between the two stable states is not effected by an impulsive trigger but simply by the d-c value of the applied signal.

(a) Thyratron Circuits. If the capacitor C_1 is removed from the circuit of Fig. 2.32(a) or if the resistance R_1 is decreased to 10,000 ohms or less, the resulting circuit has two stable states: the thyratron is either conducting or nonconducting. Both states are stable, since the first is maintained by the negative grid bias and the second

---

* This statement is not precisely true. The necessary correction is discussed under hysteresis considerations of the Schmitt trigger circuit.

by the nature of the gas discharge. The circuit passes from the non-conducting to the conducting state when the grid receives a suitable trigger, as described in Sec. 4.2 of this chapter. The circuit then remains in this state until it is "reset" by a second trigger of a different sort. Resetting can be accomplished by applying a negative pulse of 100 μsec duration to the anode or by opening the plate or cathode circuit momentarily. In some cases it is possible to effect the transition to the nonconducting state by the application of a large negative pulse to one of the grids. The waveforms that can be obtained from this circuit are essentially fast-rising steps of voltage. Most of the discussion concerning the circuit of Fig. 2.32(a) applies here as well. Circuits of this type are used occasionally in pairs to form a tallying or "counting" circuit. The circuit finds its principal use at the present time as a "locking" circuit which responds to the first of many incoming signals but which does not respond to subsequent signals until it is manually reset.

(b) The Flip-flop. Another element that can exist in each of two stable states is the well-known Eccles-Jordan trigger circuit, or "flip-flop circuit," as it will be called here. A symmetric form of this circuit is shown in Fig. 2.36(a). If the tube T-1 is conducting, its grid will be at ground potential and its plate at +100 volts. Because of the voltage-dividing action of R_2 and R_3, the grid of T-2 will be at -50 volts, more than enough to cut off the tube current. The plate of T-2 will therefore rest close to +300 volts, and the grid of T-1 will tend to be at +30 volts. Sufficient grid current, however, will be drawn by T-1 to keep its grid very close to ground, which is the potential we assumed for this grid. This state is evidently a stable one, since small changes of the plate potential of T-1 will not move the grid of T-2 above cutoff, and will therefore produce no change at the grid of T-1 and no further change at the plate of T-1. If by means of a trigger the grid of T-2 is moved to within 15 volts of ground, the circuit becomes regenerative and a rapid transition to a second stable state occurs. It is evident from the symmetry of the circuit that this second state is the "mirror image" of the first, and that a suitable trigger will return the circuit to its initial state. As with the trigger circuits previously discussed, the transition to a new stable state does not necessarily mean that static conditions will at once prevail. Evidently a certain recovery time must elapse before equilibrium is finally reached, during which time charges on the circuit capacitances redistribute themselves. Methods of triggering the flip-flop circuit are discussed in Sec. 4.4 of this chapter and also in Sec. 4.5, where the interesting case of the scaler circuit is treated. Output signals may be taken from any of a number of points in a flip-flop circuit.

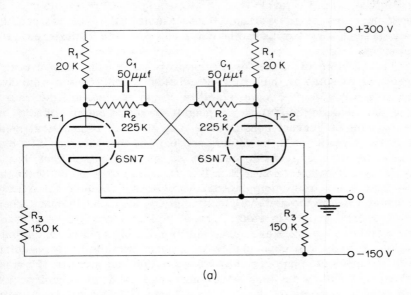

(a)

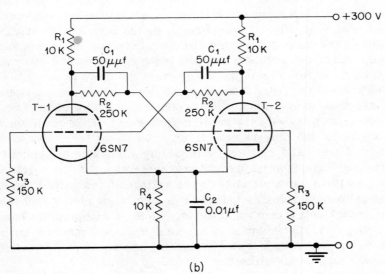

(b)

Fig. 2.36 — Flip-flops.

The particular point (or points) chosen is determined by the sign, magnitude, and d-c level desired of the signal. The signals for the most part are steady voltages that assume either of two possible values. Impulsive signals can be obtained by simple RC differentiating networks.

The selection of values for the components in a flip-flop circuit is governed by some of the following considerations. The magnitude of the resistors R_1 affects the stability of the two states, the rate of transfer between the states, the magnitude of the output signals, and the amount of current consumed by the circuit. A practical upper limit to the value of R_1 is determined both by the desired "flip-over time," or time of transfer between states, and by the fact that R_1 should be somewhat smaller than R_2. Values as high as 100,000 ohms are used in circuits employing 6SL7 tubes. A minimum value for R_1 is usually set by the plate dissipation of the tube, but in cases where a low-voltage supply is used, R_1 must be high enough to ensure that the signals at the grids are sufficient to move the grid voltage from a region of high transconductance to a point somewhat below cutoff. With sharp-cutoff pentodes (6AK5's) and a plate supply of 150 volts, values of R_1 as low as 2,000 ohms have been used successfully. With values of R_1 between the two extreme limits, flip-over times ranging from 10 to 0.1 μsec can be obtained. In some circuits, however, the flip-over time is determined primarily by the nature of the triggering signal. In this case the trigger circuit is required only to maintain a certain condition established by the trigger, and regenerative action plays only a minor role in the operation of the circuit.

The ratio of the resistances R_2 and R_3 should have a value such that the maximum grid voltage is determined by the flow of grid current and, therefore, is slightly greater than zero. This condition adds greatly to the stability of the circuit, since small changes in plate voltage of the "off" tube are absorbed by variations in grid current of the "on" tube, and so produce negligible changes in its grid voltage, i.e., little variation in the plate voltage of that tube. The value of the ratio should ensure that the minimum value of the grid voltage is somewhat below that required for cutoff. A compromise between these two conditions is usually effected in such a way that the midpoint of the grid voltage swing is midway between zero and cutoff for nominal values of the circuit parameters.

The value of the resistance $R_2 + R_3$ is limited on the one hand by current and power considerations, and on the other by recovery-time requirements. Values below 100,000 ohms for this resistance are seldom used, because of current and power limitations. Values as high as several megohms are satisfactory when long recovery times are permissible. The capacitors C_1 serve to transmit, from the plate of one tube to the grid of the other, fast signals that would otherwise be attenuated because of the presence of parasitic capacitances. Values for C_1 are usually not less than 10 $\mu\mu$f and may be as large as 100 $\mu\mu$f when signals are taken from the grids, making it necessary to drive the parasitic capacitances of several associated elements. The magnitude of C_1 should be no larger than necessary if a short recovery time is desired. Since the length of the recovery time is of primary importance in the design of scaler circuits, a detailed discussion of this point will be postponed until Sec. 4.5 of this chapter.

In Fig. 2.36, circuit (b) is an example of a flip-flop that does not require a negative supply. Its operation is essentially that of circuit (a) except that smaller voltage swings occur throughout the circuit. The resistor R_4 is so chosen that the equilibrium value of the cathode self-bias voltage is low enough to make the conducting tube draw some grid current.

(c) The Schmitt Trigger Circuit. The circuit element shown in Fig. 2.37(a) is sometimes called the "Schmitt trigger circuit."* The properties of this circuit, as well as those of related circuits, have been found to be very useful in the type of work with which this volume is concerned. Because of the nature of these properties, the circuit is sometimes known by the more generic name of "voltage discriminator." Its use will be described in Chap. 4, Sec. 2.1.

The operation of the circuit can be described simply if it is assumed that the input-signal lead is connected to a source of steady voltage whose value can be varied at will. Let us therefore consider values of the steady voltages that appear at various points in the circuit as a function of this input voltage. When the input voltage is zero, the tube T-1 is cut off, and its plate rests close to the positive supply potential. The grid of T-2 is then at +100 volts, and since T-2 acts as a cathode follower its cathode is at about +104 volts and its plate at +250 volts. If now the input voltage is raised slowly, nothing happens until it reaches the vicinity of +100 volts. Slightly below +100 volts the tube T-1 begins to conduct, and at some critical input voltage near +100 volts a regenerative condition sets in, which causes a sudden transfer of current from T-2 to T-1 to occur. The nature of this regeneration is evident if we consider the situation where the two grids are at the same potential but the grid of T-1 is held fixed. Any

---

* O. S. Puckle, op. cit.

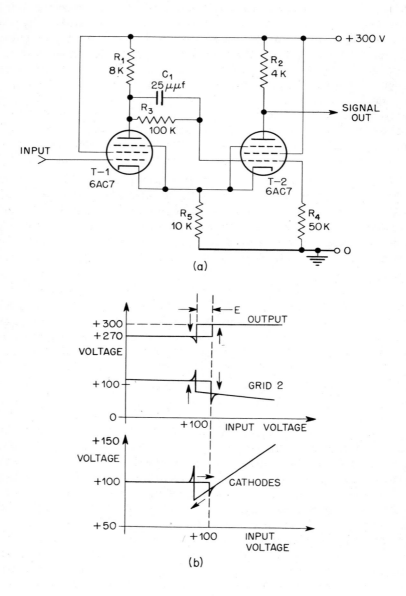

Fig. 2.37 — Schmitt trigger circuit.

small signal at the grid of T-2 appears amplified at the plate of T-1, as described under Difference Amplifiers (Sec. 3.3 of this chapter). This signal is then fed to the grid of T-2, where it has the correct phase to cause regeneration and so results in an unstable condition. The unstable state is actually reached when the grid potential of T-1 is somewhat below that of T-2, and at this point a sudden transition to a second stable state takes place. In the new state, tube T-1 is conducting and the cathodes are at about the same potential as before. However, the plate of T-1 is now at +270 volts, and the grid of T-2 is at +90 volts, or 10 volts below the cathode potential, so that T-2 is now cut off. If the input voltage is further increased, tube T-1 simply behaves as a cathode follower. The increase in cathode voltage and the decrease in grid voltage of T-2 due to the additional plate current drawn by T-1 have no further effect on the state of the circuit. Under these conditions the input signal can be increased until T-1 overloads and grid current is drawn. As long as the input voltage remains above +100 volts, the new state is maintained, and circuit voltages vary reversibly with input voltage.

If now the input voltage is decreased to the vicinity of +90 volts, a point is reached where the cathode potential is sufficiently close to the grid potential of T-2 that T-2 begins to conduct. In addition, less current is drawn by T-1, so that its plate potential begins to rise. A regenerative condition again results, and, even though the grid of T-1 is maintained at a fixed potential, the circuit changes irreversibly to its original state in which tube T-1 is cut off and T-2 is conducting. Reducing the input voltage to zero has no further effect on the circuit, which is now completely restored to its original condition.

It is convenient to exhibit the operation of a circuit of this kind by graphic means. The cyclogram of Fig. 2.37(b) shows the voltage relations that have been obtained with the circuit values shown. The transient behavior is indicated for cyclic operation at about 50 kc/sec. The voltage E indicated in the cyclogram is termed the "hysteresis" of the circuit. Values for the hysteresis between 0 and 50 volts are easily obtained by the proper choice of the circuit components.

It is evident that this type of trigger circuit differs from most others in that the state of the circuit depends on the instantaneous value of the input voltage. If the hysteresis is greater than zero, there is a small range of input voltages (from +100 to +110 volts for the above example) where either of two states may exist, depending on the immediately preceding history of the input signal. Thus, for an input voltage of +105 volts, the state in which the circuit is found depends on whether this voltage is approached from above or below.

If the amount of hysteresis is reduced below zero, the trigger circuit degenerates into an amplifier with positive feedback such that saturation is reached for small signals of either sign. The circuit voltages then become single-valued functions of the input voltage, and there no longer exists the possibility of irreversible changes in the state of the circuit. The circuit is strictly a trigger circuit only when the gain around the regenerative loop can be greater than 1 for some value of the input voltage. It should be noticed that, if the capacitance C_1 is larger than is necessary to achieve a frequency-independent voltage divider from the plate of T-1 to the grid of T-2, the gain around the loop will be greater at high frequencies than at low frequencies. Under these circumstances, if the gain at low frequencies is just less than 1, a relaxation oscillation will result when the input signal is +100 volts. It is usually necessary to avoid this condition, especially when slowly varying input signals are to be encountered.

It is possible to achieve triggering action with a wide variation in the values of the circuit components. The values for R_1, R_3, R_4, and R_5 should be so chosen that the gain from the grid of T-2 through the common cathode resistor to the plate of T-1 multiplied by the voltage-dividing factor of R_3 and R_4 is somewhat greater than 1. The extent to which the maximum gain is greater than 1 determines the amount of hysteresis in the circuit. This consideration usually determines the value of R_1, the values of the other resistances being determined by different considerations. Since it is often necessary that the input signal be allowed to assume a wide range of values without grid current being drawn by T-1, a lower limit is set for possible values of R_5. In order to get fast triggering action, as well as fast output signals, it is necessary for the plate resistors R_1 and R_2 to have low values. If sufficiently large output signals are to be obtained, this entails drawing a fair amount of plate current in the tubes. The value of this current, in connection with the value for R_5, sets the ratio of the resistances R_3 and R_4. These considerations indicate that tubes of relatively high transconductance and power dissipation must be used in the circuit. The magnitude of $R_3 + R_4$ is determined by the same reasoning as that applied to $R_2 + R_3$ for the trigger circuit of Fig. 2.36. Since the resistor R_2 plays little or no role in the operation of the circuit, its value is chosen to give a desired amplitude of output signal. The value must not be so high that the tube T-2 overloads, i.e., draws grid current, when it is conducting.

The Schmitt trigger circuit can be considered as a voltage comparison device. It gives an output signal whenever the input voltage becomes approximately equal to the voltage at the grid of T-2. It is possible to vary the "reference" voltage by varying the ratio of R_3 to R_4, although if a wide range of voltages is desired it is more advisable to replace R_3 by a capacitor and to vary the voltage at the bottom of R_4. In this case, however, the circuit has only one stable state and possesses some of the properties of the univibrator as well as those of the Schmitt circuit.

4.4 Methods of Triggering. (a) Thyratron Circuits. The method of triggering thyratron circuits, from a state in which the tube is not conducting to a state in which it is passing current, is straightforward. It is merely necessary to increase the control grid-to-cathode voltage to a point beyond a critical value, and eventually the tube will fire. The delay in firing depends upon the magnitude of the excess of the trigger voltage over the critical firing potential. If the excess is a few tenths of a volt, the time delay between the application of the trigger and the firing of the thyratron may be several microseconds. If the excess is several tens of volts or more, the delay can be as small as 0.05 μsec. The common method of applying a trigger to a thyratron is indicated in the circuits of Fig. 2.32. This method of triggering is usually satisfactory if the impedance of the triggering circuit is high or if the output signal is taken not from the cathode circuit as shown but from the plate circuit, with the cathode connected directly to ground. A positive trigger is required, and, before the tube fires, the impedance presented to the input signal is high — essentially the resistance R_2 in parallel with a stray capacitance of about 10 $\mu\mu$f. A similar method, which can be used for negative triggers coming from a low impedance source, is indicated in Fig. 2.38(a). In this case R_1 should be small, 1,000 ohms or less, and C must be suited to the nature of the input signal. Both of these methods have the property that when the tube fires, signals are introduced into the external triggering circuit. A method of triggering that overcomes this difficulty and is applicable to circuits in which fast firing is desired, is indicated in Fig. 2.38(b).

In this circuit the trigger signal is fed to the thyratron grid through a diode, which permits the grid to rise in potential unimpeded once the thyratron has fired. Hence, excessive grid current cannot be drawn even though the impedance of the source of the trigger is relatively low in order to obtain fast firing of the thyratron. Still another method of triggering a thyratron to prevent interaction with the trigger source is indicated in Fig. 2.38(c). Here a cathode follower is used to couple the input trigger to the thyratron grid. The cathode follower not only presents a high impedance to the trigger source but also serves to limit the magnitude of thyratron grid current that can

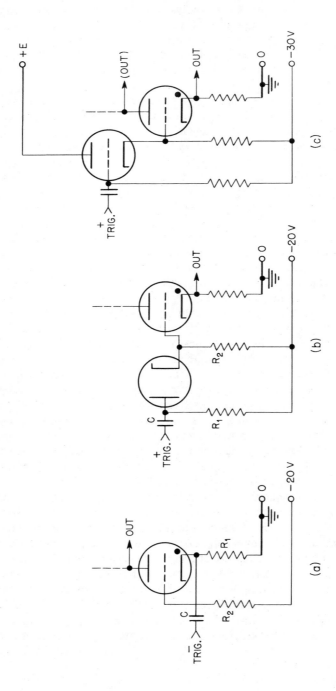

Fig. 2.38 — Methods of triggering thyratron circuits.

be drawn, since the cathode follower cuts off as soon as its cathode potential is raised much above its grid potential. Both of the circuits just described can be used only for positive input signals.

Extinguishing a thyratron in a trigger circuit is usually accomplished by opening a mechanically operated switch in the plate circuit. The same result can be achieved by applying a trigger to the cathode or to the plate so that the tube drop is reduced below 15 volts for 100 μsec or more. It is also possible to extinguish a thyratron by applying a long, very large negative trigger to the grid. This type of triggering is seldom used intentionally. It may cause trouble when a thyratron is used as a locking device.

(b) Flip-flops, Univibrators, and Multivibrators. The flip-flop circuit of Fig. 2.36 ideally has three states of equilibrium. Two of these are the stable states discussed in Sec. 4.3(b) of this chapter, and the third is a state in which corresponding points in the two halves of the flip-flop have identical voltages. The third state, of course, is highly unstable, and a small variation in any of the conditions of symmetry brings about an immediate transition to one of the stable states. If there were no capacitances associated with a flip-flop circuit, triggering could be accomplished only by forcing the circuit from one of its stable states to a point just beyond the state of symmetric equilibrium. On removing the influence of the trigger, the circuit would then assume its second stable state.

The triggering of actual flip-flops, univibrators, and multivibrators occurs under somewhat different conditions. Because of parasitic circuit capacitances, the circuit will never pass through the state of symmetric equilibrium, but will get from one stable state to the other either by passing through a new symmetric state that is not one of equilibrium or, more likely, by never assuming a symmetric configuration at all. When a circuit of the multivibrator type is triggered by a signal slow compared with the natural flip-over time, it behaves most nearly like an ideal circuit that has no parasitic capacitances.

If a fast trigger is used, i.e., one which has a rise time short compared with the flip-over time of the trigger circuit, the method of triggering is altogether different from that with a slow trigger. In fact, two methods of fast triggering can be distinguished. In one method, the trigger causes one or more points of the circuit to pass from the voltages of one stable state to the voltages of the other stable state so quickly that all the energy for the transition is supplied by the trigger. Regeneration in the circuit acts merely to bring all the other points of the circuit "up to date" a short time later. This manner of triggering is approached in circuits from which it is desired to obtain a very fast output signal. The other method of fast triggering occurs when the trigger supplies only enough energy to bring one point of the circuit quickly to a voltage such that, either immediately or shortly thereafter, regeneration occurs and completes the transition to the new state. It is not even necessary that any one point in the circuit be brought beyond the voltage at which an unstable equilibrium would occur, since the stray (or introduced) capacitances in the circuit constitute a "memory" that keeps the transition going to its ultimate end once it has been given a sufficiently good start. What constitutes a sufficiently good start is usually determined empirically, although a graphic analysis of the circuit behavior can be made if all the circuit parameters are known. This last manner of triggering is essential to the operation of certain types of scale-of-two circuits to be discussed in Sec. 4.5 of this chapter.

Practical methods of triggering flip-flop, univibrator, and relaxation oscillator circuits can be considered separately according to whether a conducting tube is "turned off" or a nonconducting tube is "turned on." The former method is ordinarily employed, since it requires less energy to accomplish a triggering action. The latter method can be used when a large positive trigger is available, or when it is desired to generate a fast output signal at the plate of the tube turned on.

Figure 2.39 illustrates six methods that are satisfactory for triggering flip-flops, univibrators, and multivibrators. Although a univibrator and a flip-flop circuit are used as examples in the figure, it is to be understood that each method of triggering applies equally well to all types of trigger circuits based on the multivibrator. Five of the methods shown operate to turn off conducting tubes, and the remaining one operates to turn on a nonconducting tube.

The simplest and most economical way of applying a trigger consists in coupling it to the grid of the conducting tube with a small capacitor, as in the case of trigger 1 in Fig. 2.39(a). To avoid interfering with the operation of the circuit, the capacitance should be as small as possible. The use of a small capacitance is especially important if the coupling is made to the grid of a univibrator, since its delay time depends in part on the value of this capacitance.

An input trigger of a few volts of either sign, provided it has the proper shape, is usually sufficient to cause triggering. A negative trigger must last at least a few microseconds so that flip-over is completed before the trigger disappears. A positive trigger should be of short duration. In this case, grid current is drawn, so that when the trigger disappears the grid is left with a negative bias, which causes the circuit to pass to its other state.

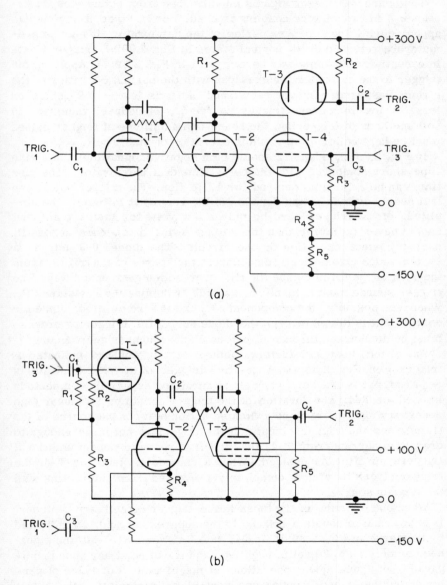

Fig. 2.39—Methods of triggering multivibrator-type circuits.

The source of trigger signals must be free from extraneous fluctu-ations when capacitance coupling is used. For instance, if any signals appear during the flip-over period of the univibrator, it may be pre-maturely returned to its normal state. In Fig. 2.39(b), trigger 1 acts in essentially the same way as trigger 1 in Fig. 2.39(a). Applying the trigger to the cathode interferes less with the normal operation of the circuit, especially as the resistance of R_4 is low—1,000 ohms or less. A low-impedance trigger source is, of course, required. In both methods of triggering, the shape and amplitude of trigger pulses must be kept uniform for reliable operation of the circuit.

In Fig. 2.39(a), trigger 2 should be a negative signal that has a rise time short compared with the delay time of a univibrator. The rise time can be as long as desired for a flip-flop. The trigger signal can last nearly as long as the duration of the regime it initiates. The am-plitude of the trigger need be only a few volts for fast signals, but should never be larger than the voltage swing that occurs across R_1 during normal operation of the circuit. The diode T-3 acts as a switch, which automatically disconnects the source of the trigger from the rest of the circuit once the flip-over action gets under way. The trigger source must evidently be capable of driving the resistance R_1. Whenever possible, the components C_2 and R_2 are omitted, since the charge that is drawn through the diode during the triggering process must be discharged through R_2 before a subsequent trigger occurs.

One of the most satisfactory methods of triggering is indicated by trigger 3 in Fig. 2.39(a). A positive trigger of at least 10 volts is required, but it can be of very short duration, especially if a pentode is used for T-4. The duration of the trigger should be no longer than necessary since there is no switching action between the source of the trigger and the trigger circuit. If the trigger is not large enough to draw grid current from T-4, the circuit is ready to accept additional triggers as often as desired. When a pentode is used for T-4, the trigger circuit is almost completely prevented from interacting with the trigger source.

When one or more of the tubes in the trigger circuit are pentodes, it is possible to couple a trigger to the suppressor grid, as indicated by trigger 2 in Fig. 2.39(b). If T-3 is a 6AS6 or an EF-50, the signal need be only 10 to 20 volts, negative, and it can be of any speed com-patible with subsequent operations of the circuit. For types of pen-todes having a poor suppressor-control characteristic, the signal must be larger, but in all cases the impedance offered to the trigger source is high.

One method for turning on a nonconducting tube by a positive trig-ger is illustrated by trigger 3 in Fig. 2.39(b). This method combines many of the desirable properties of the other methods. The resistances R_2 and R_3 are so chosen that the grid of T-1 is biased somewhat below the plate potential of T-2 when this tube is conducting. The plate of T-1, which is shown connected to the +300-volt supply bus, should preferably be connected to a somewhat higher voltage source (say +450 volts) if such a source is available. The necessary size of the trigger depends on how far below cutoff the grid of T-3 rests. A fast trigger of 25 to 50 volts will usually suffice to initiate flip-over action. A larger trigger is required if very fast output signals are to be taken from the circuit. The tube T-1 is essentially a cathode follower, and so possesses a high input impedance and a low output impedance, which is effective in driving the trigger circuit. When small triggers are used, a switching action is obtained, as in the case of trigger 2 in Fig. 2.39(a), so that triggers of either short or long duration are suitable. There is little coupling back to the trigger source.

(c) <u>Blocking Oscillators</u>. The triggering of blocking oscillators can be accomplished by methods similar to most of those discussed in connection with flip-flop circuits. An essential difference exists in that triggering may occur with input signals having a variety of shapes, provided that there exists at some time a high rate of change of voltage. The size and shape of the output signal from a blocking oscillator depend to a certain extent upon the nature of the input trigger.

Five possible methods of triggering a blocking oscillator are shown in Fig. 2.40. Trigger 1 must be positive, and trigger 2 negative. In both cases the triggers should be of short duration if multiple triggering is to be avoided. These methods of triggering have the disadvantage that signals from the blocking oscillator are fed into the trigger source. The presence of C_1 tends to slow down the action of the blocking oscillator, so that the method of trigger 2 is preferable. Particularly satisfactory methods of triggering are indicated in Fig. 2.40(a) by trigger 3 and in Fig. 2.40(b) by trigger 4. Both methods afford considerable isolation between the blocking oscillator and the source of the trigger. Trigger 3 should have a short rise time, but it can have a fairly long duration, whereas trigger 4 can have a relatively long rise time, provided its value is considerably less than the RC time constant of the grid circuit. When triggering is accomplished by the method of trigger 4, the output impedance of the cathode follower, tube T-1, appears in series with the grid circuit of the blocking oscillator and therefore affects the shape of the waveform of the output signal in much the same way that resistor R_3 in Fig. 2.35 does. The resistance R_2 can be several thousand ohms, since the output impedance of the cathode follower is determined primarily by the tube transconductance. With this method there is some coupling back to the trigger source, since the current in the grid circuit of the

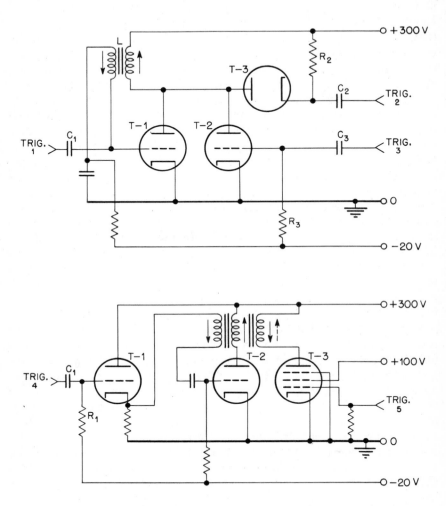

Fig. 2.40—Methods of triggering blocking oscillators.

blocking oscillator is usually large enough to cause the cathode follower to draw grid current.

The method of triggering indicated by trigger 5 in Fig. 2.40(b) can be applied for either positive or negative input signals, depending on

which way connections are made to the tertiary winding of the transformer. When positive signals are used, T-3 is biased below cutoff,
and the method is essentially the same as that of trigger 3. When
negative signals are used, T-3 must be so biased that, when its current is cut off by the trigger, an adequate signal in the tertiary winding is produced. A modification of the method of trigger 5 can be
employed when it is desired to trigger the oscillator only if several
signals appear simultaneously on several of the control elements of
tube T-3.

4.5 <u>A Scale of Two</u>. An interesting example of a trigger circuit
is afforded by a scale-of-two circuit. Such a circuit is usually based
on a flip-flop that is symmetrically coupled to a single source of
triggering and is capable of being triggered alternately from one
state to the other by successive, identical triggers. The important
properties of such a circuit, in addition to those inherent in the flip-
flop, depend on the switching mechanism by which the effect of an applied trigger pulse is different on the two halves of the circuit, depending upon which half is already conducting. Many scale-of-two
circuits have been devised, but only one circuit, which has been found
particularly satisfactory, will be discussed here. The circuit and its
associated waveforms are shown in Fig. 2.41. The circuit is similar
to the flip-flop shown in Fig. 2.36(b) except that symmetrical diode-
coupling to the trigger source is indicated. Values for the circuit
components shown in Fig. 2.36(b) can also be used for the scale of
two. The diode can be a 6H6 tube. The resistor R_9 in series with a
small neon light has a value of 1 megohm or larger and so has a
negligible effect on the operation of the circuit.

Let us now consider certain details of the operation of this particular scale-of-two circuit. If the input-signal voltage has a steady
value of +300 volts, neither of the diodes will be conducting since the
potential of the plates of the diodes is either less than or at most
equal to their common cathode potential. At the outset let us assume
that tube T-4 is conducting, so that its plate is at +130 volts, its
cathode is at +80 volts, and its grid is held at +82 volts by virtue of
grid-current flow. The plate of T-3 will then be at +280 volts and its
grid at +50 volts, cutting off the tube. Let us now slowly decrease the
input voltage so that the diode T-2 begins to conduct. Since its resistance is small compared with the resistance R_1, the plate of T-3 follows the decreasing voltage signal. The grid potential of T-4 does
not decrease in a proportionate amount but drops only slightly as long
as grid current is being drawn. A decrease in grid current takes up
the decrease in voltage across R_4. When the input signal reaches
+240 volts, T-4 stops drawing grid current and its grid then moves

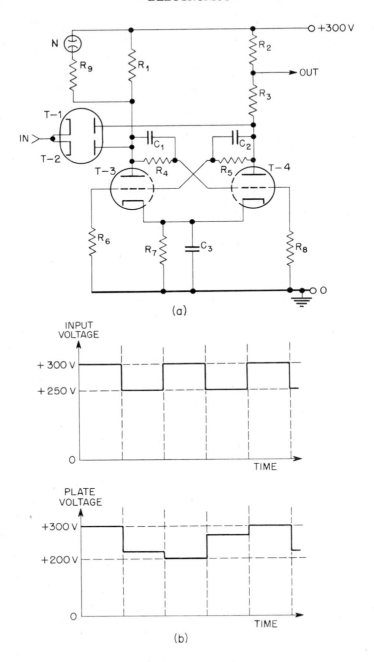

Fig. 2.41 — A scale of two.

negatively in accordance with the voltage division of R_4 and R_8. Consequently the plate potential of T-4 begins to increase very rapidly, soon reaching the potential of the input signal. A symmetric state now exists. Any further decrease in the signal voltage simply lowers the potential of the two plates and the two grids in corresponding amounts. If the signal voltage should suddenly return to its initial value, the circuit is left in a highly unstable state, from which it quickly returns to one or the other of its stable states. Evidently the final state so attained has no causal connection with the initial state since it is selected by small asymmetries in the circuit components or in the circuit potentials. The circuit possesses no memory once it exists in a stable symmetrical state.

It is important to recognize that, as long as T-4 is drawing grid current, the circuit is very stable. If the input-signal voltage is maintained constant — for instance, at +250 volts — the trigger circuit still has two stable states and, in principle, can be triggered back and forth between these states. The stability of the circuit may be accounted for in the following way: A small signal at the plate of T-3 is so reduced at the grid of T-4 (by grid current) that even after amplification by T-4 it is at most equal to the original signal. The signal reaching the grid of T-3 is approximately one-third of the signal at the opposite plate, so the gain from the plate of one tube back to its grid is small as long as the other tube is drawing grid current. It is important that an individual scale-of-two circuit be very stable when a number of circuits are to be operated in a long chain.

In the above discussion the behavior of the scale-of-two circuit has been considered for a very slow decrease of the input trigger voltage. It is evident that a quite different behavior results if the negative input trigger has a short rise time. Thus, let us suppose that the input voltage is brought suddenly from +300 volts to +250 volts. The grid of the conducting tube T-4 immediately goes negative by an amount determined by the ratio of C_1 to the static parasitic capacitance at the grid T-4. Immediately following the input signal, the plate of T-4 starts to rise rapidly, and the grid of T-3 moves positively a proportionate amount determined by the ratio of C_2 to the parasitic capacitance at the grid. The tube T-3 is soon in a conducting state, so that regeneration causes the circuit to proceed toward its other equilibrium state. However, before the state equivalent to the original state is reached, the plate of T-4 is "caught" by the diode T-1, and the circuit assumes a stable state with the plate of T-4 at +250 volts. If now the input voltage is returned either quickly or slowly to +300 volts, there is no effect on the trigger circuit other than causing it to assume the stable state, which is the exact mirror image of the original state. The application of a second trigger similar to the first causes the circuit to pass through the same cycle of the operations, but the role of T-3 is now replaced by that of T-4, and vice versa. The voltages appearing at the plate of one of the triodes are shown diagrammatically in Fig. 2.41(b) for two complete cycles of triggering.

The important properties of the scale-of-two circuit that has been described are the following: (1) The diodes, in connection with the trigger circuit, constitute a switching arrangement enabling a trigger signal to be applied to only one side of the circuit at a time, so that a definite and unilateral effect is obtained. (2) The capacitances C_1 and C_2, in conjunction with parasitic capacitances in the circuit, and especially in conjunction with the effects of grid current, constitute a memory which ensures that, once regeneration occurs, it will continue in the same direction until a complete flip-over action is accomplished. The circuit has the further desirable property that, because of its stability, any number of circuits can be connected directly together (to form scales of 64 or more) by means of the input and output connections indicated in Fig. 2.41(a). The resulting chain of scales of two is extremely stable.

Since a finite time is required for the flip-over action and since a certain recovery time must elapse after flip-over before static conditions again prevail, the scale-of-two circuit will respond to a second input signal only after a certain time has elapsed following a previous signal. The minimum resolving time is about 5 μsec for the components shown, and with no essential modifications of the circuit it can be made as short as 1 μsec. Resolving times as short as 0.3 μsec have been achieved by making certain essential modifications in the circuit. This matter is discussed in Chap. 4, Sec. 2.2, which is devoted to scaling circuits. Practical scale-of-two circuits are also given in that section, together with their resolving times.

The $\frac{1}{25}$-watt neon lamp N, in series with R_9, indicates at all times the state of the scale-of-two circuit. As soon as T-3 is conducting and its plate is at 130 volts, the lamp will fire and carry a current of 100 μa. A neon lamp so operated gives sufficient light to serve as an effective indicator for all indoor uses. When used with a chain of scaler units, the neon lamps are called "interpolation indicators."

5. OTHER NONLINEAR ELEMENTS

5.1 Clamps. A clamp is defined as a circuit element that can at one time present a low impedance (i.e., a "short circuit") and at another time a high impedance between a signal lead and ground. The

impedance that exists at any time can be controlled either by the signal itself or by an additional control signal, or "gate." Circuits that
clamp automatically when a signal of the proper nature appears are
useful as diode restorers or pulse shapers.

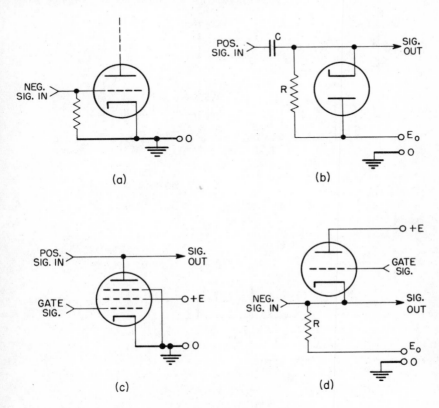

Fig. 2.42—Clamps.

Two circuits of the diode-restorer type are shown in Figs. 2.42(a)
and (b). As long as the input-signal voltage of (a) is negative, the
impedance presented to the signal source is very high, but as soon as
the signal voltage goes positive, grid current flows and the impedance
of the signal lead drops to a low value. This circuit can be used as a
means for squaring, or "clipping," pulses if the impedance of the
signal source is high (> 10,000 ohms). If the signal is coupled to this
circuit through an RC network, then d-c restoration for negative
pulses is achieved. The circuit of Fig. 2.42(b) is a similar circuit
but offers a high impedance for positive signals and a low impedance

for negative signals. This particular circuit illustrates the use of a
clamp as a d-c or diode restorer. When a positive signal is applied
at the point indicated in the diagram, the impedance of the diode is essentially infinite, but some charge flows on to the capacitor C through

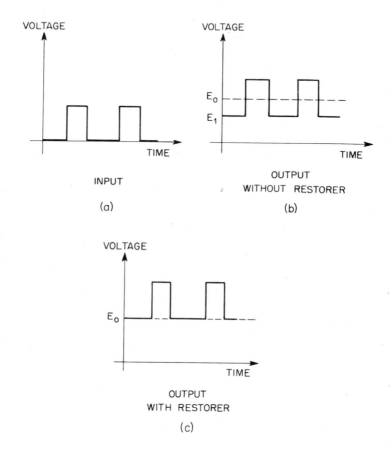

Fig. 2.43 — D-c restoration.

the resistor R. When the signal returns to its base value, the output
signal tends to go negative a small amount. The diode, however,
operates to offer a low impedance to ground (or to the voltage E_0), so
that the capacitor quickly discharges to its original value. The action
of this circuit is illustrated in Fig. 2.43. If the input signal is a
series of regularly spaced positive pulses as shown in (a), the resul-

tant output signal that would be produced if the diode were absent and if the time constant RC were large is as shown in (b). The average value of the output signal coincides with the voltage E_0. When the diode is operative, the base line of the pulses coincides with E_0, as indicated in (c). Hence, without diode restoration the voltage E_1, at which the base line is found, depends on the frequency, amplitude, and duration of the pulses, but with restoration of the base line of the output signal the voltage is always at E_0. The impedance of the source of E_0 should be small compared with the resistance R_1, and for no distortion of the pulses the time constant RC must, of course, be long compared with the duration of one pulse.

In Fig. 2.42(c) is illustrated the type of clamp that is controlled by a second signal, designated "Gate Sig." It is clear that the impedance presented to the signal lead is very high when the gate voltage is sufficiently negative to cut off the tube, but is very low when the gate voltage is zero and the signal is positive. A 6AG7 tube is most often used in a circuit of this sort.

The circuit of Fig. 2.42(d) can be used either as a gated or as a self-operating clamp. If the gate-signal lead is connected to the E_0 terminal, the clamp presents a low impedance when the signal voltage is less positive than E_0, and a high impedance when the signal voltage is more positive than E_0. If the gate voltage is made less than any signal voltage that will appear, then no clamping action takes place. By varying the clamp voltage in a prescribed manner, the clamping characteristic is readily controlled. Evidently the source impedance of the gate signal can be very high. Moreover, if the circuit is used as a d-c restorer, the source impedance of E_0 can also be very high. This particular circuit has the interesting property that it clamps to a certain reference voltage without requiring that the source of that voltage furnish any current during the process. Current, of course, is supplied through the tube from the plate supply bus.

If it is desired to clamp against both positive and negative signals, the circuits (c) and (d) of Fig. 2.42 can be used together, in which case the clamp (c) is placed in parallel with the resistor R of clamp (d).

5.2 Gates, Mixers, Coincidence Circuits. The circuits to be considered in this section have the common property that the transfer coefficient (or gain) from input to output, for signals applied to one input terminal, is a function of the voltage at a second input terminal. The choice of terminology in many cases depends more on the function of the circuit than on its nature.

(a) <u>Gates</u>. An ideal gate is a circuit element that can have either unity gain or zero gain, depending on the value of a control, or gating,* voltage. The functions of an ideal gate can be approximately realized in a number of ways by particular circuit arrangements. The

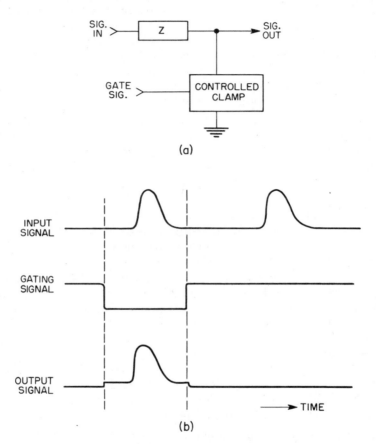

Fig. 2.44 — A clamp-type gate.

chief difficulty encountered is in preventing the gating signal from appearing at the output terminals along with the signal being gated. The output signal appearing coincident with the gating signal, but in the absence of an input signal, is called a "pedestal." In many pratical gating circuits it is possible to remove the pedestal only by sac-

---

* The term "gate" is sometimes applied to a rectangular voltage pulse, since a signal of this sort is often used in connection with gating circuits.

rificing linearity of gain for small input signals. In other circuits the pedestal itself can be removed, but there is always a small output signal that occurs at the beginning and at the end of the gating pulse.

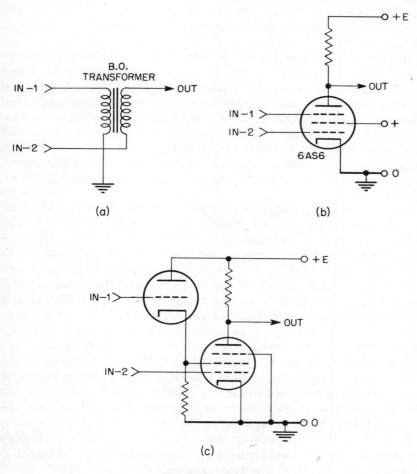

Fig. 2.45 — Mixers.

The gating of fast signals is often accomplished by means of a clamp as shown in Fig. 2.44(a). In this case the signal is applied to a controlled clamp through an impedance Z. If the impedance of the clamp can be changed from a value much smaller than Z to a value much larger than Z, effective gating action is possible. Since it is usually necessary, for the operation of the clamp, that some steady current be flowing through Z at the time the clamp is released, there is a resultant pedestal. The waveforms that are typical of a clamp-type gate are shown in Fig. 2.44(b). If only signals of a single polarity are to be gated, one of the "singled-ended" clamps of Sec. 5.1 of this chapter can be used. If both positive and negative signals must be gated, a combination of two types of clamp must be used. Some of the mixers and coincidence circuits discussed below can also be used as gates.

(b) <u>Mixers</u>. A mixer circuit is defined as a circuit in which the output signal is a function of two or more input signals. The gating circuit is a special case of a mixer circuit. In a linear mixer, the output voltage is the sum of linear functions of the input voltages. The difference amplifiers of Sec. 3.3 of this chapter are typical examples. In a nonlinear mixer, the output voltage contains additional terms that are functions of products of the input voltages. The first detector in a superheterodyne radio is a circuit of this kind. Figure 2.45 shows several useful mixer circuits whose mode of operation should be obvious.

(c) <u>Coincidence Circuits</u>. A coincidence circuit is one in which an output signal is obtained only when suitable signals appear simultaneously at each of several inputs. A circuit of this sort usually consists of several mixer circuits used perhaps in combination with other nonlinear elements. The output signal from a coincidence circuit should be independent of the amplitudes of the input signals, provided they are larger than some minimum value. The two circuits of Fig. 2.46 are useful examples of coincidence circuits. The operation of circuit (a) depends on the anode-bend characteristic of the two pentodes, and so requires a large load resistor R. It is therefore usually not suitable for fast signals. In this circuit a large output pulse is obtained when two negative input signals occur at the same time, permitting the plate voltage to rise toward the positive supply voltage. If a negative signal occurs at the grid of only one tube, the clamping action of the other tube limits the output signal to a small value. Circuit (b) is somewhat more satisfactory, although, if very fast input signals are used, there is some feed-through of signal to the output on account of the grid-cathode capacitance. This circuit requires larger signals for operation than circuit (a). For satisfactory operation the load resistor R need only be large compared with $1/g_m$ (usually about 200 ohms), and so the circuit can be used with signals that last only a few tenths of a microsecond. Figure 2.46(c) shows the response of circuit (b) to typical signals.

A modification of the previous circuit is shown in Fig. 2.47(a). This circuit has the desirable properties that it requires smaller signals to operate and does not give rise to feed-through of a signal of a polarity that impairs the operation of the circuit. In the quiescent state

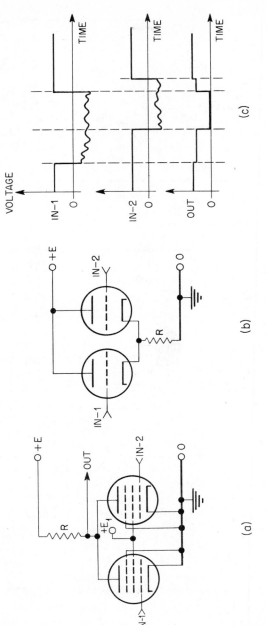

Fig. 2.46—Coincidence circuits.

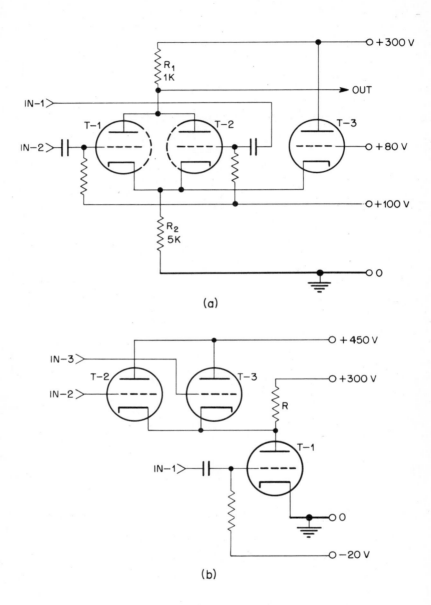

Fig. 2.47—Coincidence circuits. All tubes are ½ 6SN7.

of the circuit, tubes T-1 and T-2 carry a current of 10 ma and tube T-3 is cut off. When a negative signal of 30 volts or more is applied to an input lead, one of the tubes cuts off, requiring the other tube to draw a current of 20 ma. A negligible signal therefore appears at the output. If, however, negative signals of 30 volts or more are applied simultaneously to both input leads, both tubes are cut off, since the cathode is maintained at +80 volts by T-3. Hence a signal of +20 volts appears at the output. Larger output signals can be obtained, at the cost of increasing the rise time of the output signal, by making R_1 larger.

Another fast coincidence circuit is shown in Fig. 2.47(b). This circuit requires three input signals. It consists of an amplifier, tube T-1, which is normally biased to cutoff and whose load resistor R is shunted by two clamps, T-2 and T-3, whose grids are biased to +300 volts. If a positive input signal is applied to tube T-1, only a small output signal will appear, because of the clamping action of T-2 and T-3. If large negative signals are applied to T-2 and T-3 simultaneously with the positive signal to T-1, a negative output signal, which can in general be as large as the smaller of the two negative input signals, will be developed across R. Fast operation can be achieved with this circuit, especially if a pentode is used for T-1. All the coincidence circuits described can be modified by additional tubes so as to require the coincidence of any number of input signals before an output signal is obtained.

An anticoincidence circuit is a special case of a coincidence circuit in which the "suitable signal" at one of the input terminals is the nonexistence of a pulse simultaneous with other input pulses. Circuits of this sort are usually composed of the circuit elements just described. The signal polarities and the biases of the input grids are so arranged that the absence of one signal, together with the presence of one or more other signals, produces an output pulse. If IN-3 in Fig. 2.47(b) were biased below IN-2, positive signals at IN-3 would be in anticoincidence with conventional signals at terminals IN-1 and IN-2.

Chapter 3

VOLTAGE AMPLIFIERS

By William C. Elmore

1. INTRODUCTION

This chapter is devoted primarily to discussions of linear voltage amplifiers that are useful in nuclear physics investigations. Some consideration, however, is given to amplifiers intended to be used in oscillographs for the recording of fast electrical transients and to miscellaneous types of amplifiers that have proved useful in particular experiments. Practical circuits given in the chapter have been selected on the basis of their utility and their successful operation as research tools. Since most of the circuits consist essentially of combinations of linear circuit elements treated in Chap. 2, it is assumed that the reader will understand the general operation of the circuits and therefore will be most interested in having the important features of the circuits pointed out. Unfortunately, some quantitative information that would be of interest simply does not exist at present.

The first part of the chapter is devoted to a discussion of general matters concerning the design of pulse amplifiers used in nuclear physics. It has been written in the hope that it will clarify some of the problems that exist in the design of this type of amplifier. The latter part of the chapter contains descriptions of different amplifier circuits, all of which have been used extensively in experimental work.

2. VOLTAGE WAVEFORMS ENCOUNTERED IN PULSE AMPLIFIERS

To facilitate the design of pulse amplifiers used in nuclear physics investigations, it is necessary to have a clear notion of the nature of the input signal coming from an electrical detector and of the sort of output signal that is best suited for counting separate bursts of ionization in the detector. In this section the waveforms of these signals will be described, and certain conclusions will be drawn regarding the role a pulse amplifier must play in making nuclear measure-ments.

2.1 __Waveform from an Electrical Detector.__ A description of electrical detectors and the processes that occur in them is given

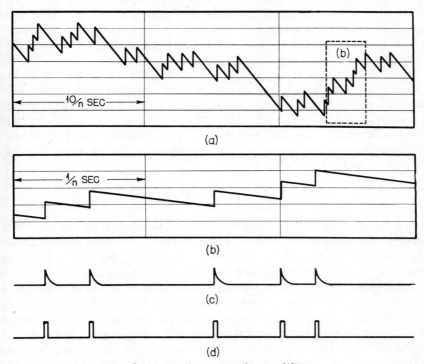

Fig. 3.1—Waveforms in pulse amplifiers.

in "Ionization Chambers and Counters" (National Nuclear Energy Series, Division V, Volume 2) by Bruno Rossi and Hans Staub. For present purposes it is sufficient to state that, as a result of the entry of a single ionizing particle into the detector, a certain amount of charge q is deposited in a time T_0 on the capacitance of the detector and the associated input circuit of the pulse amplifier.* Let C be the total capacitance involved, and let R be the grid-leak resistance of

---

* When there is no gas amplification in the detector, the magnitude of q can be esti-mated by assuming that about 30 ev of energy are absorbed from an ionizing particle to produce one pair of ions in the gas of the detector. When the detector is designed for electron collection, the magnitude of T_0 will lie in the range of from a few tenths to about 10 μsec.

the first stage of the amplifier. If, as usual, $T_0 \ll RC$, the input signal of the amplifier will rise in a time T_0 to the value q/C and will then decay exponentially with the relatively long time constant RC. Let us next consider what form the signal takes when the detector is exposed to a steady source of radiation. For purposes of illustration we can assume that each ionizing particle produces the same elementary signal or pulse. The combination of many pulses randomly distributed in time clearly results in an input signal of the type illustrated in Figs. 3.1(a) and (b).

In most cases the time intervals between successive pulses in the signal are distributed in the following way: Let n be the average rate at which pulses occur. Then the probability that a pulse will occur in a time interval dt is simply n dt. If τ represents the time elapsing between any pulse and the one immediately following it, it is simple to prove that the probability of the second pulse falling in the interval between τ and $\tau + d\tau$ is given by

$$p(\tau) \, d\tau = n e^{-n\tau} \, d\tau \tag{1}$$

The average time between pulses is given, of course, by $\bar{\tau} = 1/n$. This type of temporal distribution of pulses will be assumed in the following analysis. It should be remarked, however, that other types of distribution are sometimes met in particular experiments.

2.2 <u>Necessity for Pulse Shaping</u>. Let us now examine some consequences of the form of input signal just described. It is at once evident that, if this signal were amplified faithfully, the amplifier would tend to overload before individual voltage steps in the signal would be large enough to be measured accurately. To avoid this difficulty, it is customary to choose the low-frequency response of the amplifier so that the output signal quickly drops to zero following the rapid step rise of each pulse. The signal therefore becomes a series of narrow pulses, as suggested in Figs. 3.1(c) and (d). Figure 3.1(d) has been drawn to indicate the most desirable shape for output pulses, namely, pulses with flat tops, which make for the greatest accuracy in the determination of their height. Although it is possible to choose the low-frequency response of an amplifier so that essentially rectangular pulses are obtained in the output, the simplest and most common solution to the problem of obtaining narrow pulses is to include a single short-time-constant coupling in the amplifier, so that the pulses appear as indicated in Fig. 3.1(c).* Methods for achieving both shapes of pulses are discussed in the next section.

---

* The value of the short time constant is often referred to as the "clipping time" of the amplifier.

2.3 Fast Counting Rates. There are aspects of the signal from an electrical detector that become important when the number of pulses per second is large. For instance, it is often convenient to connect one electrode of the detector directly to the grid of the first stage of the amplifier. Since the voltage across the detector is always shifted by an amount nqR when the detector is exposed to radiation, the grid bias of the first stage is shifted by a like amount. Although the shift in grid bias is usually negligible, the effect can be important where there is a strong background radiation producing many small pulses in the detector for every large pulse that is actually counted by the recording equipment. Such a situation occurs when pulses from fission fragments are being counted in the presence of a strong α-ray background. In this case it may be necessary either to choose an unusually low value of grid resistance for the first stage or to decouple the detector from the first grid by means of a suitable capacitor. The latter method is to be preferred when the grid resistance required for the former method noticeably increases the noise output of the amplifier.

The grid biases of later stages in the amplifier are obviously independent of the mean value of the input signal, but they can be seriously disturbed by the random fluctuation of the signal level about its mean value, a behavior that is clearly indicated in Fig. 3.1(a). The magnitude of this effect determines, in part, the best location in the amplifier for the network that converts the input signal into a series of narrow pulses. To aid in estimating what magnitude of bias shifts can be expected, a statistical analysis of the type of signal shown in Fig. 3.1(a) can be made. One result of this analysis indicates that the root-mean-square value of the fluctuation voltage, taken about the mean value of the signal, is given by

$$v_s = \sqrt{\frac{nRC}{2}}\, e_p \tag{2}$$

where e_p is the value of a single voltage step in the signal. Occasional excursions of the fluctuation voltage can be expected to have several times the rms value given by Eq. 2. The statistical phenomenon giving rise to these peaks is often referred to as the "pile-up" of pulses. When reasonably fast counting rates can be expected, e.g., 1,000 counts per second or more, it is well to allow for a pile-up factor of 20 in designing the amplifier.

If, in Eq. 2, we let RC denote the value of the single short time constant in the amplifier, then v_s can be interpreted as giving the rms fluctuation voltage in the output signal. This interpretation is useful in a type of situation already mentioned, namely, the counting of large pulses from one source in the presence of a strong background of much smaller pulses from another source. To avoid an error in counting caused by an occasional large pile-up of the smaller pulses, Eq. 2 indicates that a low value of the time constant used for pulse shaping should be chosen.

Although there are evidently many advantages in having a detector-amplifier system that gives pulses having a short rise time, it is occasionally desirable to increase the rise time of the amplifier to reduce random noise, i.e., to improve the signal-to-noise ratio of the output signal. In any case, little is gained if the rise time of the amplifier is much less than the collection time of the detector.

2.4 Output Pulse Forms. Recording of output pulses usually consists in counting all pulses whose heights lie in a certain range. The circuit element used to select pulse heights in this way is termed an "amplitude discriminator" (see Chap. 4, Sec. 2.1). It consists of a voltage-sensitive trigger circuit capable of supplying standard pulses to a scaling or counting circuit. Since the voltage stability of existing types of discriminators amounts to about ±0.1 volt, the output pulses from a pulse amplifier should be at least 10 volts high for good accuracy in taking measurements. It is clear that the output impedance of the amplifier should be low enough so that pulse heights are faithfully preserved on transmission to a discriminator-scaler circuit. For this reason the output stage is always chosen to be a cathode follower, and the number of inversions of pulse polarity in the amplifier is so chosen that the output pulses are positive in sign.

The capability of the output cathode follower to reproduce exactly the trailing edge of a pulse requires some discussion in addition to that already given in Chap. 2, Sec. 3.4. If the discriminator-scaler circuit has a resolving time of 5 μsec, then there is certainly no reason for pulses having an exponential decay constant as short as a few tenths of a microsecond to be accurately reproduced as regards their trailing edge. The extremely narrow pulses obtained when a short clipping time is used to avoid pile-up are actually unsuited for counting with an ordinary discriminator-scaler circuit. Hence it may be to some advantage to have the cathode-follower output stage broaden, or "stretch," very narrow pulses. Pulse-stretching should not be pursued to such an extent that the resolving time of the entire system is increased.

3. WIDE-BAND AMPLIFIER THEORY: LOW-FREQUENCY CONSIDERATIONS

An adequate discussion of the majority of design problems concerned with the low-frequency response of multistage amplifiers is found in standard texts and handbooks.* It has been made clear in the preceding section, however, that pulse amplifiers require special treatment, since their low-frequency response characteristic is used to alter the shape of pulses that come from an electrical detector. Accordingly most of the present section will be devoted to problems in the shaping of pulses from detectors. Near the end of the section certain problems arising in the design of transient amplifiers will be given brief treatment.

3.1 Pulse Shaping by Interstage RC Couplings. In discussing the shaping of pulses by controlling amplifier response at low frequencies, it is convenient to assume that the high-frequency response of the amplifier is perfect. The gain of an amplifier idealized in this way increases from zero, at zero frequency, to a constant gain at mid-band and higher frequencies. The lower half-power frequency f_1 is defined as that frequency at which the voltage gain is $1/\sqrt{2}$ times the gain at high frequencies. The knowledge of a particular value of f_1, however, tells very little about the transient response of the amplifier. Instead we must deal directly with the time constants of the resistance-capacitance couplings between stages of the amplifier, and possibly with other time constants, such as those associated with screen and cathode self-bias. If these time constants are known, then it is possible to compute directly the transient response of the amplifier to an ideal step-wave input signal. For most purposes the transient response so computed is a close enough approximation to that excited by a pulse from a detector. For simplicity in the following analysis, we assume that the low-frequency response characteristic depends solely upon the interstage time constants.

Let us therefore consider that a step-wave signal is applied at $t = 0$ to an amplifier having n interstage time constants τ_i and at the same time having perfect response at high frequencies. It can then be shown that the output signal takes the form

$$e_o = E_m \sum_{i=1}^{n} A_i e^{-t/\tau_i} \tag{3}$$

where

$$A_i \equiv \frac{1}{\prod\limits_{j=1}^{n} 1 - \dfrac{\tau_i}{\tau_j}}, \quad (i \neq j) \tag{4}$$

and where it is assumed that no two of the time constants are equal. Equation 3 shows that the output signal consists of n superposed exponentially decaying voltages. If the n time constants are arranged so

* For instance, see F. E. Terman, "Radio Engineers' Handbook," Sec. 5, McGraw-Hill Book Company, Inc., New York, 1943.

that $\tau_1 < \tau_2 < \cdots < \tau_n$, then the coefficients A_i given by Eq. 4 alternate in sign with increasing i, and one after another of the terms in the series of Eq. 3 becomes small as time increases. Hence the value of e_o tends to alternate in sign as it diminishes in value — a type of behavior indicated in Fig. 3.2, which has been computed for the limiting case of four equal time constants.

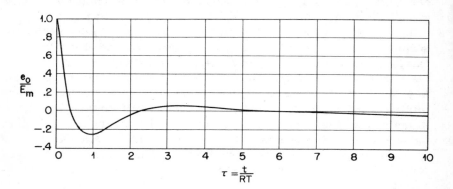

Fig. 3.2 — Transient response of amplifiers having four equal interstage time constants. Graph of $\frac{1}{6}e^{-\tau}(6 - 18\tau + 9\tau^2 - \tau^3)$.

It is obvious that the type of transient behavior shown in Fig. 3.2 is undesirable for shaping pulses from an electrical counter. Not only is a pulse that closely follows an earlier one distorted in height, but it is even possible that the peaks of some of the oscillations following a single large pulse will be counted as separate pulses.

These difficulties are eliminated if all but one of the time constants are made very long. The transient response given by Eq. 3 then reduces essentially to that of an amplifier having only a single short-time-constant coupling, i.e.,

$$e_o = E_m e^{-t/\tau_1} \tag{5}$$

when $\tau_1 \ll \tau_i$, (i = 2, 3, ..., n). An actual pulse from an electrical detector will therefore have a fast rise, determined by properties of the detector and by the rise time of the amplifier, followed by an exponential decay, which can be made as short as is consistent with loss in pulse height on account of the finite rise time of the pulse. There remain two practical questions of design: (1) Where should the single short-time-constant coupling be placed in the amplifier?

(2) How much longer than τ_1 should other time constants in the amplifier be made?

The question of where in the amplifier to place the single short-time-constant coupling finds its answer in a compromise between two requirements. On the one hand, the coupling should be placed at a point where there exists no danger that preceding stages may overload from the pile-up of pulses. On the other hand, it should be placed as far along in the amplifier as possible, since it acts as a filter for hum, microphonics, and low-frequency noise components originating in early stages. In practice the coupling is best placed after a few stages of gain.

To answer the second question, regarding the magnitude of other time constants in the amplifier, let us consider an amplifier having two short time constants such that $\tau_1 < \tau_2 \ll \tau_i$ (i = 3, 4, ..., n). The transient response, Eq. 3, then becomes

$$e_o = \frac{E_m}{\tau_2 - \tau_1} (\tau_2 e^{-t/\tau_1} - \tau_1 e^{-t/\tau_2}) \tag{6}$$

which has a minimum (negative) value at

$$t_m = \frac{2\tau_1 \tau_2}{\tau_2 - \tau_1} \ln \frac{\tau_2}{\tau_1}$$

If we let $\mu \equiv \dfrac{|e_o|_{min}}{E_m}$ and $s \equiv \tau_1/\tau_2$, then it can be proved from Eq. 6 that

$$\mu = s^{(1+s)/(1-s)} \tag{7}$$

On account of its utility, this result is shown graphically in Fig. 3.3. For an underswing of 1 per cent or less, $\tau_2 \geq 100\tau_1$.

It does not appear to be profitable to make a general analysis for cases where there are more than two short time constants. However, it is intuitively obvious that, if there is no time constant less than $100\tau_1$, the amount of undershoot will be restricted to a few per cent or less.

Now the pulse shape obtained from a single short-time-constant interstage coupling has certain undesirable features. In the first place, it has a very narrow top when extremely short clipping times are used. This shape makes it difficult to design a satisfactory circuit for measuring pulse heights. In the second place, it has a relatively long decay time in comparison with the width of its top. Another pulse, which occurs on its "tail," is incorrectly rendered in height.

In the third place, a pulse whose time of rise is comparable with the clipping time is considerably reduced in height. The extent of this effect may be judged by reference to Figs. 2.3(c) and (d), which show, respectively, a step pulse having a linear rate of rise and one having

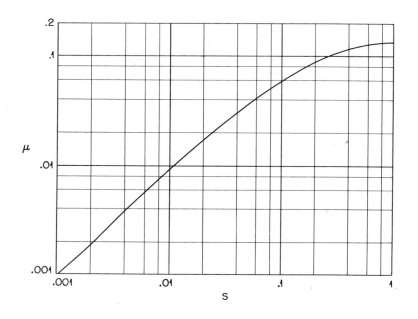

Fig. 3.3 — Amount of underswing.

an exponentially decaying rate of rise, before and after having passed through a single RC coupling.

A certain improvement in the shape of the pulse is obtained if an inductance $L = \frac{1}{4}R^2C$ is placed in series with the resistive arm of the coupling. The computed curves shown in Figs. 2.7(c) and (d) illustrate this effect, indicating that the pulses obtained are somewhat higher and decay more rapidly than pulses obtained without the inductance. Evidently the inductance first delays the discharge of the coupling capacitor and later causes it to discharge more rapidly. If the value of the inductance is made greater than that proposed, the shaped pulse will have an oscillatory decay that is clearly undesirable.

3.2 Delay-line Pulse Shaping. An alternative method of shaping pulses from an electrical detector employs a delay line shorted at

one end.* In the present application the delay line is correctly terminated at the unshorted end by its characteristic impedance $Z_c = R$,
and is used as the plate load of one stage in the amplifier. Alternately
the delay line can be used as the output portion of a potential divider

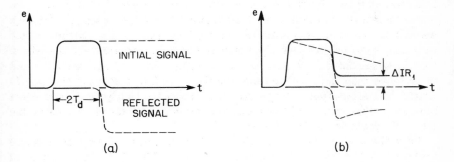

(a)   (b)

Fig. 3.4—Delay-line pulse shaping (idealized).

whose other arm may be the terminating resistance for the line. If a
step pulse of current ΔI is applied in series with the terminated end
of the line, a voltage $\Delta IR/2$ appears across the terminals and lasts a
time $2T_d$, where T_d is the time taken by a pulse traversing the line in
one direction. At the end of the interval $2T_d$ an inverted step-voltage
wave returns to the terminals of the line, thereby tending to cancel
the signal there. This situation is shown in Fig. 3.4(a), which was
drawn to indicate what would occur in the case of a lossless delay
line.

In practical applications of this method, the delay line necessarily
has a finite resistance, with the result that the reflected voltage wave
is of smaller amplitude than the initial wave. In this case the output
pulse takes the form indicated by the solid line in Fig. 3.4(b). Evidently the pulse fails to return to the base line by the amount ΔIR_1,
where R_1 is the d-c resistance of the delay line. This behavior can be
remedied by including a single short-time-constant interstage at
some point in the amplifier. All pulses then have an exponential
decay, whose time constant can be so chosen that the reflected pulse
just cancels the remaining part of the original pulse. Pulses obtained
in this manner are illustrated by the dashed lines in Fig. 3.4(b).

* Some properties of delay lines have already been discussed in Chap. 2, Sec. 2.4.

Another method of compensating the finite resistance of the delay line is based on using the line as one arm of a Wheatstone bridge, which is balanced for the d-c resistance of the shorted delay line. Until the pulse returns reflected from the shorted end of the line, the line acts like a pure resistance having a value equal to its characteristic impedance. When the pulse returns at a time $2T_d$ later, the line possesses its d-c resistance. It is assumed that the resistive network seen from the terminals of the delay line equals its characteristic impedance, to ensure that the reflected pulse is completely absorbed. Hence, when the line is used as one arm of a bridge, the bridge is out of balance by a definite amount for the time $2T_d$ following the application of a step input voltage. At later times the bridge is in complete balance. The output pulse from the bridge will therefore have the ideal form shown in Fig. 3.4(a).

To make use of this principle, the bridge can be driven by a phase inverter of the type described in Chap. 2, Sec. 3.2. On account of troubles arising from parasitic capacitances in the bridge, this method is most suitable for pulses having rise times greater than 1 μsec.

It is interesting to note that a shorted delay line, as used for pulse shaping in an amplifier, constitutes an effective means of differentiating a signal of arbitrary shape. If the input signal to an amplifier is represented by $v_i(t)$, the output of the amplifier containing a delay-line pulse-shaper is given by

$$v_o(t) = A[v_i(t) - v_i(t - T_d)]$$

where A is the effective gain of the amplifier and T_d is the one-way uelay time of the shorted delay line. This expression, in the limiting case for small values of T_d, will be recognized as expressing the definition of the time differential of the input signal $v_i(t)$.

It is evident that delay-line-shaped pulses more nearly approach the ideal form required for accurate measurement of pulse height. Moreover, their width, which need not be more than a few times their rise time, reduces the number of instances where two pulses overlap each other. It is expected that, when the advantages of this method of pulse shaping are more widely recognized, its use will more and more supplant the traditional method involving a single short-time-constant coupling in the amplifier.

3.3 Transient Amplifiers. The discussion up to this point has been concerned with methods of choosing the low-frequency response of an amplifier so as to realize certain desirable pulse-shaping characteristics. In the faithful amplification of transient signals, the reverse problem is encountered; that is, the distortion resulting from the dropping off of amplification at low frequencies must be kept less than some specified amount. A suitable criterion for this distortion can be obtained from the transient response of the amplifier to a step-function input signal. Thus we require that the transient response shall not deviate more than a certain fraction δ from its initial value in some specified interval of time T measured from the application of the step signal.

As an example of this criterion, consider a multistage amplifier whose low-frequency response is determined entirely by n interstage time constants τ_i (i = 1, 2, ..., n). If a step voltage is applied to the input terminals at t = 0, the transient response is that given by Eq. 3. Now the power series expansion of the right-hand member of Eq. 3 takes the form

$$e_o = E_m \left[1 - \left(\sum_0^n \frac{1}{\tau_i} \right) t + \cdots \right]$$

so, for small deviations, the response falls off the fractional amount

$$\delta = \left(\sum_1^n \frac{1}{\tau_i} \right) T \tag{8}$$

in time T. If all the interstage time constants are equal, it is possible to express this result in terms of the lower half-power frequency f_1 of the multistage amplifier.

$$\delta = 2\pi f_1 n (2^{1/n} - 1)^{\frac{1}{2}} T \approx 2\pi f_1 (n \ln 2)^{\frac{1}{2}} T \tag{9}$$

where the approximate relation holds for large n. Evidently the requirements on good low-frequency response are severe for accurate reproduction of transients. For instance, suppose an amplifier has five equal interstage time constants, and it is desired that the response to a step function shall drop only 1 per cent in 100 μsec, i.e., δ = 0.01 for T = 10^{-4} sec. From Eq. 9 it is found that f_1 = 8.3 cycles per second. If there is only a single short time constant in the amplifier, then f_1 = 16 cycles per second.

In practical amplifiers, the insufficient by-passing of cathode and screen-bias resistors may also influence low-frequency response, causing the initial linear drop in transient response to be greater than that indicated by Eq. 8. Although it is possible to make the ratio δ/T as small as desired by using sufficiently large values for the coupling and the decoupling capacitors involved, it is often better, for reasons of economy and of reduction in interstage parasitic capacitances, to compensate the amplifier to improve its amplification at low frequencies and thus to obtain a low value for δ/T. Methods of low-frequency compensation are well known* and will not be discussed here. Most published accounts, however, fail to consider the matter of compensation in terms of transient response. Instead, they consider it in terms of the gain and the phase-shift response characteristics. This method of treatment appears to be an unfortunate choice in the case of amplifiers intended primarily for the amplification of transient signals.

4. WIDE-BAND AMPLIFIER THEORY: HIGH-FREQUENCY CONSIDERATIONS

In the present section we shall consider the properties of an amplifier idealized to the extent that it has constant gain from zero frequency up to a frequency region where the gain progressively falls to zero. The upper half-power frequency f_2 is that frequency at which the voltage gain has fallen to $1/\sqrt{2}$ times the gain at low frequencies. The frequency f_2 is often termed the bandwidth of the amplifier, and its value is intimately related to the number of amplifying stages, the properties of the amplifying tubes, and the gain per stage. Before investigating the nature of this relationship, let us consider another fundamental aspect of wide-band amplifiers, namely, their transient response to a rapidly changing input signal. The connection between transient and frequency response can then be stated in a form useful in designing amplifiers.

4.1 Transient Response. The transient behavior of an amplifier is best exhibited in the response of the amplifier to an input step voltage of the type shown at (a) in Fig. 3.5. Typical amplifier response curves are indicated by curves (b), (c), (d), and (e), where for convenience all curves have had their final amplitudes normalized to unity. The response approaches its final value monotonically in the case of curves (b) and (c), whereas in the two remaining curves the final value is temporarily exceeded. Curve (c) is meant to represent a response having the shortest possible rise time with no transient overshoot. An amplifier having this response is said to be "critically compensated." At least two distinct types of overcompensation exist, as suggested by curves (d) and (e). Amplifiers described later in the chapter are intended for applications where it is highly desirable that they be critically compensated, i.e., that they have the steepest possible transient rise with no appreciable transient overshoot. With

---

* For instance, see F. E. Terman, loc. cit.

this end in view, a wide-band amplifier is ordinarily designed to have certain adjustable circuit components that control the degree of compensation. The proper adjustment of these components can be accomplished with the aid of test equipment described in Chap. 6.

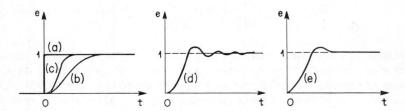

Fig. 3.5 — Typical transient-response curves of amplifiers.

The important aspects of amplifier transient response are expressed by the rise time T_R and the delay time T_D, which can be defined in several approximately equivalent ways. In making the following definitions, we assume that the step wave, as shown in Fig. 3.5(a), is always applied at a time $t = 0$ and that the transient response $e(t)$ has been normalized to unity. The conventional definition of delay time is then expressed by $e(T_D) = \frac{1}{2}$. If, at the point $e(t) = \frac{1}{2}$, a tangent is drawn to the response curve, T_R is the reciprocal of the slope of this tangent line. Rise time can also be defined as the time elapsing between $e(t) = 0.10$ and $e(t) = 0.90$. Each of the two definitions of rise time is convenient for laboratory use, but both are awkward in making computations. When the transient response is monotonic, it is possible to define delay time and rise time in a form extremely convenient for computation. The new definitions lead to numerical results that in most cases differ but little from those obtained from the conventional definitions. If $e(t)$ is the normalized response of the amplifier to a unit-step signal and if $e'(t) \equiv de/dt$, then we define

$$T_D = \int_0^\infty t e'(t)\, dt \tag{10}$$

and

$$T_R = \left[2\pi \int_0^\infty (t - T_D)^2 e'(t)\, dt \right]^{\frac{1}{2}}$$

which can be written

$$T_R = \left\{ 2\pi \left[\int_0^\infty t^2 e'(t)\, dt - T_D^2 \right] \right\}^{\frac{1}{2}} \tag{11}$$

The usefulness of the new definitions is made evident in the following: For any wide-band amplifier, the portion of the complex gain pertaining to high-frequency response G(p) takes the form

$$\frac{G(p)}{G_m} = g(p) = \frac{1 + a_1 p + a_2 p^2 + \cdots + a_n p^n}{1 + b_1 p + b_2 p^2 + \cdots + b_m p^m} \tag{12}$$

where G_m is the mid-band amplification, p is the complex angular frequency, a_i and b_i are real constants whose values depend on the values of lumped circuit parameters in the amplifier, and $m > n$. Now the derivative of the transient response to a step wave $e'(t)$ is related to g(p) by the Laplace transformation

$$g(p) = \int_0^\infty e'(t) e^{-pt} dt \tag{13}$$

Let us expand e^{-pt} in a power series, so that Eq. 13 becomes

$$g(p) = 1 - p \int_0^\infty t e'(t) \, dt + \frac{p^2}{2!} \int_0^\infty t^2 e'(t) \, dt \cdots \tag{14}$$

since $\int_0^\infty e'(t) \, dt = 1$. But Eq. 12 may be expanded to give

$$g(p) = 1 - (b_1 - a_1) p + (b_1^2 - a_1 b_1 + a_2 - b_2) p^2 + \cdots \tag{12a}$$

By comparing Eqs. 14 and 12a we obtain the first and second moments of $e'(t)$ about the $t = 0$ axis. These moments enable the delay time T_D and rise time T_R, as defined by Eqs. 10 and 11, to be determined, with the result that

$$T_D = b_1 - a_1$$
$$T_R = \left\{ 2\pi \left[b_1^2 - a_1^2 + 2(a_2 - b_2) \right] \right\}^{\frac{1}{2}} \tag{15}$$

This analysis is useful only when the constants a_i and b_i have been so interrelated, by choosing values of amplifier circuit parameters, that e(t) is a monotonic function of time. It is to amplifiers of this type that the following results apply.

The values of T_D and T_R for a single R-coupled stage with parasitic capacitance C may be determined from Eq. 15. They are

$$\left. \begin{array}{l} T_D = RC \\ T_R = \sqrt{2\pi} \ RC \end{array} \right\} \tag{16}$$

For a shunt-compensated stage having an inductance $L = \frac{1}{4}R^2C$ in series with the resistor R,

$$\left.\begin{array}{l} T_D = \frac{3}{4}RC \\ T_R = \sqrt{7\pi/8}\ RC \end{array}\right\} \tag{17}$$

Hence, critical shunt compensation decreases the rise time about 34 per cent below that of a simple R-coupled stage. The corresponding delay time is decreased 25 per cent. In most applications the magnitude of the delay is of no consequence.

Let us next consider an n-stage amplifier whose individual stages have delay times $T_{D_1}, T_{D_2}, \cdots, T_{D_n}$ and rise times $T_{R_1}, T_{R_2}, \cdots, T_{R_n}$. From the definitions, Eqs. 10 and 11, it can be proved that the following expressions give the over-all delay time T_D and rise time T_R:

$$T_D = \sum_1^n T_{D_1} \tag{18}$$

$$T_R = \sqrt{\sum_1^n T_{R_1}^2} \tag{19}$$

It is evident from Eq. 19 that the rise time of an n-stage amplifier is $\sqrt{n}\ T_{R_1}$ when all stages have the same rise time, T_{R_1}. Equation 19 can be used to estimate how much the rise time of a pulse increases on passing through an amplifier.

A simple approximate relation exists between the rise time and upper half-power frequency f_2 of a multistage amplifier that is either undercompensated or critically compensated. The relation proves to be

$$T_R f_2 \approx \sqrt{\frac{\ln 2}{2\pi}} \approx \frac{1}{3} \tag{20}$$

The error made in using Eq. 20 amounts to a few per cent when the amplifier has as many as five stages, and decreases progressively with an increased number of stages.

Now the gain and the rise time of any amplifying stage are both linearly related to the value of the plate-load resistor. Hence, if a number of stages are used in cascade to obtain an over-all mid-band gain G_t, the product of the rise times of individual stages is independent of how the gain G_t is distributed among the stages. But according to Eq. 19 the over-all rise time is given by the square root of the sum of the squares of individual rise times. It follows from a simple analysis that the amplifier will have the shortest possible rise time when the rise times of individual stages are made equal to one another. Often, however, some sacrifice in rise time must be made in the output stage to achieve a sufficiently linear, as well as large, output signal. In a feedback amplifier, the rise times of the individually fed-back sections should be kept approximately identical by suitably distributing the total gain among the sections.

    4.2   Gain-bandwidth Computations.   Let us now investigate the bandwidth and the gain requirements of an individual stage in an n-stage amplifier when it is necessary to realize a mid-band gain G_t

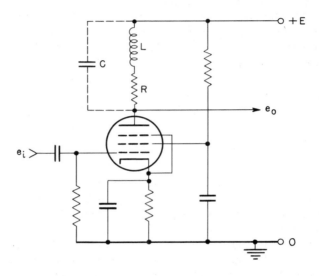

Fig. 3.6 — Shunt-compensated amplifier stage.

and a bandwidth f_2 for the entire amplifier. The analysis will be made for the shunt-compensated stage, shown in Fig. 3.6. The simple R-coupled stage will be considered to be a special case of this circuit. The gain of such a stage may be written

$$G(f) = g_m R_g(f) = g_m Rg(f)$$

where $R_g(f) \equiv Rg(f)$ is the absolute value of the plate-load impedance at any frequency f. Equation 2 of Chap. 2 shows

$$g(f) = \left[\frac{1 + \alpha^2 F^2}{(1 - \alpha F^2)^2 + F^2} \right]^{\frac{1}{2}}$$

where $F \equiv f/f_0$, $f_0 \equiv 1/(2\pi RC)$, and $\alpha \equiv L/R^2 C$. For n identical stages in cascade, the total gain is

$$[G(f)]^n = (g_m R)^n \; [g(f)]^n$$

Hence, the bandwidth f_2 is found by solving

$$[g(f_2)]^n = 1/\sqrt{2}$$

giving the result

$$f_2 = f_0 \phi(n) \tag{21}$$

where $f_0 \equiv 1/(2\pi RC)$, as defined previously, and

$$\phi(n) = \left[\sqrt{A^2 + B^2} - A \right]^{\frac{1}{2}} \tag{22}$$

$$A \equiv \frac{1}{2} \left(\frac{1}{\alpha^2} - \frac{2}{\alpha} - 2^{1/n} \right)$$

$$B^2 \equiv \frac{2^{1/n} - 1}{\alpha^2}$$

For an uncompensated amplifier, $\alpha = 0$, so Eq. 22 becomes

$$\phi(n) = \sqrt{2^{1/n} - 1} \tag{23}$$

Equation 21 indicates that the value of f_0 must be

$$f_0 = \frac{1}{2\pi RC} = \frac{f_2}{\phi(n)}$$

in order that the bandwidth of n stages shall be f_2. Hence the plate-load resistance required for any stage is

$$R = \frac{\phi(n)}{2\pi f_2 C}$$

Moreover, the mid-band gain G_n of each of the n stages is

$$G_n = \frac{g_m}{2\pi f_2 C} \phi(n) \tag{24}$$

It is interesting to note that the mid-band gain of a single R-coupled amplifier stage of bandwidth f_2 is given by

$$G_0 = \frac{g_m}{2\pi f_2 C} \qquad (25)$$

permitting us to write Eq. 24 in the form

$$G_n = G_0 \phi(n) \qquad (26)$$

Equation 26 shows that the mid-band gain of each stage of the n-stage amplifier may be separated into two factors. The first factor, G_0, is the value of the mid-band gain of a single-stage R-coupled amplifier of bandwidth f_2. The second factor, $\phi(n)$, is a function of the number of stages n and of the amount of shunt compensation as measured by the value of α. The mid-band gain of the entire amplifier, of course, is given by

$$G_t = G_n^n = [G_0\phi(n)]^n \qquad (27)$$

The above analysis is an aid in designing an amplifier of bandwidth f_2 and total gain G_t, if such an amplifier is possible. The method of design is as follows: First, a value of G_0 is computed from Eq. 25. Next, a guess is made concerning the required number of stages; a value of α having been chosen, a value of G_n is computed, using Eqs. 26 and 22. The total gain is then computed and compared with the desired gain. The process is repeated until a satisfactory number of stages has been decided upon, or until it is clear that there is no solution to the problem. To aid in carrying out these computations, three nomographs have been prepared for values of $\alpha = 0$, 0.25, and 0.414, respectively. For convenience they have been placed in the next section, along with a description of their use.

The figure of merit for tubes used in wide-band amplifiers is evidently the quantity g_m/C, where C is ordinarily taken to be the sum of the input and output capacitances of the tube. The figure of merit for a single amplifying stage of the type here considered may be expressed by the gain-bandwidth product

$$G_1 f_2 = \frac{g_m}{2\pi C} \phi(1)$$

where $\phi(1) = 1$ for $\alpha = 0$, $\phi(1) = 1.414$ for $\alpha = 0.25$, and $\phi(1) = 1.721$ for $\alpha = \sqrt{2} - 1$.

As a last point of interest, let us determine the gain per stage giving greatest over-all bandwidth in a many-stage amplifier of total gain G_t. It turns out that optimum gain per stage is conveniently found by maximizing the total gain G_t, considered as a continuous function of n, while keeping the bandwidth f_2 constant. Thus, let us equate the derivative with respect to n of G_t (Eq. 27) to zero, and so obtain

$$\ln G_n = -\frac{n}{\phi}\frac{d\phi}{dn} \tag{28}$$

Now $\phi(n)$, as given by Eq. 22, can be expanded in a converging series of the form

$$\phi(n) = \frac{a}{n^{\frac{1}{2}}} + \frac{b}{n^{\frac{3}{2}}} + \cdots \tag{29}$$

where the first term is a good approximation to $\phi(n)$ when n is large, and $0 \leq \alpha \leq \frac{1}{4}$. This range of α includes all cases where there is no overshoot on a fast transient. On evaluating Eq. 28, it is found that $\ln G_n \approx \frac{1}{2}$, or that

$$G_n \approx e^{\frac{1}{2}} = 1.65 \tag{30}$$

A stage gain of less than $e^{\frac{1}{2}}$ will result in a narrower pass band for a given total gain than that obtained with a stage gain of $e^{\frac{1}{2}}$. The number of stages required for maximum bandwidth is usually prohibitive. For instance, if $G_t = 10^5$, n = 23 stages.

When $\alpha = \sqrt{2} - 1$, the form of the expansion of $\phi(n)$ becomes

$$\phi(n) = \frac{a}{n^{\frac{1}{4}}} + \frac{b}{n^{\frac{3}{4}}} + \cdots \tag{31}$$

so that $G_n \approx e^{\frac{1}{4}}$ when n is large. For values of α between $\alpha = \frac{1}{4}$ and $\alpha = \sqrt{2} - 1$, the expansion of Eq. 29 is correct, but it converges more and more slowly as the value of α approaches $\sqrt{2} - 1$. Hence, for a reasonable number of stages—for instance, 10 to 20 stages—the optimum gain per stage will gradually decrease from $e^{\frac{1}{2}}$ to $e^{\frac{1}{4}}$ as α increases from $\frac{1}{4}$ to $\sqrt{2} - 1$. Higher values of α are not considered here since the frequency-response characteristic then has a hump at its high-frequency end.

5. DESIGN NOMOGRAPHS FOR WIDE-BAND AMPLIFIERS

Three separate nomographs have been prepared as aids in design-ing R-coupled and shunt-compensated wide-band amplifiers.* They are based on Eqs. 25 and 26 developed in Sec. 4 above. Equation 25 gives the mid-band gain G_0 of a single R-coupled stage having a bandwidth f_2, interstage parasitic capacitance C, and a tube transcon-ductance g_m. Equation 26 gives the mid-band gain G_n of one stage of a shunt-compensated n-stage amplifier having the values of g_m, f_2, and C that are used in computing G_0. The function $\phi(n)$, which con-tains the shunt-compensation parameter $\alpha = L/R^2C$, is given by Eq. 22. The following three cases are of particular interest: $\alpha = 0$, the uncompensated resistance-coupled case; $\alpha = 0.25$, the critically shunt-compensated resistance-coupled case; and $\alpha = 0.414$, the shunt-compensated case giving a flat frequency response of greatest band-width. The nomographs for the three cases are given in Figs. 3.7, 3.8, and 3.9, respectively.

The method of using the nomographs is illustrated by an example using the three dashed lines on each of the charts. The example is based on an amplifier of 3-megacycles-per-second bandwidth, con-sisting of seven 6AC7 tubes. It is assumed that $g_m = 0.009$ mhos, which determines a point on line 1. The interstage parasitic capaci-tance is taken to be C = 25 $\mu\mu$f, which determines a point on line 3. The line between the two points is extended to line 5, and from the point of intersection a second line is drawn to the point $f_2 = 3$ mega-cycles per second on line 2. On line 4 the value of G_0 (= 19) is found. From the value of G_0 on line 4 a third line is drawn through the point n = 7 on line 5 and extended to line 6, where the value of G_n is ob-tained. The gain G_n is that which each stage of the seven-stage am-plifier must have in order to realize a 3-megacycles-per-second band-width with the assigned values of g_m and C.

The more general case of an amplifier with stages having different values of g_m and C may be handled as though the amplifier consisted entirely of one kind of stage, then of another, and so on. The band-width f_2 and the number of stages n remain as invariant points on the nomograph during the calculation. By this analysis one arrives at the correct gain for each stage.

---

* The construction of these nomographs has been suggested by similar nomographs for i-f amplifiers, prepared at the Radiation Laboratory of the Massachusetts Institute of Technology.

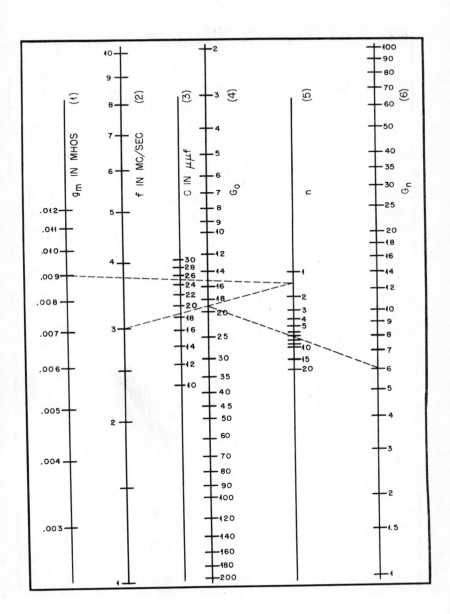

Fig. 3.7 — Nomograph for wide-band amplifier design ($\alpha = 0$).

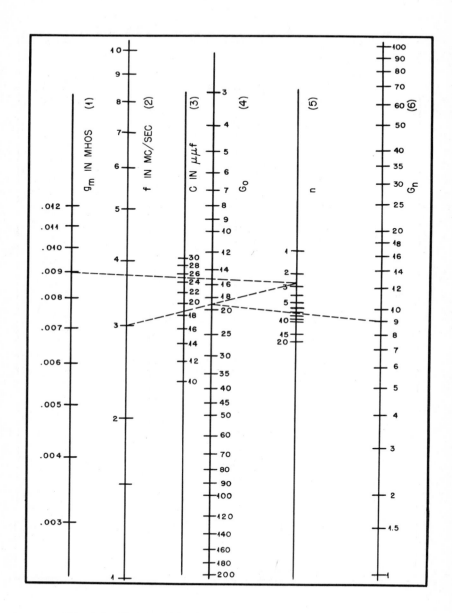

Fig. 3.8 — Nomograph for wide-band amplifier design ($\alpha = 0.25$).

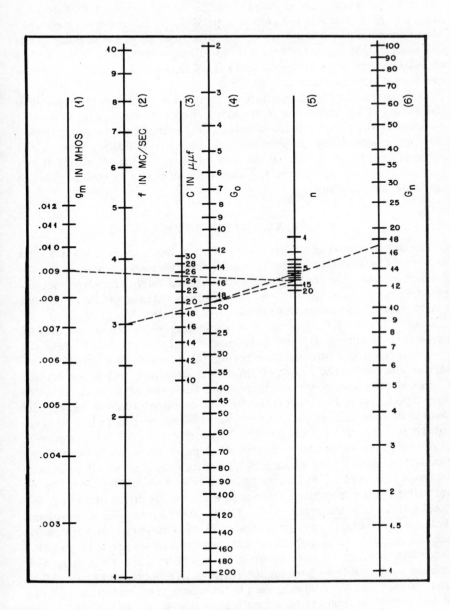

Fig. 3.9 — Nomograph for wide-band amplifier design ($\alpha = 0.414$).

When it is necessary to determine the correct number of amplifier stages to give an assigned gain and bandwidth, the method of successive approximations must be used. If it appears at some point in the calculation that the gain of an individual stage must be as low as $G_n = e^{\frac{1}{2}} = 1.65$, then it is impossible to design such an amplifier with the given values of g_m and C.

The present type of analysis can be applied, with less accuracy, to the design of certain types of feedback amplifiers that are critically compensated. Usually it is sufficient to consider the feedback amplifier as replaced by an equivalent R-coupled amplifier having the same net gain and the same number of tubes as the amplifier it replaces. The nomograph for R-coupled amplifiers can then be used to estimate the bandwidth.

6. AMPLIFIER NOISE

The output signal of an amplifier usually has superimposed on it a variety of extraneous signal components termed "noise." In the present section we shall discuss the various sorts of noise encountered in wide-band amplifiers and suggest certain precautions that can be taken to improve the signal-to-noise ratio.

It is convenient to classify the various types of noise that may be present as follows: (1) noise termed "hum," introduced from the power supply; (2) microphonic noise; (3) noise picked up from external sources as the result of imperfect shielding; (4) noise arising from defective components; (5) inherent tube and resistor noise. The only type of noise that theoretically cannot be eliminated by careful design is tube and resistor noise, whose origin lies in the discrete nature of electricity and matter. In practical amplifiers, however, simplicity and convenience in operation must sometimes be weighed against the possibility of completely eliminating noises listed above as types 1, 2, and 3. Evidently noise of type 4 should be absent in all amplifiers, since defective components can be identified and replaced.

6.1 Hum and Microphonics. There are several noise problems that are particularly serious in the case of wide-band amplifiers, on account of the high g_m pentodes that are used to secure a large gain-bandwidth product. These tubes are extremely microphonic, as well as very susceptible to hum pickup from an a-c operated heater. When an amplifier has appreciable gain in the audio-frequency range, a d-c heater supply is found to be essential for low-level stages, which may also require careful shock mounting against mechanical vibrations. Pulse amplifiers whose low-frequency response has been reduced for the purpose of shaping pulses from an electrical detector are naturally less sensitive to hum and microphonic pickup. In such amplifiers it is often satisfactory to use a common a-c heater supply for all stages. When this is done, the ungrounded side of the heater leads should be kept away from low-level, signal-carrying circuits. As an example of a precaution of this sort, experience shows that pin 3 of a 6AK5 tube should be grounded, leaving pin 4 for the high side of the heater connection.

In the case of pulse amplifiers, even if no trouble is experienced with hum pickup from the heater circuit, power-line transients that have high-frequency components may couple into the heater leads and ultimately appear in the output signal of the amplifier. Often it is difficult to determine just where these transients find their way into signal-carrying circuits. Pickup of these transients can often be reduced by using a heater transformer that has an electrostatic shield.

6.2 Extraneous Transients. Noise picked up electromagnetically, in spite of complete shielding, is perhaps one of the major sources of annoyance to anyone using a pulse amplifier. Pickup of this sort appears to be associated particularly with the finite impedance of the shield covering a group of leads between parts of an amplifier when the amplifier is divided into a main section and preamplifier. Often the preamplifier and attached detector are connected directly to other equipment, such as an accelerating device for nuclear particles, and the output of the amplifier is at the same time grounded to other electronic equipment for recording pulses. The multiplicity of grounds is obviously poor practice when the amplifier has high gain over a range of several megacycles. Nevertheless it is often difficult to arrange ground connections in a sensible fashion. Even under favorable conditions of grounding, there is evidence that a single layer of shielding is not entirely adequate to prevent the pickup of strong electromagnetic disturbances. For this reason, considerable grief can be avoided by choosing an electrically quiet room or building for carrying out nuclear experiments. When this is impossible—for instance, where large acceleration equipment is involved—no entirely adequate solution to the pickup problem has been found. It is suggested, in severe cases of noise pickup, that a system of double shielding be tried. This method requires a separate electrostatically shielded isolation transformer for bringing power through the outer detector-amplifier enclosure. The minor inconvenience of having a slightly enhanced background counting rate is ordinarily not worth the inconvenience of double shielding.

6.3 Tube and Resistor Noise.* In the case of a well-designed amplifier that has been properly installed, the upper limit to useful amplification is set by noise originating in tubes and resistors, the major contribution coming from the first stage of the amplifier. We shall not attempt to discuss noise limitation of this sort for the general case of wide-band amplifiers having a variety of different input circuits, but shall restrict ourselves specifically to pulse amplifiers used with an electrical detector connected to the grid of the input stage. On account of the low gain of pulse amplifiers at audio frequencies, it will not be necessary to consider noise from the flicker effect, whose frequency components lie mostly below 5 kc/sec. We shall therefore consider only thermal-resistor noise, noise from fluctuations in grid current, and noise from the shot effect.

In making an approximate computation of noise contributions from these sources, it is convenient, first of all, to express each source of the noise as if it came from an equivalent resistance suitably connected in the input circuit of the amplifier. Then, instead of computing noise as so many rms volts, either in the output of the amplifier or at the grid of the first stage, it is advantageous to express it in terms of an equivalent rms noise charge q_n on the capacity of the detector. Thus a particular value of q_n corresponds to the same output signal as would be produced if an actual charge of this amount were placed on the capacitance of the input circuit. This manner of expressing noise is particularly useful since it makes possible an immediate estimation of the signal-to-noise ratio when a charge q is released in the detector as a result of the entry of an ionizing particle.

If $g(\omega)$ denotes the relative gain of the amplifier expressed as a function of $\omega \equiv 2\pi f$, then it can be shown that

$$q_n^2 = \frac{1}{2\pi} \int_0^\infty [g(\omega)]^2 \left[\frac{4kT}{\omega^2 R} + \frac{4kT}{\omega^2 R_g} + 4kTR_s(C + C_1)^2 \right] d\omega \qquad (32)$$

where R is the input resistance between grid and ground, as measured with tube cold; R_g is the equivalent input noise resistance of first tube, taking into account grid current, buffeting of grid by space charge, etc.; R_s is the equivalent series grid noise resistance, commonly used to express the magnitude of shot-effect voltages arising in the plate circuit; C is the capacitance of attached electrical detector; and C_1 is the input capacitance of amplifier, as measured with the potentials of all tube elements held fixed.

---

* For general reference to this subject see E. B. Moullin, "Spontaneous Fluctuations of Voltage," Oxford University Press, New York, 1938.

In deriving Eq. 32, it has been assumed that it is correct simply to add the mean-square equivalent noise charges arising from the various sources of noise. Some error is probably made in neglecting a possible interrelation between shot noise and noise originating in the grid because of the buffeting of the grid by fluctuations in the space charge.* It should be noted that C_1 may not be the actual input capacitance of the amplifier. An analysis of a variety of types of input stages shows that C_1, as defined, is the proper value of capacitance to use when computing signal-to-noise ratios. The true input capacitance differs from C_1 in the case of a triode input stage, and in the case of a feedback loop where feedback to the cathode of the input tube takes place.

The integrals in Eq. 32 can be evaluated in a simple closed form for a pulse amplifier having a single RC cutoff at low and at high frequencies. For such an amplifier

$$[g(\omega)]^2 = \frac{\omega^2}{\omega_1^2 + \omega^2}\frac{\omega_2^2}{\omega_2^2 + \omega^2}$$

where $\omega_1 = 2\pi f_1$ and $\omega_2 = 2\pi f_2$. The frequencies f_1 and f_2 are the lower and the upper half-power frequencies, respectively. For this case Eq. 32 becomes

$$q_n^2 = \left(\frac{kT}{2\pi R} + \frac{kT}{2\pi R_g}\right)\frac{f_2}{f_1(f_1 + f_2)} + 2\pi kTR_s(C + C_1)^2\frac{f_2^2}{f_1 + f_2} \qquad (33)$$

The important aspects of the results expressed by Eq. 33 have been verified by noise measurements on several of the pulse amplifiers described in a later section. In making these measurements, rectangular pulses occurring at a constant repetition frequency are fed into an amplifier through a known capacitance C, which simulates the detector capacitance.† The output of the amplifier is connected to a discriminator-scaler circuit that counts all pulses whose height is greater than a fixed pulse height. A curve can then be taken of the number of counts per second as a function of the size of pulses coming from the pulser.

All curves that have been taken by this method can be fitted reasonably well by a Gauss error function of the form

$$n = \frac{n_0}{\sqrt{\pi}}\int_{-\infty}^{v}\exp\left[-\frac{(v - V_0)^2}{2V_n^2}\right]dv \qquad (34)$$

---

* See. for instance. P. O. North and W. R. Ferris, Proc. I.R.E., 29: 49 (1941).

  † The Model 100 pulser, described in Chap. 6, Sec. 3, can be used as a source of pulses.

where V_0 is the magnitude of input pulse giving a counting rate n = $n_0/2$ and where $V_n C = q_n$ can be interpreted as the rms value of the equivalent charge noise. The most probable value of the charge noise is evidently $Q_n \equiv 0.6745 q_n$. On determining values of Q_n for several

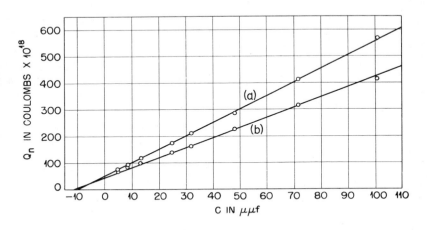

Fig. 3.10 — Equivalent charge-noise curves for Model 500 amplifier.

different values of C, the type of relation shown in Fig. 3.10 is obtained. The curves there are for a Model 500 amplifier (see Sec. 7 of this chapter) having a 100-megohm input resistor and the 6AK5 input tube connected as a pentode for curve (a) and as a triode for curve (b). The clipping time, or low-frequency short time constant in the amplifier, is about 5 μsec. Since both curves represent a linear relation between Q_n and C, the first two terms in Eq. 33, which are due to thermal noise and grid-current noise, respectively, must be negligible, indicating that practically all noise comes from the shot effect. Other curves, taken with lower-valued input resistors, have a curvature at low values of C. This can be attributed to the first term in Eq. 33.

An experimental result to be especially noted is that the equivalent charge noise from the input tube is less when the tube is triode-connected than when it is pentode-connected. The advantage of a triode input stage has not been fully recognized in the past use of pulse amplifiers in making nuclear-physics measurements. However, the reasons that such a stage is better than a pentode stage are not difficult to find. Let us consider the effect of a parasitic capacitance between grid and plate of the input stage. In reality this capacitance constitutes a true inverse-feedback element when the input signal itself is generated across a capacitance. Since both noise and signal voltages are fed back in the same ratio, the signal-to-noise ratio (S/N ratio) is unchanged, although the greater input capacitance of a stage having a parasitic grid-plate capacitance results in a smaller output-voltage signal. Now it is well known that the mean-square shot noise of a pentode is generally found to be about three times greater than that of the same tube triode-connected.* Hence, a given tube that is triode-connected should have an appreciably greater S/N ratio than if it were pentode-connected. This conclusion is in accord with the data in Fig. 3.10, although the improvement is perhaps not so great as might be expected.

It should be pointed out that the use of a triode input stage for a wide-band pulse amplifier does not noticeably increase the rise time of the amplifier. This point has been carefully checked for the Model 500 amplifier used in obtaining noise data on triode input stages.

The figure of merit of a tube for low shot noise is $g_m/(C_i I_p^{\frac{1}{2}})$. On this basis, several miniature triodes, including the 9001 and the 6C4, were selected for comparison with the triode-connected 6AK5 as an input stage for a pulse amplifier. None of these tubes, however, seemed to show as low a noise curve as indicated by curve (b) in Fig. 3.10. Not all 6AK5 tubes are found to make satisfactory input tubes. Some 6AK5 tubes have a larger grid current than others, and these particular tubes show an appreciably greater noise output than is found if the grid current is low. Although it is to be expected that this effect can be accounted for by the second term in Eq. 32 or in Eq. 33, no quantitative study of this source of noise has been made.

It is evident that experimental noise curves of the type described are extremely useful in estimating the S/N ratio to be expected with an electrical detector of known capacitance. It is desirable that curves of this sort should be taken for all amplifiers used in investigations where noise is a limiting factor in the experiment. It should be remarked that, other than comparing the relative merits of triode and pentode input stages, little attention has been given to the problem of obtaining the best possible S/N ratio in the amplifiers described later in the chapter. These amplifiers have been designed with emphasis placed primarily on good stability, linearity, and short rise time.

---

* See W. A. Harris, RCA Rev., 5: 505 (1941).

As a final point concerning the S/N ratio, it is of interest to inquire how the ratio varies with clipping time, $\tau_1 = 1/(2\pi f_1)$, of the amplifier. An approximate calculation, substantiated by noise measurements,

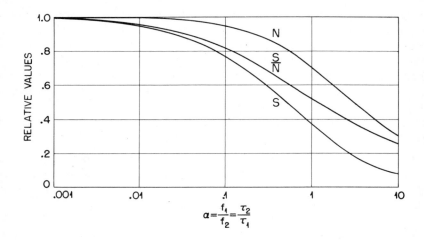

Fig. 3.11 — Signal, noise, and signal-to-noise relations.

indicates that the S/N ratio decreases with decreasing clipping time, contrary to the supposition of many experimentalists. In other words, the output-signal height decreases more rapidly than the amount of noise as the lower half-power frequency of the amplifier is raised.

The magnitude of this effect can be calculated exactly for an amplifier having a single RC cutoff at low and at high frequencies — the case for which the equivalent charge noise, Eq. 33, has been computed. If a step voltage is applied to the input stage at t = 0, i.e., if at this time some charge is suddenly placed on the capacitance of the detector, the output pulse takes the form

$$e_0 = E_\infty \frac{\tau_1}{\tau_1 - \tau_2} (e^{-\tau/\tau_1} - e^{-\tau/\tau_2}) \tag{35}$$

where $\tau_1 = 1/(2\pi f_1)$, $\tau_2 = 1/(2\pi f_2)$, and E_∞ is the amplitude of the output signal if $\tau_1 \to \infty$. If we let $\alpha \equiv f_1/f_2 = \tau_2/\tau_1$, then the maximum value of the output pulse e_0 is found from Eq. 35 to be

$$e_{om} = E_\infty \alpha^{\alpha/(1-\alpha)} \tag{36}$$

Since experiment shows that the predominating noise in the output of the amplifier arises from the shot effect, Eq. 33 indicates that the output-noise voltage depends on the frequencies f_1 and f_2 as follows:

$$e_n = \text{const.} \times \sqrt{\frac{f_2}{1 + \alpha}} \qquad (37)$$

The output S/N ratio therefore depends on α according to

$$\frac{e_{om}}{e_n} \left(= \frac{S}{N} \right) = \text{const.} \times \sqrt{\frac{1 + \alpha}{f_2}} \; \alpha^{\alpha/(1-\alpha)} \qquad (38)$$

Equations 36, 37, and 38 are presented as graphs in Fig. 3.11, where each quantity is normalized to unity for $\alpha = 0$ and where the three

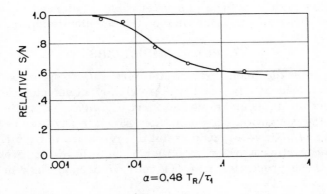

$$\alpha = 0.48 \, T_R/\tau_1$$

Fig. 3.12 — Experimental signal-to-noise ratio as a function of clipping time.

equations are identified by S, N, and S/N, respectively. Evidently an appreciable loss in S/N ratio begins to set in when $\alpha > 0.01$.

The above calculation is inaccurate for the usual pulse amplifier, whose upper-frequency cutoff will approximate the shape of a Gauss error curve rather than that of a single RC plate load. The calculation, however, does show the order of magnitude of the decrease in S/N ratio to be expected as the amplifier clipping time is decreased.

Some measurements of the decrease in S/N ratio for a Model 500 amplifier are presented in Fig. 3.12. In interpreting this result, it should be recalled that the upper half-power frequency f_2 is related to the amplifier rise time T_R by the relation $T_R f_2 \approx \frac{1}{3}$ (Eq. 20), so that

$$\alpha = \frac{f_1}{f_2} \approx 3 T_R f_1 \approx 0.48 \frac{T_R}{\tau_1}$$

where τ_1 is the clipping time. Thus if the amplifier has a rise time of 0.1 μsec and a clipping time of 5 μsec, $\alpha \approx 0.01$, and it is for about this value of α that the curve shown in Fig. 3.12 begins to decrease fairly rapidly, in qualitative agreement with the predicted behavior.

If the pulses from an electrical detector have a rise time appreciably longer than the rise time of the amplifier, the S/N ratio will be correspondingly decreased. For this reason the amplifier should never have a rise time much in excess of that required by the collection time of the particular detector with which it is being used. Furthermore, it appears that the clipping time should be kept as long as is consistent with avoiding a pile-up of pulses, but need not be more than about fifty times the rise time of the detector-amplifier system.

7. PULSE AMPLIFIERS

In this book the term "pulse amplifier" refers specifically to an amplifier intended to be used with an electrical detector for making measurements in nuclear-physics investigations. Certain factors affecting the design of a pulse amplifier have already been pointed out in this chapter. However, it is useful to review and to supplement the various properties a pulse amplifier should possess, even though some of these properties may not yet have been attained in existing amplifiers.

The gain required of a pulse amplifier depends on the magnitude of the signal received from the electrical detector with which it is used. Since a wide spread in input-signal levels is encountered with different detectors and with particles having different energies, it is usual to have the maximum amplifier gain large enough to make the random peaks of noise voltage in the output no less than 10 volts high. This somewhat arbitrary figure is chosen because the voltage discriminator employed to measure output heights is rarely used below a 10-volt level. (See Chap. 4, Secs. 2.1 and 2.5, for a discussion of discriminators.)

Experience with various wide-band amplifiers indicates that a lower limit to the equivalent noise voltage at the first grid, under most favorable circumstances, has an rms value of perhaps 3.5 μv, corresponding roughly to 10-μv peaks. Hence a gain of 10^6 is not unreasonable for some pulse amplifiers. In most cases, however, a maximum gain between 10^5 and 5×10^5 is sufficient. When highly energetic fission fragments are being counted or when gas amplification is used in the electrical detector, maximum gains 10 to 100 times smaller than those stated are satisfactory. To meet various gain requirements, it is customary to provide two attenuators: one having four or more steps, each reducing the gain by a factor of 2, and the other having either a continuous or a step control covering but a single factor of 2. The simple resistance attenuator described in Chap. 2, Sec. 2.1, makes a satisfactory element for the coarse gain control. It should be placed at a point where preceding stages are not overloaded when the amplifier gain is set at a minimum and the amplifier is delivering pulses of maximum amplitude at the maximum counting rate that will ever be used.

The output pulses from a pulse amplifier are always chosen to have a positive polarity so that a low-impedance cathode-follower output stage is suitable. The minimum usable amplitude of output pulses is about 10 volts, and the amplifier should be capable of delivering pulses of at least a 50-volt amplitude, with the same rise time and linearity afforded smaller pulses. This requirement is reasonable only if the parasitic-capacitance load of attached electronic devices is less than some specified value. Since pulses of a single polarity (usually negative) are obtained from a given electrical detector, the high-level stages in the amplifier can be asymmetrically biased for most efficient operation with one sign of pulse. The amplifier gain, as a function of output-pulse height, should be constant to 1 per cent for output pulses up to 50 volts in height.

The amount of gain stability of a pulse amplifier becomes very important when the electrical detector does not posses a good "plateau" on its counting-rate, pulse-height characteristic. Short-time gain changes in an unfed-back amplifier are usually caused by changes in heater voltage and not by changes in the plate power supply, which is always electronically stabilized. Changes of gain of a few per cent for a 1 per cent change in line voltage are usual for a wide-band shunt-compensated amplifier.* In the case of feedback pulse amplifiers, gain drifts from this cause are sufficiently reduced so that they become inconsequential. Perhaps a change in output-pulse height of

---

* Principally because of lack of gain stability, but also because of poor linearity, unfed-back pulse amplifiers were used but little at Los Alamos once suitable wide-band feedback amplifiers were designed. Only where very narrow pulses, perhaps 0.2 μsec wide, have been needed for fast timing experiments, have shunt-compensated pulse amplifiers continued to be popular. To avoid drifts in gain, the heaters of the tubes in an unfed-back amplifier have been powered by a storage battery floating on a charger, by a stabilized 110-volt a-c generator, or by the lamp-bridge heater-voltage stabilizer described in Chap. 7, Sec. 8.

0.1 per cent for a line voltage variation of 1 per cent is a reasonable stability requirement. Long-time drifts in gain caused by changes in ambient temperature, by the aging of tubes, and by the aging of carbon resistors (when this type must be used) usually do not cause trouble.

The low-frequency response of a pulse amplifier determines the shape of output pulses, in the manner described in Sec. 3 of this chapter. The network responsible for pulse shaping is ordinarily placed in the amplifier very near the coarse gain control. All other short time constants in the amplifier should be about 50 to 100 times longer than the single short time constant used for pulse shaping in order to avoid an appreciable undershoot of the output pulse. The maximum value of the clipping time need never be more than 50 to 100 times the rise time of the amplifier, and it is sometimes made as short as the rise time.

The high-frequency response characteristics of a pulse amplifier are usually expressed in terms of amplifier rise time, which is defined precisely in Sec. 4 of this chapter. Pulse amplifiers should normally have a monotonic transient response to an input step voltage, and values of rise time ranging from 0.05 to 1 μsec are needed, depending on the experiment at hand. This range of rise times corresponds to a range of upper half-power frequencies from 6 megacycles per second to 300 kilocycles per second. The rise time of an amplifier suitable for use with a given detector should be somewhat less than the collection time of the detector, except, of course, when one is investigating the finite rate of collection of the detector. In this case an amplifier with a much shorter rise time than the collection time is needed.

The noise in the amplifier output should consist almost entirely of shot noise from the first tube, which must be selected for its low-noise properties. Although most pulse amplifiers have in the past employed a pentode input stage, a better S/N ratio is obtained if this particular stage is based on a triode (see Sec. 6 of this chapter). It is difficult to propose a requirement in regard to noise originating in the first amplifier stage, but the noise data presented in Fig. 3.10 may be taken as a reasonable upper limit to the noise that is characteristic of an amplifier having a 0.1-μsec rise and a 5-μsec clipping time. An amplifier with a longer rise time should have a higher S/N ratio than this amplifier.

The shielding and the physical layout of a pulse amplifier are of considerable importance. It has been pointed out in Sec. 6 of this chapter that trouble is often encountered with pickup of transient electrical disturbances that give rise to spurious counts in the pulse-recording equipment. The pickup of severe transients has never been completely eliminated in the amplifiers to be described, although in nearly all applications the amplifiers have proved satisfactory when sufficient care has been taken to install them properly. It is usually necessary to divide a pulse amplifier into two portions—a so-called

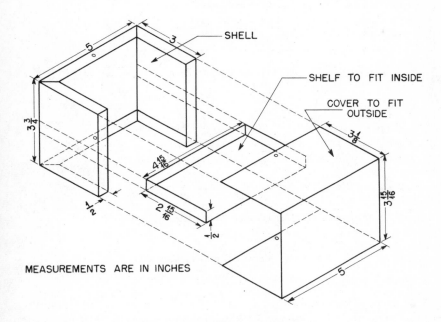

Fig. 3.13—Model 100 preamplifier case.

"preamplifier" and a "main amplifier." There are several reasons for this division. The grid of the input stage must be as close as possible to the electrical detector in order to keep capacitance at a minimum. It is often necessary, however, either on account of space limitations or, on account of the unduly large nuclear cross section of the complete amplifier, to locate as much of the amplifier as possible several feet or more from the electrical detector. A voltage gain of from 1 to 100 is usually taken in the preamplifier, and a maximum gain of perhaps 10,000 is taken in the main amplifier, where the coarse and fine gain controls are located. Usually the preamplifier contains from one stage (a cathode follower) to four stages (as in the Model 500 amplifier described later).

A convenient standard preamplifier case is shown in Fig. 3.13, and a standard cable to connect the two parts of the amplifier is shown in Fig. 3.14. In any laboratory where a number of different amplifiers are used, it is wise to standardize on a single type of preamplifier cable, even though the style of construction of the preamplifier may have to be chosen to suit the experiment at hand.

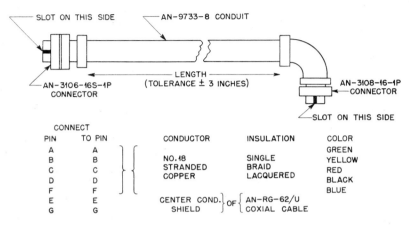

Fig. 3.14 — Model 100 preamplifier cable.

7.1 Unfed-back Amplifiers. In Fig. 3.15 is shown the complete wiring diagram of a Model 50 shunt-compensated amplifier, which has an over-all gain of about 150,000 and a rise time of about 0.06 μsec.* This amplifier delivers positive output pulses having an amplitude of 40 volts with reasonable linearity, and it requires negative input signals from the electrical detector. Gain is controlled by switching the plate-load resistors in the plate circuit of the first stage of the main amplifier and by varying the screen potential of the same tube. The pulse-shaping time constant is located just following this stage. Neither the method of controlling gain nor the location of the pulse-shaping network is ideal. A somewhat better amplifier would result if a step attenuator were used at the termination of the coaxial cable from the preamplifier and if the short time constant were located as in the Model 100 or in the Model 500 amplifier to be described later.

---

*Although the Model 50 amplifier has been successfully used in a large number of investigations, it is now considered more or less obsolete in comparison with more recently designed feedback pulse amplifiers. An unfed-back amplifier with more desirable properties than the Model 50 can undoubtedly be designed.

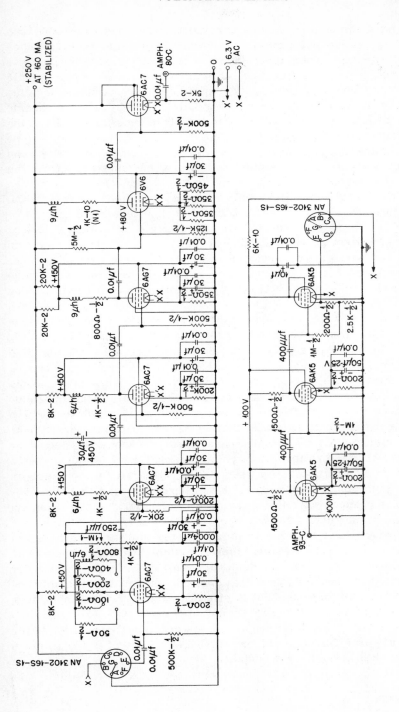

Fig. 3.15 — Model 50 pulse amplifier.

The stage preceding the output cathode follower is a type 6V6 tube biased to draw a plate current of 70 ma. This stage has an unbypassed cathode resistor of 125 ohms, in order to increase its linearity of response for large signals. The gain of this stage is only a little more than 3, so the preceding stage has to supply a maximum negative signal of about 15 volts, requiring a plate current change of nearly 20 ma through its plate-load resistor of 800 ohms. On account of the large current swing required, a type 6AG7 tube, instead of a type 6AC7, is used for this stage. The nonlinear characteristics of the two high-level stages tend to cancel each other, and thus to improve the over-all linearity of the amplifier.

Each stage of the main amplifier is shunt-compensated with an inductance whose value is intended to be that computed from $L = \frac{1}{4} R_L^2 C_L$. The values indicated in the diagram are slightly high if parasitic interstage capacitances are kept at a minimum by careful layout and wiring. The inductances can be made by unwinding turns from sections of small r-f chokes or by winding turns on a high-value composition resistor (1-watt size), which makes a convenient winding form.

Each of the first four stages of the main amplifier, and the preamplifier as a unit, is decoupled from the plate power supply. Decoupling is done in this way chiefly for reasons of convenience. In the main amplifier, for instance, a dual electrolytic tubular capacitor can be mounted near each stage to serve for both cathode- and plate-supply by-passing. Screen biases have been so chosen that separate decoupling is not required. The resulting saving in parts avoids congestion near the signal-carrying leads, thereby keeping parasitic capacitance at a minimum. All electrolytic capacitors are shown by-passed by mica capacitors, in a manner often recommended for television video amplifiers. This precaution may not be required for good quality electrolytic capacitors; in fact, it has been observed that this procedure sometimes introduces damped oscillations in the transient response of the pulse amplifier.

The preamplifier contains two amplifying stages, each having a gain of about 6, and a cathode follower to drive the capacitance of an unterminated 6-ft coaxial cable leading to the main amplifier. For simplicity, no shunt compensation has been used in the preamplifier, although a small improvement in rise time would result if inductance of about 6 μh were placed in series with each plate-load resistor. The rise time of the entire amplifier, however, has been adequate for nearly all experiments, and therefore the design of a faster pulse amplifier has never been undertaken.

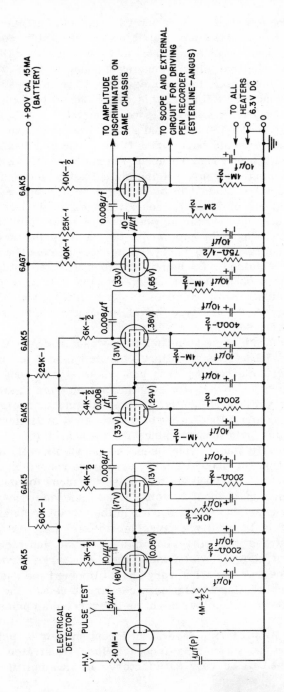

Fig. 3.16 — Model 75 pulse amplifier for recording the infrequent occurrence of fission.

It is interesting to estimate the practical limit in rise time that can be obtained with a shunt-compensated amplifier which contains a reasonable number of stages and which has a gain of 2×10^5 with a linear output for positive signals having an amplitude of 30 or 40 volts. Since the bottleneck in any pulse amplifier is the stage preceding the output cathode follower, this stage should perhaps consist of a type 807 tube having a large figure of merit, $I_{p_{max}}/C_0$. With a plate-load resistance of 750 ohms and a parasitic load capacitance of 20 $\mu\mu$f, such a stage would have a rise time, computed from Eq. 17, of 0.01 μsec, and it would require about 100 ma plate current for the desired linear output response. If the plate-load resistor of each of the other stages were made 600 ohms, with an average interstage parasitic capacitance of 25 $\mu\mu$f, then all stages would have a rise time of about 0.01 μsec. Assuming an average stage gain of a little more than 4, nine stages of gain would be required for an over-all gain of 2×10^5, and according to Eq. 19 an over-all rise time of 0.03 μsec would be obtained. By using four-terminal interstages (not described in this book), a rise time of perhaps 0.02 μsec could be obtained. Experience with compensated amplifiers suggests that practical amplifiers of this type could be constructed if need for them should ever arise.

A second unfed-back pulse amplifier to be described, the Model 75, is shown in Fig. 3.16. It is a battery-operated model for use at a remote point where electrical pickup can cause no spurious counts. It is intended to be used only for counting pulses from fission fragments that occur very infrequently, so that continuous operation for several days is required to obtain reasonably good statistics. There is no provision for gain control since the values of the plate-load resistors in the early stages have been chosen empirically to give a sufficiently great pulse, about 10 volts, to operate recording devices. It is claimed that, in response to test pulses, narrow output pulses are obtained which rise about 20 volts in 0.2 μsec and decay with a comparable time constant. What appears in the circuit to be an output cathode follower is in reality a pulse lengthener, i.e., the positive output pulse charges the stray capacitance of an interconnecting coaxial cable (not shown), which must then discharge through the 1-megohm cathode resistor. The very short clipping time used in the amplifier following the input stage is necessary to reduce the pile-up of small background pulses that might be interpreted as pulses from fission fragments.

7.2 Feedback Amplifiers. Several different models of pulse amplifiers based on the three-tube feedback loop illustrated in Fig. 2.20(b) have proved to be very satisfactory. In an amplifier of this type, three separate feedback loops are normally required. One loop with a gain of 30 to 100 can serve as the preamplifier, and the other two loops, each with a gain of 100, can serve as the main amplifier. Additional cathode followers may be required to couple the preamplifier to the main amplifier and the main amplifier to pulse-recording

Table 3.1 — Some Properties of Models 100 and 500 Pulse Amplifiers

	Model 100	Model 500
Rise time	0.5 μsec	0.1 μsec
Maximum gain	10^6	3×10^5
Range of gain control	2^9	2^5
Maximum usable output pulse having stated rise time	+150 volts	+75 volts
Polarity of input pulse	Positive or negative	Negative
Maximum recommended pulse-shaping time constant	50 μsec	10 μsec
Provision for plug-in delay-line pulse shaper	Yes	No
Feedback resistors determining gain	Wire-wound	Carbon
Stability of mid-band gain	Excellent	Good
Stability of rise time	Excellent	Fair
Linearity	Excellent	Excellent

devices, since it is undesirable to place an appreciable capacitive load on the output of the three-tube feedback loop (see Chap. 2, Sec. 3.5). In the present section, three amplifiers of this type will be described, the Models 100, 500, and 220. Since the Models 100 and 500 tend to supplement each other for general laboratory use, they will be discussed at the same time.

The circuit diagrams for the two amplifiers are shown in Figs. 3.17 and 3.18. Some of the important features of the two amplifiers are listed in Table 3.1. Most of the essential differences between the two amplifiers, as noted in the table, are dictated by the differences in rise time for which the amplifiers are designed. The Model 100 amplifier should normally be used for most experiments except where the short rise time of the other amplifier is of primary importance. Random noise data for the Model 500 amplifier have been given in Figs. 3.10 and 3.12. Some preliminary measurements of random noise for the Model 100 indicate that it is somewhat less than for the Model 500.

The upper half-power frequency of the Model 500 amplifier is about 3.5 megacycles per second. The amplifier contains three ceramic trimming capacitors across the feedback resistors in each feedback

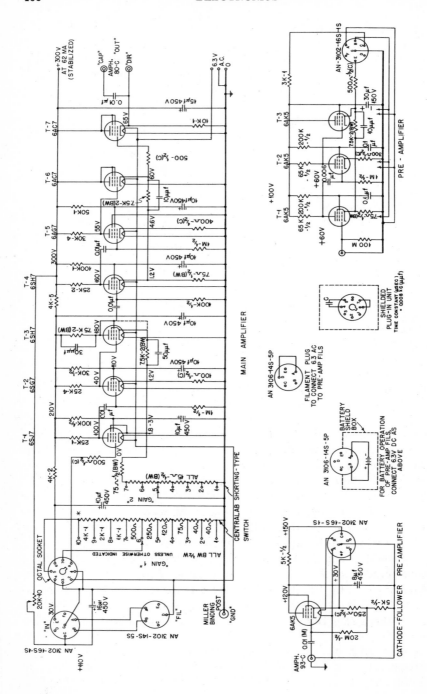

Fig. 3.17—Model 100 pulse amplifier.

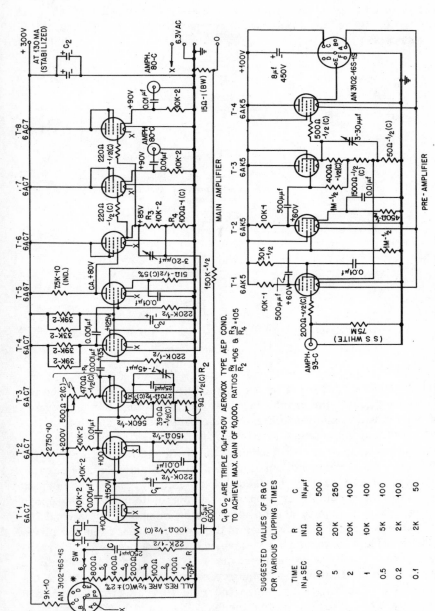

Fig. 3.18 — Model 500 pulse amplifier.

SUGGESTED VALUES OF R & C
FOR VARIOUS CLIPPING TIMES

TIME IN μ SEC	R IN Ω	C IN μμf
10	20K	500
5	20K	250
2	20K	100
1	10K	100
0.5	5K	100
0.2	2K	100
0.1	2K	50

loop. These must be empirically adjusted so that there is no transient overshoot on a test step wave having a rise time at least as short as 0.05 μsec. When the amplifier is compensated in this way, its high-frequency response characteristic is similar in shape to that of an

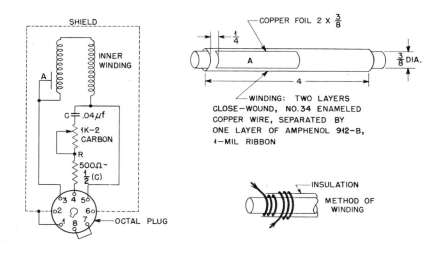

Fig. 3.19 — Plug-in delay-line pulse shaper for the Model 100 amplifier.

R-coupled amplifier of nine stages having a gain of 3×10^5 and employing the same tubes. This experimental evidence justifies the use of the amplifier nomograph (Fig. 3.7) for predicting the upper half-power frequency (and therefore the rise time) of an amplifier of this sort, provided it is compensated for good transient response.

The upper half-power frequency of the Model 100 amplifier is about 700 kilocycles per second. In this amplifier, fixed values of capacitance are placed across the feedback resistors. They have been so chosen for the preamplifier loop and the output loop that these loops possess a flat frequency response extending considerably beyond 700 kilocycles per second. The upper half-power frequency and the shape of the transient-response curve are determined mostly by the relatively larger feedback capacitance used in the second feedback loop. This method of limiting the frequency response tends to stabilize the rise time of the amplifier, since the rise time is then determined primarily by a property of the feedback path and not by the plate-circuit time constants of the amplifier. A stable rise time is important when short clipping times are used and when the electrical detector has a collection time comparable to the rise time of the amplifier. In such a case the pulse height is sensitive to changes in amplifier rise time.

Different methods of placing the gain control and the short time constant are used in the two amplifiers. In both amplifiers, pulse inversion occurs at the output of the first loop of the main amplifier, and the gain of this loop is determined by the ratio of the plate-load resistance of T-3 to the resistance in the cathode of T-1. In the case of the Model 500 amplifier, it is necessary to obtain additional grid bias for T-1 from a resistor in series with the negative power-supply lead. The Model 100 amplifier has been so designed that the signal from tube T-3 can be taken from the cathode instead of from the plate circuit. This change enables the amplifier to be used with positive input pulses. The necessary alteration in wiring is indicated by a dashed line in Fig. 3.17.

The short time constant in the Model 100 amplifier can readily be changed by removing a plug-in unit and substituting a unit having a coupling capacitor of a different value. If it is so desired, a delay-line pulse-shaping network can be substituted for the capacitor. (See Sec. 3.2 of this chapter for a discussion of this method of pulse shaping.) A plug-in unit of this type is illustrated in Fig. 3.19. The network contains a double-layer shorted delay line of the type described briefly in Chap. 2, Sec. 2.4. The line illustrated has a one-way delay of about 0.8 μsec. The piece of copper foil cemented to the solenoid near its input end is connected as indicated at A in the diagram. It is found empirically that the capacitance afforded by the foil improves the transient response of the line, evidently giving a certain amount of correction to its high-frequency, phase-delay characteristic. The resistance R, in parallel (in the a-c sense) with the input attenuator of the amplifier, constitutes the terminating impedance of the line. Part of R is made adjustable to enable an accurate termination of the line to be made. The capacitance C, in conjunction with the various resistances in the circuit, introduces the proper exponential decay to the signal, to compensate for the finite d-c resistance of the shorted delay line. The delay line must be carefully shielded to avoid the pickup of electrical transients.

Two preamplifiers are provided for the Model 100 amplifier. The cathode-follower preamplifier is used in conjunction with a proportional counter that generates relatively large pulses. The other preamplifier, which has a gain of approximately 100, is the preamplifier most often used.

The Model 100 amplifier is provided with a plug to enable power from either a transformer or a storage battery to be used for the

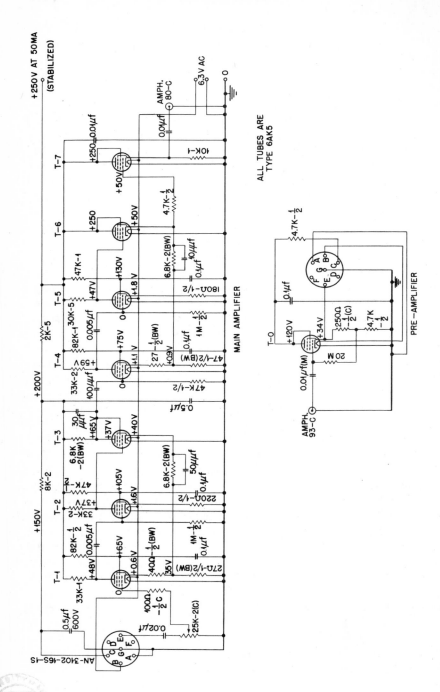

Fig. 3.20 — Model 220 pulse amplifier for use with a proportional counter.

heaters in the preamplifier. The preamplifier should be run on a storage battery when long clipping times are used, or when trouble is experienced from the pickup of transients from the power-supply mains. The storage battery is ordinarily placed in a shielded box.

The Model 220 amplifier, Fig. 3.20, is based entirely on type 6AK5 tubes. It has a mid-band gain of about 25,000, with a rise time of 0.5 μsec. It is intended primarily for use with a proportional counter having some gas amplification. Components have been chosen to enable the amplifier to be constructed compactly for applications where portability is of importance.

The preamplifier consists of a cathode follower. The ideal gain of the first feedback loop is about 250, whereas that of the second loop is about 140. A pulse-shaping time constant of 5 μsec is placed between the two feedback loops. Since the maximum height of individual pulses at this point is about 1 volt, the preceding feedback loop will never have to furnish an output signal, due to random fluctuations, of greater than 20 volts. (See Sec. 2 of this chapter for a discussion of this matter.) Hence there is no danger of the first loop overloading as the result of pulses piling up when reasonably fast counting rates are encountered.

8. TRANSIENT AMPLIFIERS

All the amplifiers to be considered here are intended for amplifying transients for their ultimate presentation on a cathode-ray oscillograph. Two sorts of problems are met in experimental investigations. It may be necessary to amplify signals to obtain an accurate timing of events, as indicated by abrupt changes in signal level, or it may be necessary to record faithfully the actual shape of a transient signal. In the former type of problem it is sufficient to use a shunt-compensated amplifier, and no effort need be wasted in obtaining good stability and linearity of response. The requirements placed on the amplifier are much more severe in the latter type of problem, so that considerable feedback must be used in the amplifier to obtain the requisite stability and linearity of response. When it is necessary to achieve an accuracy of a few per cent in the amplification of a transient lasting as long as 200 μsec and having a rise time of perhaps 0.5 μsec, the amplifying system must have an extremely flat mid-band frequency response, with lower and upper half-power frequencies of about 30 cycles per second and 3 megacycles per second, respectively. The bases for these requirements on frequency response have been discussed in Secs. 3 and 4 of this chapter. In view of the need for two types of transient amplifiers, let us first consider some of the

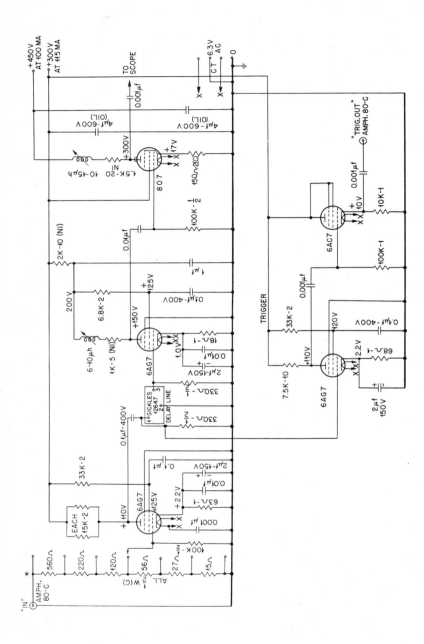

Fig. 3.21 — Model 200 transient amplifier for narrow pulses.

unfed-back shunt-compensated amplifiers useful for timing experiments and then turn to the consideration of several feedback amplifiers having good gain stability and linearity of response.

8.1 Unfed-back Amplifiers. Occasionally the problem arises of measuring with fair accuracy the time between two events separated by at most a few microseconds. If it is not known exactly when the two events will take place — as evidenced by two narrow pulses or by the leading and trailing edges of a single pulse — it is necessary not only to use the signal itself as a trigger to start an oscillograph sweep but also to pass the signal through a delay line before an amplified version of it is presented on the oscillograph, whose sweep is already under way. The Model 200 amplifier, shown in Fig. 3.21, represents one simple solution to a problem of this sort. A positive input signal containing the desired information at a minimum level of 1 volt passes through a 1,000-ohm attenuator to an amplifier stage whose plate load is essentially a delay line. The undelayed signal is amplified about seven times to serve as a positive trigger pulse for the sweep circuit, and the delayed signal is amplified by two asymmetrically biased stages for presentation on a cathode-ray tube having deflecting-plate connections brought out along the neck of the tube (for instance, a 5JP11 tube). The plate cap of the type 807 output stage can be conveniently located near the connection to one deflecting plate of the tube in order to minimize parasitic capacitance. The opposite deflecting plate can be used for putting narrow timing marks on the oscillograph trace.

The shunt-compensation of the amplifier is adjusted by varying slug-tuned chokes whose range of values is indicated in the drawing. The cathode resistor of the 807 tube is unby-passed in order to improve the linearity of response of the amplifier. Although the rise time of the system is about as good as that of the delay line, a little better than 0.1 μsec, no attempt has been made to achieve a good low-frequency response. Indeed, the 0.1-μf capacitor coupling the plate of the first stage to the delay line constitutes a short time constant of about 15 μsec. The amplifier would have to be modified if pulses longer than a few microseconds were to be recorded.

Another unfed-back transient amplifier, Model 300 shown in Fig. 3.22, is also used primarily in timing applications. Here two stages of gain are followed by a cathode-coupled phase inverter (see Chap. 2, Sec. 3.2) which drives a pair of type 807 tubes in push-pull. The amplifier has a gain of about 4,000, with a rise time of 0.06 μsec when it is compensated for no transient overshoot. It is intended to be built near a cathode-ray tube of the type 5JP11, so that the plate caps of the type 807 tubes can be located conveniently near the deflecting-plate connections on the neck of the cathode-ray tube.

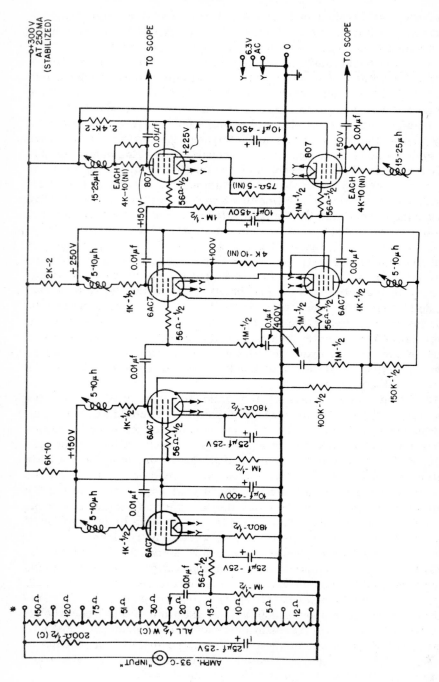

Fig. 3.22 — Model 300 transient amplifier.

The Model 300 amplifier, which has better linearity than the Model 200, is suitable for pulses of either sign. It will deliver a push-pull output signal of about ±150 volts with reasonable linearity. The input attenuator is intended to serve both as a proper termination for a coaxial cable and as a cathode resistor for a cathode follower located at a remote point. The attenuator should be modified to suit the needs of particular applications. The low-frequency response characteristic of the amplifier is essentially that given by the four 0.01-sec time constants of the grid circuits. It would be possible to apply low-frequency compensation to the amplifier if a better low-frequency characteristic were desired.

8.2 **Feedback Amplifiers**. The Model 600 transient amplifier, Fig. 3.23, has a maximum gain of about 15,000, a rise time of about 0.15 μsec, and a lower half-power frequency of about 15 cycles per second. This amplifier is intended to be used for the high-fidelity amplification of electrical transients lasting at most 200 μsec and having rise times as short as 0.5 μsec. It will handle signals of either sign, delivering an undistorted output signal of at least ±20 volts, which must be further amplified before presentation with a cathode-ray tube. The Model 1000 amplifier, described later in this section, has been designed as a high-level amplifier to be used in conjunction with the Model 600.

The Model 600 amplifier is constructed in two sections, a preamplifier and a main amplifier. The preamplifier consists of a three-tube feedback loop using 6AK5 pentodes, and has an ideal gain of 11. The cathode of T-3 is connected directly to a 200-ohm coaxial cable (Amphenol 72-30T), terminated at its far end by the attenuator in the main amplifier. It is necessary to supply the heaters of the tubes in the preamplifier with direct current to avoid hum pickup. The large plate-supply decoupling capacitor used for the preamplifier is found to be necessary to avoid peaking of the low-frequency response characteristic. As a matter of fact, there probably is some low-frequency compensation afforded by regeneration, since the measured lower half-power frequency of the entire amplifier is about 15 cycles per second, whereas the expected value is 25 cycles per second. This value is computed from the 0.01-sec time constants in the grid circuits at the input of each of the two feedback loops in the main amplifier.

The input circuit of the preamplifier is arranged for calibrating the over-all gain of the amplifying-recording system. The input terminals of the amplifier are short-circuited, and a known current is passed through the precision 1-ohm resistor R_1 in Fig. 3.23. The current is then abruptly cut off by electronic means, shortly after the

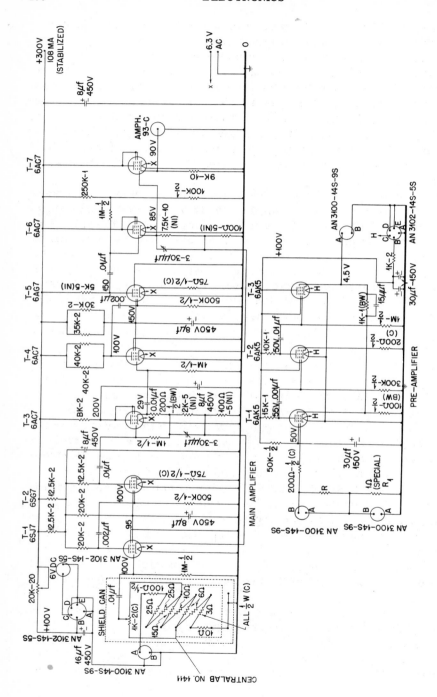

Fig. 3.23—Model 600 transient amplifier.

oscillograph sweep gets under way. By taking a series of photographs of the step signal appearing on the cathode-ray tube, for currents of different magnitudes and sign, calibration is made of the entire system. This type of calibration is necessary in careful work, since a certain amount of distortion is produced both by the cathode-ray tube and by the optical system used for photography of the trace.

The main amplifier consists of two three-tube feedback loops and an output cathode follower. The 6SJ7 and 6SG7 tubes used in the first loop have been chosen to reduce hum pickup, since it is convenient to operate all heaters in the main amplifier on alternating current. The measured rms hum voltage in the output of the main amplifier is normally less than 0.1 volt unless an unusually noisy 6SJ7 tube happens to be used for the first amplifier stage. The ideal gain of the first loop is 23, and that of the second loop 70. The gain of the second loop could be increased to 100 without increasing the amplifier rise time, which is limited primarily by the first loop of the main amplifier, where some sacrifice in rise time is taken for the advantages of using the type 6SJ7 tube.

The Model 1000 amplifier, shown in Fig. 3.24, is intended to be used following the Model 600 amplifier for the purpose of driving — in a push-pull connection — the plates of a cathode-ray tube. It has a gain of only 8, with a rise time of less than 0.1 μsec, provided very short leads are used to couple it to the deflecting plates of a 5CP11 cathode-ray tube. The input stage of the amplifier consists of a phase inverter based on a triode-connected 6AC7 tube drawing a current of 12 ma. It is found necessary to compensate the inverter capacitively by placing a small trimmer capacitor across the cathode-load resistor, in the manner described in Chap. 2, Sec. 3.2. Following the inverter are two identical two-tube feedback loops of the type discussed in Chap. 2, Sec. 3.5. On account of variations in the bias required by different 6AG7 tubes, part of the cathode resistance of the output stages is made variable so that the quiescent plate voltages of the two stages can be made equal to each other. The amplifier will deliver a push-pull output signal of ±150 volts without distortion. If greater voltage swings are required, it is possible to make minor modifications in the circuit so that a 400- or 450-volt supply can be used for the two 6AG7 tubes. It is desirable that the plate-load resistors of the output stages be of the inductively wound type, to aid the amplifier in delivering fast signals of considerable amplitude. The trimmer capacitors across the feedback resistors are adjusted so that no overshoot occurs on a fast step pulse. The amplifier has excellent gain stability and linearity of response. It is possible to bias the output stages asymmetrically if the amplifier is to be used for pulses of only one polarity.

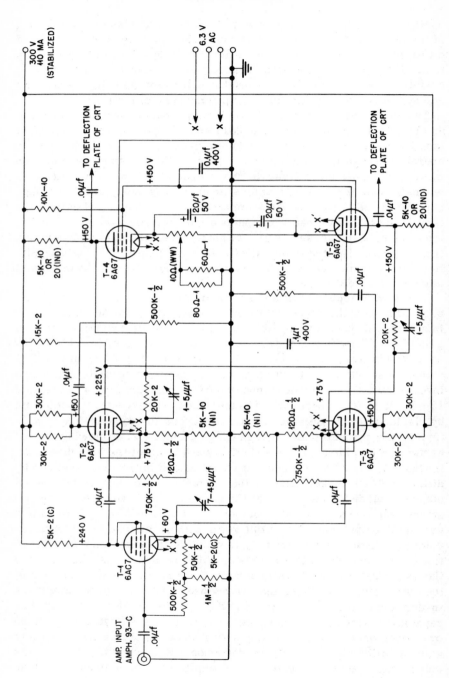

Fig. 3.24 — Model 1000 transient amplifier.

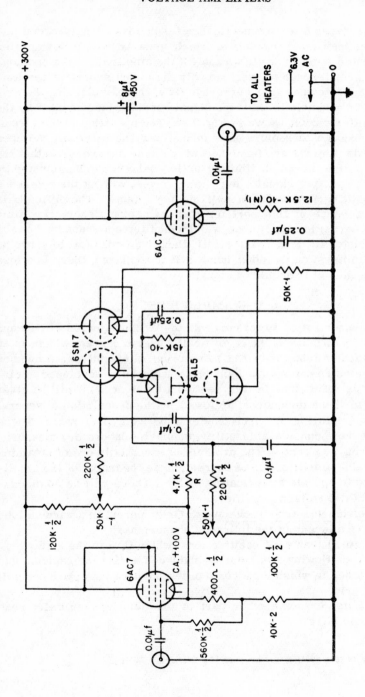

Fig. 3.25 — Limiter circuit for high-level signals.

In certain types of experiments, large spurious signals occur just prior to the legitimate transients, which must be faithfully amplified and presented with an oscillograph. If the amplitude of the spurious signals is great enough to overload only the output stages of the amplifier, i.e., to cause grid current to flow, thereby blocking the amplifier, it is possible to limit the signal reaching these stages by the type of limiter circuit shown in Fig. 3.25. The operation of the circuit is simple enough to require no explanation. The reference voltages for the diode limiters are furnished by cathode followers, so that the signal amplitude at which limiting action sets in can be adjusted by means of repetitive signals, e.g., sine waves, without the reference voltages shifting as a result of self-biasing effects. The difficulty in designing a device of this sort for signals having a short rise time lies in the parasitic capacitance, which constitutes a shunt load on the series resistor R. If R is too small, then the diodes fail to serve as effective limiters; on the other hand, if R is too large, there is a loss in the rise time of transmitted signals.

9. D-C AMPLIFIERS*

The measurement of direct currents of 10^{-8} amp (or less) by means of electronic circuits is made difficult by grid current which, in an ordinary vacuum tube, is of the same order of magnitude. A number of special electrometer-tube techniques have been developed to circumvent this difficulty. In this section a brief account will be given of certain of these techniques, followed by the description of several amplifiers employing an electrometer tube as a first stage. These amplifiers have considerable utility in making laboratory measurements of small currents. The problem is essentially one of obtaining a considerable amplification of current, since the output of the amplifier is used to operate an indicating meter. There will be no discussion here of d-c voltage amplifiers.

9.1 Electrometer-tube Techniques. Grid current in a vacuum tube may be caused by any of the following phenomena:

1. The cathode can emit positive ions, which flow to the grid.

2. Electrons flowing from grid to plate can ionize the residual gas left in the tube, in which case some of the positive ions produced will flow to the grid.

3. The plate, or some other part of the tube, can emit electrons (photoelectric effect).

---

* The draft of this section was prepared by Richard J. Watts.

4. Electrons impinging on the plate can have enough energy to cause the emission of soft x-rays. These x-rays, in turn, can bombard the grid and release electrons.

5. Electrons can reach the grid from the cathode by virtue of the finite velocity with which electrons are emitted.

6. Leakage currents can occur over the inside or the outside of the tube.

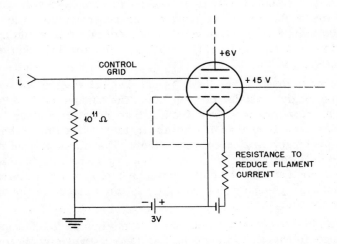

Fig. 3.26 — Typical operating conditions for an electrometer tube.

To minimize or eliminate these various sources of grid current, it is necessary to operate a vacuum tube in the way indicated in Fig. 3.26. With only +6 volts on the plate, no positive ions are produced in the vicinity of the grid, since the electron energy is below the ionizing potential of the residual gas molecules. By operating the screen at +15 volts, no positive ions emitted by the cathode can reach the grid. A further reduction in grid current is obtained by operating the filament at a reduced temperature. Photoelectrons are avoided by mounting the tube in a lighttight shield. When these precautions are taken, the tube is usually termed an "electrometer tube." With special manufacture the grid current of an electrometer tube can be reduced to 10^{-17} amp, which permits currents of the order of 60 electrons per second to be detected.

One of the most commonly used commercial electrometer tubes is the General Electric FP-54. When this tube is used with an input resistence of 10^{10} ohms, it will give a current amplification of 2.5×10^{5}.

The voltage amplification, however, is less than unity. If a galvanometer with a sensitivity of 10^{-10} amp/mm is connected in the plate circuit, a sensitivity of 2.5×10^5 mm/volt can be obtained. An electrometer-tube amplifier can therefore be substituted for a sensitive galvanometer or electrometer. Many commercial radio tubes can be used as electrometer tubes when operated at potentials low enough to reduce grid current. In the case of a pentode, grid G_1 is usually connected to the cathode, grid G_2 is biased to about +15 volts, and grid G_3, at a few volts minus, is used as the control grid. The plate is ordinarily biased at about +6 volts. Tubes often used in electrometer applications include the RCA types 38, 22, 954, and 959 and the Western Electric type 259-B.

A number of precautions must be observed if an electrometer-tube circuit is to give satisfactory service. The surface of the electrometer tube must be kept free from all sources of surface leakage. Before the tube is placed in the apparatus, it should be thoroughly washed, preferably with alcohol or ether. The glass around the control grid is often dipped in ceresin wax to reduce surface leakage. The air in contact with the bulb should be kept free from moisture. A drier, such as phosphorus pentoxide, is often placed in the box surrounding the tube.

Since an electrometer tube has an extremely high input impedance, any change in the capacitance of the control-grid circuit to ground will cause a marked change in the control-grid potential. This effect is especially annoying when it is desired to switch resistors in the grid circuit to cover various current ranges. The effect can be minimized by using a shorting-type switch. In any event, an appreciable length of time is required for the grid potential to come to an equilibrium value after it has been altered.

A source of disturbance that must be avoided is caused by changing external magnetic or electric fields. For this reason the electrometer tube is usually built into a shielded compartment, which can be made airtight and be evacuated when extremely low currents are to be measured. Evacuation eliminates the current due to ionization of the air around the control-grid lead by cosmic or other penetrating rays.

Great care must be exercised in constructing the circuit to avoid introducing sources of current leakage to the grid circuit. The grid lead and all connections to it should be run as directly as possible, without the use of insulators. When it is necessary to run the lead through the shield, Ampehnol 912-A or quartz will make the most satisfactory bushing. To reduce leakage over these surfaces, guard rings are frequently employed. It has been found advantageous to coat the outside of the bulb with Aquadag to within 1½ inches of the control-grid connection and to use the coating as a guard ring for the grid lead.

The precautions described should be rigidly followed for currents of less than 10^{-13} amp. For greater currents it is not necessary to evacuate the container, and commercial radio tubes instead of a special electrometer tube are satisfactory. A less expensive and more compact electrometer tube than the FP-54 is the Victoreen V-124B. This tube, which has a grid current of about 10^{-15} amp, was designed for use in portable equipment where a low filament drain is desirable.

Three types of high resistors are commercially available for use in the input grid circuit. These resistors are made by IRC, by S. S. White, and by Victoreen. They can be secured in various values up to 10^{12} ohms. A value greater than 10^{11} ohms is rarely used, since the time constant of the grid circuit becomes unduly long.

9.2 DuBridge-Brown Circuit. The DuBridge-Brown circuit is too well known to require comment.* Figure 3.27 shows a complete diagram for the instrument in a form suitable for use with a mass spectrograph. The FP-54 tube is mounted in an evacuated housing, and the rest of the circuit is mounted in a metal box on the control panel of the spectrograph. Shielded leads are used to connect the two parts of the circuit. The Ayrton shunt and filter are built as integral parts of the circuit. A two-conductor shielded cable 15 ft long is used for galvanometer leads. With a galvanometer having a sensitivity of 0.00037 μa/mm, the instrument has a sensitivity of 3×10^{-16} amp/mm. Considerably more stability of operation is achieved by allowing the instrument to run continuously.

9.3 A Bridge Amplifier. Bridge amplifiers are adaptations of the circuit first built by Wynn-Williams.† Although used originally for measuring small potentials, this type of circuit can be adapted nicely for use with electrometer tubes to measure small currents.

The circuit of a bridge amplifier using RCA type 959 tubes is shown in Fig. 3.28. This circuit represents an attempt to produce a portable instrument capable of adapting type 959 tubes (as electrometer tubes) to a bridge circuit and of measuring an intense source of gamma radiation as accurately as possible.

* L. A. DuBridge and H. Brown, Rev. Sci. Instruments, 4: 532 (1933).

† "Medical Physics," ed. Otto Glasser, p. 1117, The Year Book Publishers, Chicago, 1944.

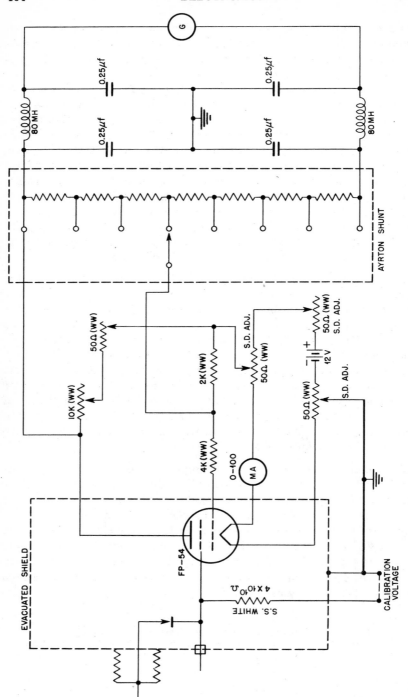

Fig. 3.27 — The DuBridge-Brown circuit for an FP-54 electrometer tube.

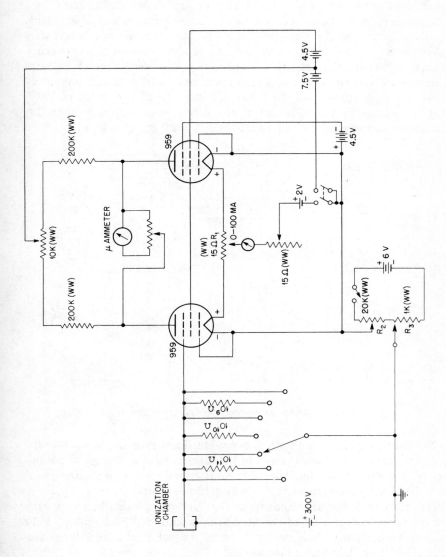

Fig. 3.28 — A bridge amplifier.

It can be shown that by choosing a suitable setting for the potentiometer R_1 in the filament circuit, there will be no change in the galvanometer deflection for small changes in filament current. The instrument is therefore stabilized against drift from this cause.

Measurements with the circuit can be made independent of any lack of linearity by using a null method. For this purpose two calibrated potentiometers, R_2 and R_3, are used to insert a known compensating voltage in series with the grid resistor. The potentiometers are equipped with vernier dials, which make accurate readings possible. Since the grid current of the type 959 tube is of the order of 10^{-13} amp, no appreciable deflection of the galvanometer occurs when the resistance in the grid circuit is changed from 0 to 10^{11} ohms.

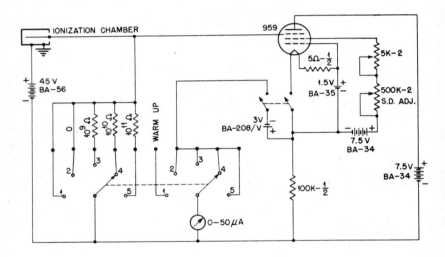

Fig. 3.29 — An electrometer-tube cathode follower.

The galvanometer used with the bridge amplifier has a sensitivity of 0.016 μa/mm. It makes possible the detection of a change of potential of 1.4 mv at the input grid, which corresponds to a current of 1.4×10^{-14} amp through the 10^{11}-ohm grid resistor.

The input tube and the ionization chamber are placed in a separate box connected to the rest of the circuit by a shielded 30-ft cable. This construction enables the operator to be at some distance from the radiation while it is being measured.

9.4 Electrometer-tube Cathode Follower. Figure 3.29 illustrates a simple electrometer-tube circuit that may be used for a variety of purposes. Although the drawing shows its use as a roentgenometer, it makes an excellent high-impedance voltmeter.

The warm-up position on the range switch prevents damage to the meter when the instrument is first turned on. Resistors made by S. S. White are used in the grid circuit. Since the lower end of these resistors is mounted on a switch, the switch must have a resistance between contacts considerably greater than 10^{11} ohms. It is found that by carefully cleaning a steatite switch and then dipping it in ceresin wax, a resistance in excess of 10^{14} ohms can be achieved. The zero position on the switch makes it possible to check the instrument for grid-current leakage. If the meter indicates no change in current between 0 and 10^{11} ohms in the grid circuit, it may be assumed that the grid current is negligible.

The voltage sensitivity of the instrument is about 1.75 volts for full-scale deflection. Hence, in the most sensitive range a current of 1.75×10^{-11} amp can be measured.

In constructing the instrument, the usual precautions required for electrometer tubes should be taken. Current drains are low, and, with the batteries indicated, instruments of this type have run continuously for seven days with no apparent exhaustion of the batteries.

9.5 A D-c Feedback Amplifier. The feedback amplifier shown in Fig. 3.30 is an adaptation of the well-known Vance circuit.* The original circuit has been modified in the direction of measuring smaller currents by using an electrometer tube as the first stage. Since this stage has a voltage gain of less than unity, it is necessary to employ five instead of the usual three stages to obtain a sufficient unfed-back gain. To avoid oscillations, the grid of the last stage is by-passed to ground with an 8-μf capacitor. Although the capacitor slows down the response time of the amplifier, this is no drawback, since the amplifier is used for measuring currents that vary but slowly with time.

If G is the unfed-back gain of the amplifier and A the gain with feedback, it can be shown that

$$A = \frac{1}{1 + \dfrac{1}{G}}$$

Hence, to a good approximation, the input and output voltages are equal. Therefore, if R_i and R_o are the input and output resistances, and I_i and I_o the input and output currents, respectively, then

$$I_o = \frac{R_i}{R_o} I_i$$

* A. W. Vance, Rev. Sci. Instruments, 7: 489 (1936).

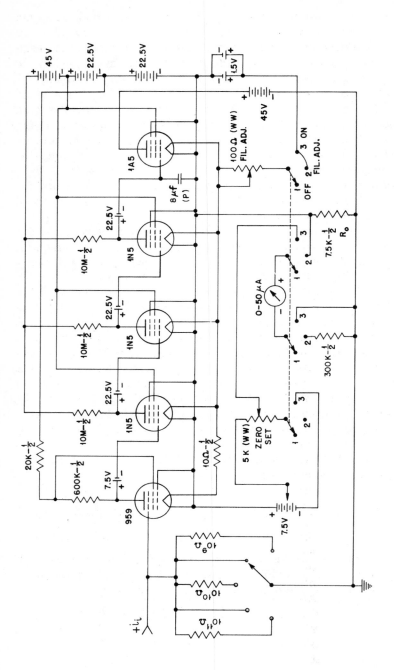

Fig. 3.30 — A d-c feedback amplifier.

This relation between input and output currents is very desirable since the scale of the indicating meter can be made linear to at least 1 per cent, and its calibration will be little affected by fluctuations in battery voltages.

The amplifier illustrated in Fig. 3.30 has a full-scale voltage sensitivity of 0.1 volt, so a current of 10^{-12} amp will give a full-scale reading. The circuit is very stable after a warm-up period of $\frac{1}{2}$ hr. A drift in the zero setting of less than 1 per cent of full scale will occur during 6 hr of continuous running. The circuit can be used for automatic recording by connecting a Micromax Recorder across the output-load resistor R_o. It is possible to adapt the circuit to an FP-54 input stage if lower currents are to be measured.

9.6 An A-c Operated D-c Amplifier. The greatest single difficulty with d-c amplifiers is drift of the zero setting of the indicating meter. This drift is found to consist of two effects: (1) a short-time drift of considerable magnitude, usually lasting about $\frac{1}{2}$ hr, which is due in part to various components coming to a new temperature equilibrium; and (2) a long-time drift, whose origin is not well known, but which may be due to changes in the emissive properties of the cathode, or what may be termed the "effective contact difference" of potential between grid and cathode.

Recent experiments have shown that this long-time drift will disappear or become negligibly small after a tube has been run continuously for a long period of time. If the tube is turned off and allowed to cool, and then turned on with the precaution that the cathode is allowed to come to equilibrium temperature before the plate voltage is turned on, no change in long-time drift is observed. If, however, the plate voltage is turned on simultaneously with the filament current, long-time drifts will again occur. It is postulated that destabilization of the emitting properties of the cathode occurs when the emission capability of the cathode is exceeded, even for a very short time. This observation requires additional confirmation before it can be accepted as well established.

To minimize drifts, it is customary to run the filaments of an a-c–operated d-c amplifier in series from the stabilized supply, which also furnishes plate voltage. The amplifier can be left running continuously in order to avoid short-time drifts and to allow the long-time drift to become small.

Figure 3.31 illustrates a type of a-c–operated d-c amplifier that is very useful for monitoring purposes. By grounding the positive side of the power supply, the entire amplifier circuit is negative with respect to ground. If a power failure occurs, the output signal will rise to ground and can be used as a warning signal. For instance, it can be used to fire a thyratron.

The output signal is suitable for operating a 0- to 1-ma Esterline-Angus recording meter. The sensitivity of the circuit is 0.5 volt for full deflection of the meter. Drift is less than 1 per cent of full scale in any 24-hr period. The simplicity of the circuit contributes greatly to its reliability. Circuits of this type have been operated continuously for more than one year with no troubles developing.

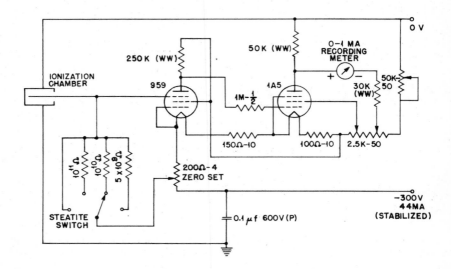

Fig. 3.31 — An a-c—operated d-c amplifier.

10. MISCELLANEOUS AMPLIFIERS

A number of special-purpose amplifiers have been designed to suit the needs of particular experiments. A few of these amplifiers are of sufficient general interest to warrant describing their circuits. It is thought that these circuits may be immediately useful in other experimental work, or at least may incorporate ideas that can be carried over into the design of new circuits suitable for the problem at hand.

10.1 An Amplifier Having Good Response at Low Frequencies. The Model 800 amplifier, shown in Fig. 3.32, has half-power frequencies at approximately 0.03 and 1,500 cycles per second, and a gain of about 1,700. It is intended to be directly coupled, through a suitable source of bucking voltage, to a recording meter for the purpose of obtaining permanent records of very slow transients.* The output

---

* The Heiland Recorder (type C galvanometer) has been used with this amplifier.

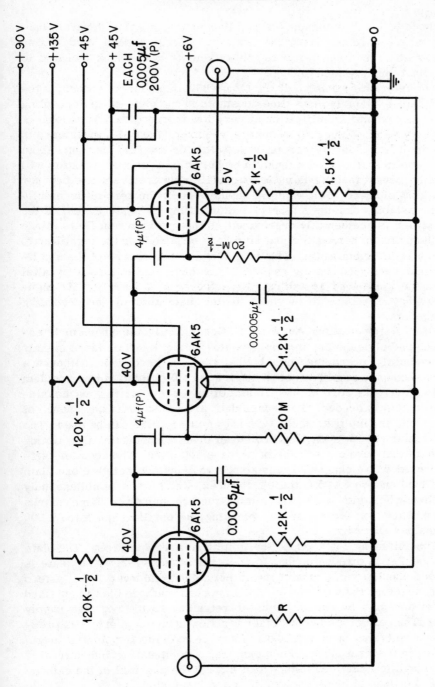

Fig. 3.32 — Model 800 amplifier.

cathode follower is biased for positive output signals. Separate batteries are used to supply the indicated plate, screen, and heater voltages. The amplifier must be extremely well shock-mounted to eliminate microphonic pickup.

The interesting feature of the Model 800 amplifier, of course, is the fact that extremely long time constants in the plate-to-grid coupling networks permit amplification at very low frequencies. On account of the high value of the grid resistors required, the 6AK5 tubes used in the amplifier must be carefully selected for low grid current. About one tube in four has been found to be suitable. Systematic testing will usually reveal that tubes made by certain manufacturers are best for low grid current. Grid current tends to make the zero of the amplifier unstable, causing a type of motorboating in some cases. If the amplifier is accidentally overloaded, so that grid current flows at one of the grids, a period of about 20 min is required for the amplifier to reach equilibrium again. The high-frequency response of the amplifier has been deliberately reduced by including capacitors in parallel with the plate-load resistors, since there is no need for its high-frequency response to be much better than that of the recording equipment.

10.2 A Nonblocking Amplifier. Occasionally the problem is encountered of designing an amplifier that cannot block on large signals immediately preceding signals that must be recorded. Although a direct-coupled amplifier constitutes a possible solution to a problem of this sort, the zero of such an amplifier tends to drift when considerable gain is needed. To reduce drift and yet to avoid any chance of blocking, an amplifier of the type shown in Fig. 3.33 can be used. The particular circuit shown has been used in the recording of slow timing signals that have a rise time of perhaps 500 μsec. The complete set-up included five channels, each amplifier being connected to one plate of a bank of five 3AP5 cathode-ray tubes, which were simultaneously photographed with a 35-mm motion-picture camera. Time marks were placed on the record by blanking the oscillograph trace 1,000 times per second.

The following features of the amplifier are of interest. The plate of tube T-1 is direct-coupled to the grid of tube T-2, whose plate is direct-coupled to the grid of the output cathode follower T-3. Instead of connecting the cathode of T-2 to ground, cathode bias is obtained by means of a by-passed resistor returning to the negative supply bus. The gain of the second stage for slow changes in signal is practically unity, so no amplification is given to drifts in potential originating in the first stage. Furthermore, a computation indicates that no signals reaching this stage can change the potential of the cathode of T-2 enough to block the amplifier for large signals.

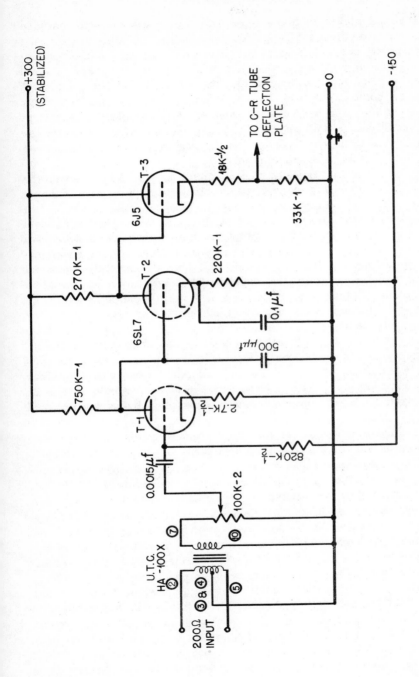

Fig. 3.33 — A nonblocking amplifier.

The output signal is taken from a point part way down the cathode resistor of the output follower. The maximum possible voltage swing at this point is not sufficient to deflect the spot of the cathode-ray tube off the face of the tube. This precaution is necessary to avoid losing track of the blanking marks that furnish the time scale. It should be pointed out that, if signals sufficient in amplitude to draw current at the grid of T-1 are expected, the capacitor in the first grid circuit can be omitted by connecting one end of the transformer secondary and the gain control to the negative supply bus and the other end directly to the input grid.

10.3 **A Wide-band Band-pass Amplifier.** In Fig. 3.34 is shown the circuit of a wide-band band-pass amplifier having a gain of about 5×10^4, which is suitable for driving the deflection plates of a 5JP11 cathode-ray tube. An oscillograph of this sort is intended to be used for observing and recording abrupt changes in the modulation of a carrier waveform. The Model 400 amplifier has its pass band centered at 10 megacycles per second and has a bandwidth somewhat greater than 2 megacycles per second. This bandwidth is equivalent in transient response to a bandwidth of 1 megacycle per second in a low-pass amplifier. According to Eq. 20 the rise time for the carrier envelope will be about 0.3 μsec.

The first three stages and the push-pull output stages of the amplifier are single-tuned by the inductances L_1, L_2, L_3, and L_4, respectively, which resonate at 10 megacycles per second with the stray circuit capacitances. The inductors are wound as single layers on forms having a $\%_{32}$-in. diameter and can be tuned by permalloy-dust slugs.

The bandwidth of each of the single-tuned stages is determined primarily by the value of the plate-load resistor and by the parasitic circuit capacitance, just as in the case of a low-pass R-coupled amplifier. In fact, the same equations hold for the bandwidth of the two types of amplifiers, so that the amplifier design nomograph, Fig. 3.7, can be used as an aid in designing a single-tuned band-pass amplifier. Although it is desirable that all stages of the amplifier have the same bandwidth, some sacrifice in bandwidth of the Model 400 amplifier is made in the output stages in order to provide a large output voltage swing with reasonable plate currents for the 829-B tube.

A specially constructed transformer L_4 is used to transfer from single-sided to push-pull operation. The primary winding is wound in two sections, connected in parallel, with the end turns at a-c ground, as indicated in Fig. 3.34. The adjacent turns on the two secondary windings are also at a-c ground. This mode of construction is chosen to reduce capacitive coupling between primary and secondary. The

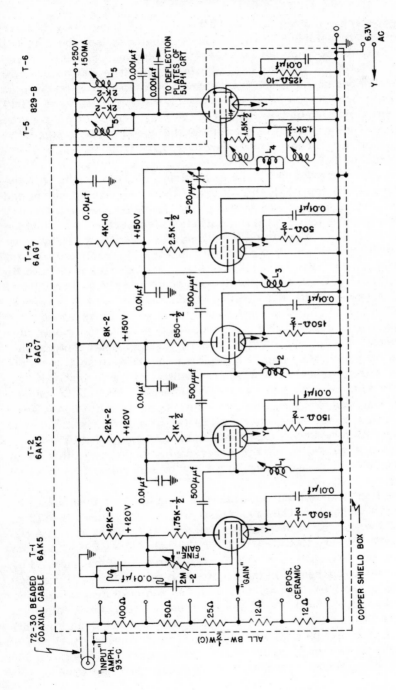

Fig. 3.34 — A wide-band band-pass amplifier.

two secondary windings are tuned by slugs entering the two outer ends of the transformer. The primary winding is so wound that a small capacitance supplied by a ceramic trimmer capacitor is required, in addition to stray capacitance, to tune it to resonance at 10 megacycles per second. The transformer is damped by resistance so chosen that both primary and secondary circuits have nearly identical Q's, approximately equal to the Q's of the single-tuned circuits in the amplifier. The coefficient of coupling of the transformer is somewhat less than critical. The estimated voltage gain from the plate of T-4 to the grids of T-5 and T-6 is slightly greater than unity.

The entire amplifier should be constructed inside a shield, with the exception of the top of the 829-B tube, which can extend out of the shield to be near the deflecting-plate terminals of a type 5JP11 cathode-ray tube to which the amplifier is connected. As a further precaution against interaction between input and output circuits, the entire oscillograph should be mounted in a metal box. If precautions of this sort are taken with the shielding, a short "antenna" can be hung on the input connection with no sign of the circuit oscillating.

10.4 <u>A Pulse-lengthener Circuit</u>. Occasionally it is necessary to determine the height of a single voltage pulse that has a rise time of about 1 μsec. Although it is possible to present the pulse on a cathode-ray oscillograph and to record its amplitude photographically, it is somewhat simpler to lengthen the pulse to such an extent that its height can be read with a d-c voltmeter. For instance, the pulse can be used to charge a capacitor through a diode. If the capacitor has a sufficiently long time constant associated with it, the voltage to which it has been charged can be read with a vacuum-tube voltmeter. However, when the pulse has an extremely short rise time, the current required to charge a reasonably large capacitor is so excessive that it is necessary to resort to several stages of pulse stretching.

In Fig. 3.35 is shown a circuit that has been used for measuring the heights of a fast pulse. The input pulse, whose height may range from +15 to +50 volts, is fed to a cathode follower T-1, which charges the capacitor C_1 through the diode T-2. If the pulse rises 50 volts in 0.5 μsec, an average current i = C(dV/dt) = 50 ma must be supplied by T-1 in order to charge C_1 in the required length of time. In practice a fraction of the 50-volt pulse is lost in the potential drop across the diode, and another fraction in a change of bias of the cathode follower. Hence the 6SN7 tube T-1 is just able to furnish the required current, somewhat less than 50 ma, without drawing grid current.

Before a capacitance considerably larger than 500 $\mu\mu$f can be charged, it is clearly necessary to increase the rise time of the

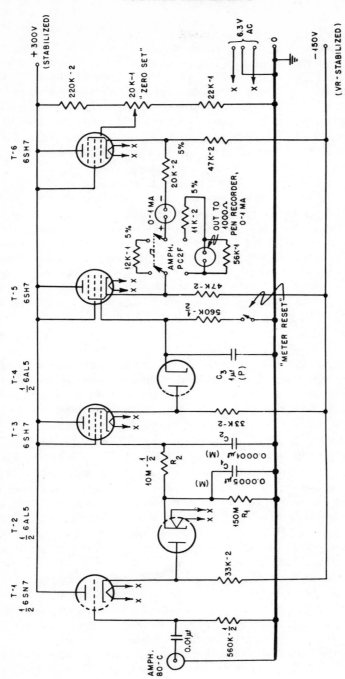

Fig. 3.35 — A pulse-lengthener circuit.

pulse. This is accomplished by the resistance R_2 connecting C_1 to a second capacitance C_2 whose value is only a fraction of C_1. The initial rate of rise of the pulse appearing across C_2 is governed by the time constant $R_2 C_1 C_2/(C_1 + C_2) \approx 600$ μsec. The cathode follower T-3 will therefore have to furnish a maximum charging current of perhaps $i = 10^{-6}$ f $\times$ 40 volts/600 μsec ≈ 60 ma. Again, this is about the limit for the tube without its drawing grid current. However, the current now decreases exponentially with a 600-μsec time constant, so that the capacitor C_3 has received all the charge it will get in a few milliseconds. In the meantime, charge is leaking off the capacitors C_1 and C_2 through the high resistor R_1, with the time constant $R_1(C_1 + C_2) =$ 90 msec. Since this time constant is long compared with the time taken to charge C_2, only a small fraction of the transmitted pulse height is lost. The capacitor C_3 has no resistor across it, so the charge on it will leak off at a rate determined by leakage resistance and the grid current of T-5. In practice the meter in the vacuum-tube voltmeter circuit will hold its peak value for at least 10 sec, which makes an accurate reading possible. Provision is made to couple the vacuum-tube voltmeter to a recording meter so that a permanent record can be obtained.

Some of the difficulties of lengthening fast pulses have been made evident in the foregoing discussion. A circuit such as that in Fig. 3.35 must be calibrated with pulses of known heights, similar in shape to the pulses with which it will be used. When so calibrated, the circuit can be depended on for measurements accurate to several per cent.

10.5 An Integrator Circuit. An electronic integrating circuit may be considered a type of amplifier in which the output signal is proportional to the integral of the input signal. A convenient form of integrating circuit is illustrated by the Model 100 integrator shown in Fig. 3.36. This particular integrator has been designed to accept input signals having peak values of about $\pm$20 volts and lasting anywhere from 5 to 200 μsec. The magnitude of the output signal is controlled by selecting a suitable value of the time constant RC. Values of RC from 5 to 320 μsec are available in convenient steps, and a value should be so chosen that the maximum amplitude of the integrated signal does not exceed $\pm$20 volts.

A transient analysis of the circuit of the Model 100 integrator indicates that the output signal will ordinarily depart from a true integral of the input signal by less than 1 per cent when the integrated signal has reached an amplitude of 20 volts. Measurements show that for a step input signal the duration of the curvature at the start of the linear rise of the output signal is less than 0.1 μsec. In practical applications the integrator is intended for use preceding the Model 1000

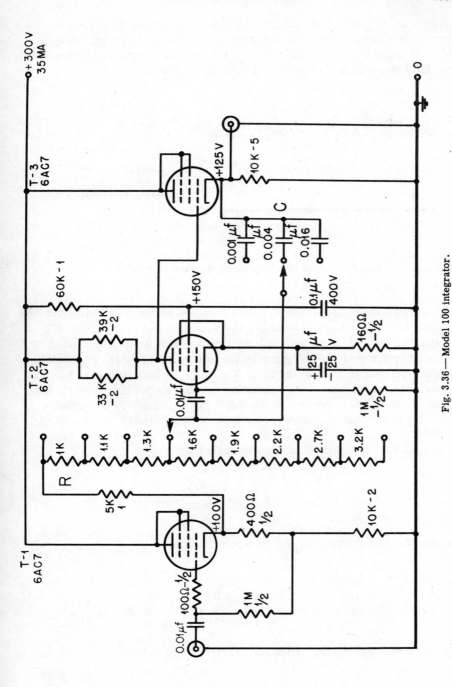

Fig. 3.36 — Model 100 integrator.

amplifier as part of an oscillograph for recording the integral of a
transient voltage signal. If the integrator is used following an amplifier that has a cathode-follower output stage, the input cathode follower of the integrator, tube T-1, can be omitted.

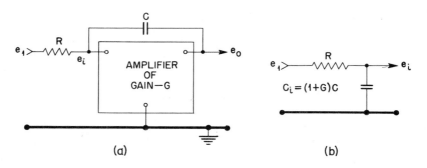

Fig. 3.37 — Approximate equivalent circuit of integrator.

An approximate analysis of the operation of the integrator can be
made as follows: Let $-G$ be the mid-band gain from the grid of T-2
to the cathode of T-3, with all resistive loads (including that of R)
taken into account. The approximate equivalent circuit of the integrator, therefore, is that shown in Fig. 3.37(a). Now the input capacitance of the amplifier, with capacitive feedback, is $C(1 + G) \equiv C_i$ (see
Chap. 2, Sec. 3.8). Hence the signal at the input of the amplifier can
be computed from the simple equivalent RC network shown in Fig.
3.37(b).

If $e_1(t) = 0$ for $t < 0$, it is easy to show that

$$e_i(t) = \frac{1}{RC_i} \int_0^t e_1(x)\ dx - \left(\frac{1}{RC_i}\right)^2 \int_0^t \int_0^y e_1(x)\ dx\ dy + \cdots$$

Hence the output signal of the amplifier will be

$$e_o = -Ge_i$$

$$= -\frac{1 - 1/G}{RC} \int_0^t e_1(x)\ dx + \frac{1}{G}\left(\frac{1}{RC}\right)^2 \int_0^t \int_0^y e_1(x)\ dx\ dy + O\left(\frac{1}{G^2}\right)$$

where terms only to the order of $1/G$ have been retained.

To demonstrate the accuracy of integration, let $e_1 = At^n$ where $n > -1$. For this case we have

$$e_0(t) = -\frac{1 - 1/G}{RC} \frac{At^{n+1}}{n+1} \left[1 - \frac{1}{G(n+2)} \left(\frac{t}{RC}\right) + O\frac{1}{G^2}\right]$$

When the output signal is equal to the input signal, $t/RC \approx n + 1$; the magnitude of the second term inside the bracket then becomes $(1/G)(n+1)/(n+2) \leq 1/G$. Since $G > 100$ in the Model 100 integrator, this simple analysis indicates that the accuracy of integration, for a signal of the form At^n, is better than 1 per cent. A complete analysis of the circuit involves taking into account the frequency-response characteristics of the amplifier as well as its finite output impedance. The complete analysis indicates that the finite gain of the amplifier is the chief source of error.

Chapter 4

ELECTRONIC COUNTERS

By Matthew Sands and William C. Elmore

1. INTRODUCTION

This chapter is devoted to the consideration of several practical circuits that record the occurrence of a large number of electrical pulses possessing certain restricted properties of amplitude and of time of occurrence. Particular attention is given to voltage pulses from a pulse amplifier of the sort discussed in Chap. 3. A circuit for recording the occurrence of pulses is called a "counter." First to be described are several counters that are suitable for the measurement of the amplitude distribution of pulses; then consideration will be given to counters whose function is to record the occurrence of groups of pulses, all of similar magnitude, which appear with a specified time relationship among themselves.

Counters that fall into the first category are composed of three essential parts: (1) a discriminator, (2) an electronic tallying circuit, or scaler, and (3) a circuit for operating an electromechanical impulse register. Several forms of each of these basic circuits are discussed before complete counter circuits are described.

Counter circuits that fall into the second category will be discussed in the latter part of the chapter.

2. COUNTERS FOR AMPLITUDE MEASUREMENTS

2.1 **Amplitude Discriminators.** A simple amplitude discriminator should possess the property of giving out a standard pulse whenever it receives an input pulse that has an amplitude greater than some minimum value.* Any trigger circuit with one stable state, such as

---

*More complicated discriminators, which respond only to pulses whose amplitudes lie in a certain interval, generally consist of simple discriminators in combination with other circuit elements. Discriminators of this type will be discussed in later sections.

those described in Chap. 2, when combined with any one of the means of triggering discussed there, has this property. Most of these circuits, however, do not possess the following properties, which are usually desired of a discriminator: (1) A discriminator should be able to discriminate reliably between pulses that differ in amplitude by a small fraction of a volt, and the amplitude at which discrimination occurs should be stable to a similar extent. (2) A discriminator should be capable of accepting narrow pulses, such as those produced by a pulse amplifier. (3) It should present a high impedance to the signal source, and respond to each of many pulses that occur in rapid succession. (4) It should not overload on a pulse of amplitude much greater than the critical amplitude, i.e., it should not distort large signals that it receives, nor should its operation depend upon the size of previous input pulses. (5) It should have an easily adjustable discrimination voltage.

Circuits which, in practice, have been found to meet most of these requirements satisfactorily are various modifications of the Schmitt trigger circuit described in Chap. 2, Sec. 4.3(c). As an example of a discriminator of this type, let us consider the circuit shown in Fig. 4.1(a), which is very similar to the one shown in Fig. 2.37(a). In the present circuit the value of the steady voltage at point A depends on the setting of the potentiometer R_4. It is recalled that a circuit of this type is triggered to a new state when the voltage at the point A goes above some critical value, say +100 volts, and returns to its original state when the voltage drops a little below +100 volts. If the value of steady voltage at A is adjusted to be, say, +80 volts, the circuit will be triggered when an input signal greater than +20 volts is impressed on it. The circuit remains in the new state as long as the input signal is above +20 volts, and returns to its original state when the input signal falls a little below this value.* If an input signal has an amplitude less than +20 volts, no output signal is obtained. The output signal is always a square wave with an amplitude of 40 volts and with a duration equal to the time spent by the input signal above the 20-volt level. The magnitude of the signal that will just trigger the discriminator is called the "bias voltage" (or "bias setting") of the discriminator. For the circuit shown, the bias voltage can be adjusted by means of R_4 to lie in the range 0 to +100 volts. The potentiometer R_4 is usually supplied with a dial that reads from 0 to 100, and by means of the variable resistors R_2 and R_{10} it is possible to adjust voltages in the circuit to make the dial read the bias voltage of the discriminator directly. It is possible to operate discriminators of this kind with

---

*It is assumed that the signal lasts only for a time that is short compared with the time constant R_1C_1.

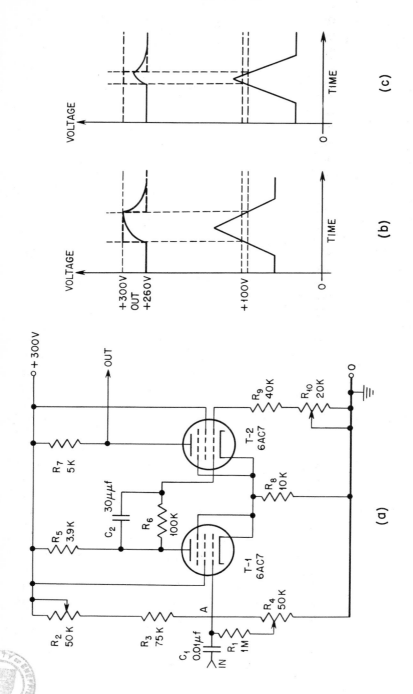

Fig. 4.1 — The 6AC7 discriminator.

negative input signals. For this type of operation the point A is biased above +100 volts, and negative output signals are obtained from the plate of T-2.

The stability of the bias setting of the discriminator depends on the stability of the positive supply voltage, on the constancy of the resistors R_2, R_3, R_4, R_6, R_9, and R_{10}, and to a lesser extent on variations of cathode emission and of contact potentials in the tubes. Because of the symmetric form of the circuit, these variations tend to balance out, especially when the hysteresis of the trigger circuit is kept small. The circuit shown in Fig. 4.1(a) has a hysteresis of about 1 volt, and the bias voltage is reliable to 0.1 or 0.2 volt over long periods of time and for reasonable variations in the heater voltage (± 10 per cent).

For a large input pulse having a short rise time, the output-pulse shape depends only on the resistance R_7 and the parasitic capacitance across it. If the input signal is fast but just large enough to trigger the circuit, the rise time of the output signal is somewhat longer, since it depends mainly upon the value of R_5. Some increase in the rise time of the output signal can be obtained by applying shunt compensation to the plate loads of both tubes. Figures 4.1(b) and 4.1(c) show the output waveforms for identical input signals but for different bias settings of the discriminator. The broken heavy line is the waveform obtained if the input signal is of considerable duration, and the solid curve is the signal obtained if the input signal lasts only 1 μsec. The output signal may never reach its full value if the input signal does not remain above the bias voltage for a sufficient length of time. For this reason it is desirable that narrow pulses, if used, should either be rectangular in shape or at least have a sufficiently long nearly flat top.

Since it is often necessary to count small pulses in the presence of much larger pulses, it is important that the discriminator should not overload easily. Tube T-1 in the circuit shown does not draw grid current on slow signals until the point A reaches approximately +200 volts. If the discriminator bias is set at a few volts, the circuit will therefore not overload for pulses of 100-volt amplitude. If the input pulses have a very short rise time and the cathode-to-ground capacitance of the discriminator is unduly high, grid current will be drawn for somewhat smaller signals. Grid-current flow is objectionable since it alters the charge on the input capacitor and results in a shift of the bias setting of the discriminator. Although it may appear desirable to make the time constant $R_1 C_1$ short, in order that the circuit might recover quickly if the shift should occur, this particular time constant is essentially one of the time constants of the preceding pulse amplifier, and the discussion in Chap. 3, Sec. 3, applies to it, as well as to the other short time constants in the amplifier.

The tube T-1 acts as a cathode follower, once the critical voltage of the discriminator has been exceeded. When large, narrow pulses are impressed on the circuit, its cathode may not precisely follow the negative return of each pulse. This behavior tends to limit the resolving time of the discriminator, for, if a pulse occurs within a few tenths of a microsecond after an earlier pulse, the second pulse may pass unnoticed. This limitation is usually not important since the scaling circuit following the discriminator ordinarily will not respond to pulses so close together.

Another difficulty with the circuit may be encountered when it is used with input pulses of very short rise time. If the bias voltage is made large (for instance, if the point A is biased to -100 volts), then a fast pulse that is large, but not large enough to trigger the discriminator in the usual manner, may still give rise to an output signal because of capacitive feed-through from the grid to the cathode of T-1. No trouble from this source has been found to occur with the circuit of Fig. 4.1(a) when the input pulse has a rise time of 0.1 μsec or longer and an amplitude of 100 volts or less.

Examples of other discriminator circuits based on the Schmitt trigger circuit occur in the Model 220 counter, Fig. 4.6, and in the Model 600 counter, Fig. 4.8. The discriminator in the Model 220 counter can be built more economically as regards cost, compactness, and power consumption than the discriminator in Fig. 4.1(a). Its bias settings, however, are subject to a certain amount of long-time drift since carbon resistors have been used throughout the circuit. The discriminator in the Model 600 counter has been designed to operate on particularly narrow pulses (0.1 to 0.2 μsec duration).

When it is desired to use a discriminator for pulses that are fairly uniform in amplitude, trigger circuits of other kinds are suitable. The discriminator given in Fig. 4.7 as part of the Model 400 counter operates directly from a Geiger-Mueller tube, and it triggers reliably on negative pulses of 1 volt. This circuit is a cathode-coupled univibrator, and when triggered it remains in a second state for a few hundred microseconds. Since the counter is intended for use with self-quenching Geiger-Mueller tubes that have recovery times somewhat longer than this, the "dead" time of the discriminator is an advantage since it prevents multiple counting of individual pulses having minor oscillations superposed on them.

2.2 Scaling Circuits. A circuit that can record $k-1$ pulses occurring regularly or at random and that recycles when the k pulse

occurs is termed a "scale of k." A scale of k has k different, absolutely stable states. If such a circuit is to be of most use, a convenient means must be available for determining in which of its k states
it exists at any moment. One of the most successful circuits of this
type is obtained if m of the scale-of-two circuits described in Chap.
2, Sec. 4.5, are connected in a chain, making a scale of 2^m. The
precise state of the scale of 2^m is indicated by the use of one interpolation indicator for each scale of two. Before discussing particular
scaling circuits of this type, let us first consider the general nature
of the task faced by any counting circuit.

If the arrival of pulses to a counting circuit is perfectly random
(i.e., if the occurrence of any one pulse is independent of the occurrence of all other pulses and cannot be influenced by the observer),
and if the pulses occur at an average rate of n per second, then the
probability of observing a pulse in any small interval of time Δt is
$n \Delta t$, provided $n \Delta t \ll 1$. If the counting circuit possesses a dead time
T following each pulse it records, during which time it is incapable of
recording another pulse, the observed counting rate will evidently be

$$n_1 = n(1 - nT)$$

provided $nT \ll 1$. The deviation of the observed counting rate from the
true counting rate n is not to be confused with errors introduced by
statistical fluctuations in the rate of occurrence of pulses. The time
T is usually referred to as the "resolving time" of the counting circuit, and the quantity nT is termed the "fractional counting loss." It
is apparent that, if one wishes to count random pulses occurring, for
instance, at a rate of 1,000 pulses per second, with only a 1 per cent
counting loss, the resolving time of the counter must be 10 μsec. A
resolving time of this magnitude, however, does not necessarily require that the counter be capable of handling 10^5 regularly spaced
pulses per second, since, for example, the average power requirements for the two cases may be quite different.

Counting circuits are sometimes used for recording pulses not
randomly distributed in time. In certain applications the pulses are
produced by an oscillator, giving pulses evenly spaced in time. Hence
the resolving time of the circuit need be only slightly less than one
period of the oscillation. A very similar situation exists in timing
measurements where random pulses are gated at a regular rate and
where the gate is so narrow that there is little likelihood of obtaining
two pulses in any one gate. Therefore the time between successive
gates determines the necessary resolving time for the counting circuit. If one wishes to count pulses from a source such as a chain-
reacting system (e.g., a pile), it should be realized that for a given

average counting rate there is a higher than normal probability that one pulse will be followed by another in a given short time interval following the first pulse. Hence, if the maximum counting loss is specified, the resolving time of the counter must be less than that required for counting pulses randomly distributed in time.

In the foregoing discussion it has been assumed that a single resolving time completely characterizes a counting circuit. This is true if the counter comprises a long chain of identical scaling elements or if the resolving time of each element in the chain is just sufficient for it to pass along the pulses that occur when entering pulses come at the maximum rate $1/T_1$, where T_1 is the resolving time of the first element of the chain. In practical counting circuits it is not convenient, nor is it economical, to meet this requirement in a strict sense. Usually an electronic scaling circuit is terminated by an electromechanical register that can record a large number (10^4 or more) of impulses. Since the resolving times of commercially available registers lie in the range 0.1 to 0.01 sec, it would be necessary to precede the register by a scale of 10^4 if a counter with an ideal resolving time of 10 μsec were to be achieved. Fortunately it can be demonstrated that, when randomly occurring pulses are being counted, a considerable "smoothing" effect exists after the counting rate has been reduced by a large scaling factor. For instance, if a scale of 256 is used, negligible errors are introduced when the register is only slightly faster than would be required for the accurate recording of regularly spaced pulses occurring at the same rate.*

(a) Scales of Two. It appears to be most convenient to build counters based on chains of scales of two where the resolving time of the first scaler is as short as necessary and where the resolving time of subsequent scalers of the chain is sufficient to meet the ideal requirement of no further counting losses. A sufficient number of scales of two are then used to reduce the pulse rate to a point where it can be handled by a register, which, however, will not meet the ideal requirement. It has been found that little is gained in economy or in operating reliability by using a scale of two that has a resolving time of more than 20 μsec.

The circuit of the scales of two, which are built as plug-in units and which have become stock items at Los Alamos, is given in Fig. 4.2. The operation of a scaler of this type has already been discussed in Chap. 2, Sec. 4.5. Scales of 2^m can readily be constructed from m of these units, with only a small amount of additional circuit wiring.

---

*A rigorous discussion of counting losses with scaler-register combinations appears in W. B. Lewis, "Electrical Counting," The Macmillan Company, New York, 1942.

It is found that the use of plug-in units also simplifies the servicing problem. The numbers that identify the external connecting leads in Fig. 4.2 refer to pin numbers of an octal plug on which the unit is mounted. The function of each lead should be clear upon examination of the circuit diagram of the Model 200 counter, Fig. 4.5, which makes use of these units.

When a scale of two is constructed of the components listed under (a) in Fig. 4.2, it has a resolving time of about 20 μsec, dissipates a total of 4.3 watts, and is perfectly reliable in operation. It is known as the "6SL7 scaler unit." The components listed under (b) are used for the "6SN7 scaler unit," which is similar to the other unit except that it has a resolving time of 5 μsec and dissipates about 8 watts. It is customary to precede a chain of 6SL7 units by two 6SN7 units, except in counters for use with Geiger-Mueller tubes or for applications where there is a negligible chance that the shorter resolving time will be useful.

Two minor improvements in these scaler units have been suggested by certain difficulties encountered in practice. Since the 6H6 tube will operate satisfactorily with a voltage difference of 300 volts between its heater and cathode, it would appear desirable to connect its heater in parallel with that of the double triode. This change would eliminate the necessity for having two heater transformers when only a few scaler units are employed. The extra terminal thus made available could be left free so that any point in the scaler unit could be reached for special circuit applications — for instance, when it is used in certain switching circuits. A second improvement in the units would result if a 1-megohm resistor were inserted in series with the lead to terminal 3, since in the present design this resistor must be supplied externally.

It is believed that most operational failures of scaler units are caused by aging or poor matching of the two units of the double triode. Occasionally, however, a direct or contributing cause of failure can be traced to poor symmetry in the flip-flop when components with 20 per cent tolerance ratings are used. It would appear advisable to use either 5 or 10 per cent components in the units. Excellent reliability and long life have been obtained by using matched components at corresponding positions in the two sides of the flip-flop.

A somewhat different scale-of-two circuit, having a resolving time less than 1 μsec, is used in the Model 600 counter, described in Sec. 2.4(d).

(b) A Scale of Ten. The use of diodes for directly coupling scale-of-two circuits to form a chain can also be applied to relatively intricate automatic-switching circuits. This method of switching is used in the scale-of-ten circuit, shown in Fig. 4.3, which has been

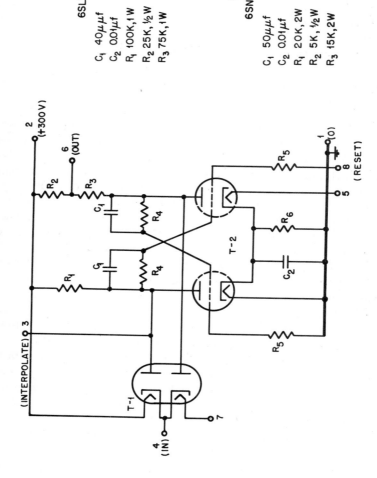

(a)

6SL7 UNIT

		T-1 6H6
		T-2 6SL7
C_1	40μμf	
C_2	0.01μf	R_4 1.0M, ½W
R_1	100K, 1W	R_5 500K, ½W
R_2	25K, ½W	R_6 40K, ½W
R_3	75K, 1W	

(b)

6SN7 UNIT

		T-1 6H6
		T-2 6SN7
C_1	50μμf	
C_2	0.01μf	R_4 200K, ½W
R_1	20K, 2W	R_5 100K, ½W
R_2	5K, ½W	R_6 10K, 1W
R_3	15K, 2W	

Fig. 4.2—Scales of two.

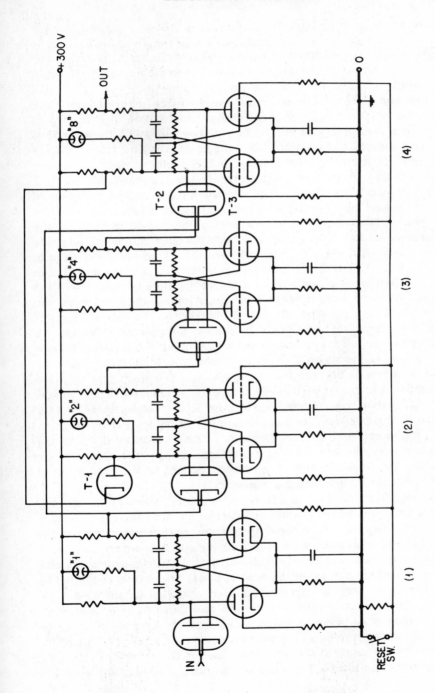

Fig. 4.3 — A scale of ten.

found to operate satisfactorily. A circuit of this sort is suitable for applications where it is worth the extra expense in order to be able to have the data appear immediately in the decimal system. The scale-of-ten circuit consists essentially of a scale-of-eight circuit, a flip-flop circuit, and three diodes (or the elements of a scale of sixteen plus one diode). When the reset switch has been opened momentarily, the left-hand tube of each scale of two and of the flip-flop is placed in a nonconducting state. The cathode of T-1 will be at +300 volts and the plate of T-3 at +130 volts, so that these tubes will not enter into the first few operations of the scale of eight. If seven pulses are now impressed on the circuit, the left-hand tube of each scale of two becomes conducting. An eighth pulse causes the scale of eight to "reset" and the flip-flop to be triggered to its other equilibrium state. The diode T-1 now prevents the left-hand plate of the second scale of two from going to +300 volts, but "catches" and holds it at perhaps +250 volts. It will be recalled, from the discussion in Chap. 2, Sec. 4.5, that the second scale of two is still in a stable state. A ninth input pulse has no other effect than to cause the first scale of two to be triggered. A tenth input pulse again triggers the first scale of two, but since its output signal drops to only +250 volts, it will not trigger the second scale of two, both plates of which are at +250 volts or lower. It does, however, trigger the flip-flop circuit (4) by means of the diode T-3, so that after the tenth input pulse the circuit is again in its original state and has produced one negative output pulse which can be used to trigger a succeeding scale of ten. It is evident that the numbers next to the interpolation lights in Fig. 4.3 give the proper indication of the number of pulses received.

2.3 **Registers and Driver Circuits.** Since economy dictates the use, wherever possible, of electromechanical impulse counters, or registers, the final function of a counter circuit is the production of signals suitable for operating a register.

Most registers consist of a ratchet-operated mechanism that involves a dial or a wheel counter indicating one digit for each electrical impulse received. The capacity of most registers is 10^4 or more counts for one complete cycle. The limiting speed at which a register will record impulses faithfully is dependent on the mechanical inertia of the mechanism and on the amount of power that can be supplied to effect the necessary mechanical motion. Energy is supplied to a register by means of current through a coil that has a large inductance. Evidently the rate at which a register can operate depends in part on the driving voltage, the maximum value of which is limited by the breakdown voltage of the insulation used in the register windings, which is too often insufficient. If a mechanical inertia of the register mechanism is to be the limiting factor in the speed of operation, it is necessary that the impedance of the driving source be high enough so that the time constant L/R of the register and its associated circuit will be short compared with the time for mechanical motion. For this reason registers are usually operated in the plate circuit of a tube, preferably a pentode, with the highest voltage available used for the plate supply. For reliable and fast operation, the pulse used to actuate the register must have a shape best suited to the particular make of register to be used.

One type of register commercially available is designed specifically for use with electronic counters. Registers of this type can be obtained from the Cyclotron Specialties Company (C. S. Co.) and the Central Scientific Company. The C. S. Co. registers, because they have been more readily available, have been used in large numbers at Los Alamos, where they have been found to be reasonably satisfactory. Their minimum operating current is 10 ma, and they have an inductance of 3.3 henrys and a d-c resistance of 1,000 ohms. They can be operated at continuous counting rates of 50 impulses per second (with careful adjustment, still higher rates are possible) with the driving circuit shown in Fig. 4.5 as part of the Model 200 counter.

Other types of registers that have been used include Western Electric registers and two registers made by the Production Instrument Co.—the Wizard register (Catalogue No. EC8) and the Mercury register (110-volt d-c model).

The Western Electric registers have an inductance of 7.5 henrys and a resistance of 2,500 ohms, and they require a current of 10 ma for reliable operation. They can be operated at a maximum speed of 5 counts per second by the type of circuit shown in the Model 400 counter, Fig. 4.7, provided the time constant in the grid circuit is lengthened somewhat.

The Wizard register has a very high inductance and resistance — 150 henrys and 15,000 ohms — and requires a current of about 10 ma for operation. It is a difficult register to drive properly by an electronic circuit but has the advantage that it can be set to zero readily. The circuit used in the Model 400 counter, Fig. 4.7, can also be used for this register, provided that the grid time constant is lengthened by increasing the coupling capacitance. This register has a maximum reliable counting rate of about 10 counts per second.

The Mercury register is considerably less expensive than the other registers mentioned and it appears to be a satisfactory solution to the register problem. It has an inductance of 16 henrys and a resistance of 6,000 ohms, and it will operate reliably on a current of about 15 ma, with a maximum counting rate of about 20 counts per second. It requires a somewhat longer pulse to operate than does the C. S. Co. register, but any circuit that will operate the C. S. Co. register is suitable for the Mercury register if the pulse is lengthened somewhat. When a negative bias is available, the circuit shown in Fig. 4.4 has proved to be very satisfactory.*

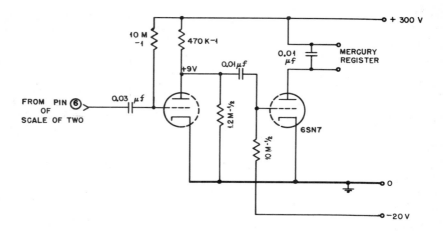

Fig. 4.4 — Circuit for driving a Mercury register.

In designing an electronic counter containing a driver circuit for a register, care must be taken to prevent transients on the power-supply bus — arising when the counter is actuated — from interacting with the scaler portion of the counter and causing extra counts. For this reason it is best either to secure plate voltage for the output stage of the driver circuit from the unstabilized side of the power supply or to use a resistance-capacitance filter for isolating the stage from the stabilized plate-supply bus. Also care must be taken to avoid loading the final scaler stage to such an extent that its operation becomes unreliable. Furthermore, the driver stage must not produce pulses that feed back through the coupling network to the scaler unit. To prevent the occurrence of large voltage surges across the windings of the register when the current through it is broken, it is customary to connect a suitable capacitor across the winding.

It will be observed that these various register driver circuits function by differentiating the square wave signal that appears at one or

---

*A suitable negative bias can usually be obtained from a stabilized supply by inserting some resistance in the ground lead between the filter and the ground terminal of the VR tube furnishing the comparison voltage in the supply.

the other of the plates of the final scale of two. The problem is essentially one of placing a sufficiently high voltage across the register until it closes, and then removing this voltage to enable the register to recover in preparation for the next count. If the square voltage pulse is slightly too short, the register may occasionally miss, whereas if it is too long the maximum counting rate is reduced. For any particular register it is usually necessary to determine empirically the best duration for the pulse, although approximate values can be estimated from data supplied by the manufacturer of the register.

Usually the tube in whose plate circuit the register is located is driven, at least temporarily, into the positive grid region. There is, of course, no reason for drawing a large surge of grid current when the positive signal first reaches the grid, so it is customary to make sure that the grid signal comes from a relatively high-resistance source. The grid therefore draws grid current either for a length of time set by the source resistance of the grid signal and the coupling capacitance used or for a length of time determined by the time constant in the grid circuit of the coupling stage that is often used between the final scaler unit and the driver stage. In the latter case, the signal applied to the grid of the driver tube is very nearly a square pulse. When the scale of two furnishing the signal to the driver circuit flips into its other stable state, a negative signal is applied to the grid of the driver tube or to that of the coupling stage, and charge must now flow back on to the coupling capacitor or capacitors before the circuit is ready to operate again. Normally the grid-circuit time constants involved can be so chosen that mechanical motion in the register and not the electrical time constant of the driving circuit sets the maximum possible counting rate.

When it is undesirable that the leads to the register be at high voltage, it is possible to couple the driving pulse to the register through a large blocking capacitor, as is done in the driver circuit of the Model 200 counter, Fig. 4.5. Values for this capacitance from 2 to 20 μf are usually satisfactory.

A driver circuit of another type involves making the register the plate load of the "off" tube in a univibrator. Each time the univibrator is triggered, a square voltage pulse of definite duration is applied to the register. Circuits of this type have not ordinarily been used, but they should be satisfactory, particularly if a negative bias supply is available.* Without a negative bias supply, the univibrator requires cathode biasing, which somewhat reduces the amplitude of the voltage pulse available for the register. A driver circuit of the

---

* A register driver circuit of the univibrator type appears in Fig. 4.33.

univibrator type is needed if the circuit to which it is coupled supplies only short pulses.

Still another type of driver circuit for a register can be based on a thyratron. Ordinarily the circuit is so arranged that the thyratron discharges a fairly large capacitor and the recharging current of the capacitor passes through the register to operate it. This type of circuit does not appear to be so reliable as circuits based on hard tubes, and its use is not especially recommended.

2.4 Some Complete Counter Circuits. The counter circuits used at Los Alamos have gone through a considerable evolution, and the circuits chosen for description here represent standard models that have proved to be very satisfactory. Changes in the near future will probably lie in the direction of improved physical construction, and possibly in the development of practical counters based on scales of ten. Some simplification in the construction of scaling circuits would result if double-triode – double-diode tubes should become commercially available to replace a 6SN7 and 6H6, and also a 6SL7 and 6H6, in the scaler units.

It has been customary to construct a counter circuit, including an amplitude discriminator, as one electronic unit, and a pulse amplifier as a separate unit. Although this division has many points in its favor while both types of circuit are undergoing development, it has led to certain abuses on the part of experimentalists who have not been keenly aware of the problem of faithfully transmitting fast pulses from a pulse amplifier to a counter circuit. For instance, there is a tendency to run unduly long coaxial cables between the amplifier and the counter, thus placing a considerable capacitive load on the output stage of the amplifier. It would appear better to consider the amplitude discriminator to be part of the amplifier, since, until the signal from an electrical detector has passed through the discriminator, pulse heights are usually of paramount importance. Following the discriminator, all pulses have standard shapes, and the circuit requirements are not particularly stringent. If the discriminator were constructed in the same chassis as the amplifier, the stabilized power supply for the amplifier could also be used for the discriminator. The counter circuit, which would then include only a scaler and a register driver circuit, could possibly be operated from an unstabilized supply, with a resulting economy in parts. This mode of construction has not been used, but it should be seriously considered by anyone designing new electronic equipment for nuclear research.

The counters to be described here all include an amplitude discriminator, a scaler, and an output circuit. Two different types of counter circuits are of importance, one of which is used with pulse amplifiers and the other with self-quenching Geiger-Mueller tubes.

The Model 200 counter is the standard counter circuit used for routine measurements where a pulse amplifier is involved. It has a resolving time of 5 μsec. The Model 220 counter has been designed to use only miniature tubes and it is particularly suitable for applications where portability of equipment is of importance. It has a resolving time of about 20 μsec. The Model 400 scaler is always used with a self-quenching Geiger-Mueller tube. It includes a high-voltage power supply, so that no additional equipment other than a register is necessary in order to make measurements. The Model 600 counter, which has a resolving time of 0.7 μsec, furnishes standard output pulses scaled down by a factor of 8 over the input pulses. It is always used preceding a Model 200 or similar counter, whose discriminator bias is set to accept all output pulses from the Model 600 counter.

(a) Model 200 Counter. The circuit for the Model 200 counter is shown in Fig. 4.5. It employs the plug-in scale-of-two units whose circuit has been given in Fig. 4.2. Since the operation of the discriminator of the scaler units and of the driver stage has been discussed earlier in the chapter, it will be necessary here only to point out a few properties of the complete circuit.

The input signal will normally come from a pulse amplifier, although the counter can be used for recording any periodic or non-periodic series of pulses that have sufficient amplitude to trigger the discriminator and are spaced more than 5 μsec apart. For making accurate nuclear measurements, pulses whose amplitudes lie in the range 10 to 100 volts are ordinarily used. Experimental tests show that to operate the counter the input pulses should remain above the bias setting of the discriminator for at least 0.1 μsec. It is desirable that the pulses should have more or less flat tops of greater duration when accurate pulse-height distributions are being determined. If the pulses are narrow enough for the discriminator to remain in its triggered state for less than 5 μsec (the resolving time of the scaler), there is no danger that a noise peak occurring on the tail of the pulse will cause an accidental count. For testing purposes the counter can be operated with a sine-wave input signal.

The potentiometer controlling the bias setting of the discriminator is usually made direct reading in volts. The dial used reads from 0 to 100 over an angle of 270 deg; it is placed on the potentiometer in such a way that the two end portions of the potentiometer are not used. Relatively narrow pulses of accurately known height are fed into the discriminator to enable the adjustment of the bias control to be made.* The pulse height is first set at a low value—for instance,

---

* The Model 50 pulse generator described in Chap. 6, Sec. 3.1, is used for this purpose.

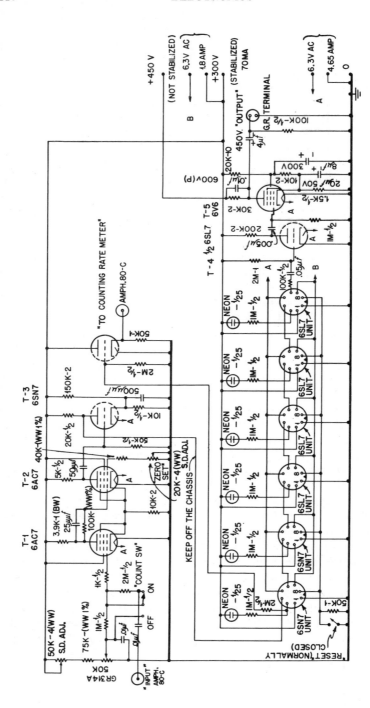

Fig. 4.5—The Model 200 counter.

10 volts — and the bias control is set to read 10. The "zero set" control is varied until the discriminator just triggers. The pulse height is then adjusted to 100 volts, and the bias control is set to read 100. The 50,000-ohm variable resistor in series with the bias potentiometer is then varied until the discriminator barely triggers again. This process is repeated, and by successive approximations the entire range of bias control is made direct reading to an accuracy of a fraction of 1 volt. It should be pointed out that the duty ratio of the waveform of the signal from the pulse generator must be less than 1 per cent if the bias adjustments are to be accurate to 1 per cent.

The input signal to the counter first passes through a "count" switch, which has been arranged to avoid the insertion of a count when it is closed. The circuit used also prevents the input capacitor from acquiring the wrong amount of charge through leakage when the count switch is in the "off" position. Each time the signal triggers the discriminator, a positive square pulse is generated at the plate of T-2. This signal, of about 40-volts amplitude, is differentiated with an RC-coupling element having a time constant of 5 μsec and is impressed on the grid of T-3, which constitutes an inverter stage for driving the first scaler unit. The inverter is normally' biased off, so its plate rests at +300 volts, which is at the correct d-c level for direct connection to the cathodes of the diodes in the first scaler unit (pin 4).

The Model 200 counter employs two 6SN7 units followed by four 6SL7 units, all direct-connected in a chain. In manual operation of the reset switch or button, the reset lead (pin 8) to each scale of two is allowed to rise in potential about +50 volts. All scalers are thus put in the same state, with the interpolation lights out. A much greater rise in potential, such as would occur if the resistance of 50,000 ohms across the reset switch were absent, disturbs the cathode potential of the scales of two and may cause some of the units to flip into the wrong state when the reset switch is closed.

From the connection used for the interpolation light (pin 3) of the first scale of two, a square-wave signal is taken through a 2-megohm resistor to a cathode-follower output stage, which can serve to drive an external counting-rate meter. The Model 200 counting-rate meter described in Sec. 2.6(c) is designed to be used with this circuit.

Although the use of a counting-rate meter is optional, it permits a rapid determination of the approximate counting-rate pulse-height distribution that is characteristic of the experiment at hand. It is felt that in many instances data of needless accuracy are taken in preliminary investigations with a new experimental setup. A less accurate but more rapid method of taking data constitutes a worth-while supplement to an accurate counter based on a scaling circuit.

The circuit used for driving an external register in the Model 200 counter has been so designed that it is basically suitable for driving a variety of registers. It is, of course, necessary to choose the time constant in the grid circuits of the coupling stage and of the 6V6 driver stage so as to give a pulse of suitable length for reliable operation of the register. The circuit constants indicated in Fig. 4.5 are correct for operating a C. S. Co. register. Most other registers require somewhat longer time constants. The series resistance of 100,000 ohms in the coupling network serves primarily to limit the magnitude of grid current drawn by the 6SL7 and does not limit the rate at which the register can be driven. It is customary to use the other half of the 6SL7 tube in the amplifier of the stabilized power supply.

Since the resolving time of the Model 200 counter is 5 μsec, it is possible to count at the rate of 2,000 random counts per second with a 1 per cent counting loss. The register will then have to run at an average rate of about 30 counts per sec. Although this rate is well within the range of operation of a C. S. Co. register that is in good adjustment, when it is desired to count fast it is advisable to add one or two more scales of two to enable the register to operate at a more leisurely pace. Indeed, it is probably economically sound to add scales of two until the counting rate is low enough so that an inexpensive register — for instance, the Mercury register — can be used. This register can be conservatively operated at 10 counts per second.

(b) Model 220 Counter. The Model 220 counter, Fig. 4.6, which is basically similar to the Model 200, has been designed for semiportable applications where the counting rates are not very high. It employs only miniature tubes, and the use of electrolytic capacitors has been avoided. The circuit shown is a scale of eight, but additional scales of two, identical to the ones used in the circuit, can be added if desired.

The discriminator in the Model 220 counter is as fast as the one used in the Model 200, but its stability will not be so good, since it employs carbon resistors instead of precision wire-wound resistors for determining the bias setting. The count switch is placed in the cathode circuit of the inverter stage, which couples the output of the discriminator to the first scaler unit. This method of turning on the counter has many points in its favor and should possibly be adopted in the Model 200 counter. Essentially it places a high positive cathode bias on the inverter when the counter is turned off. The counter is turned on by reducing the bias to a value where positive pulses impressed on the grid will produce negative pulses at the plate of the

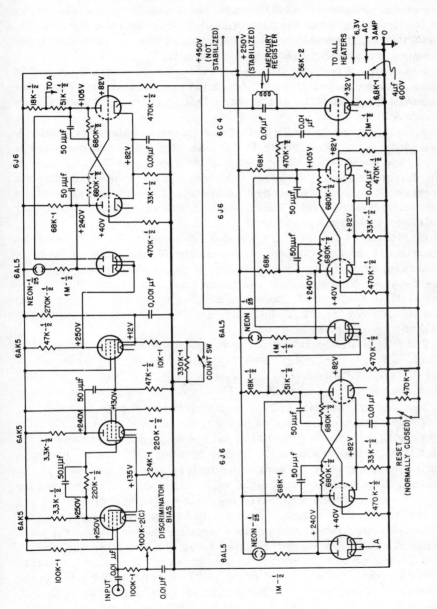

Fig. 4.6—The Model 220 counter.

inverter and so trigger the first scaler stage. This method of switching cannot produce accidental counts, and it avoids the use of a switch in the signal lead from the pulse amplifier, thereby reducing parasitic capacitance. If necessary, the count switch can be located at some distance from the inverter with no ill effects.

The scales of two are all identical and have a resolving time of 20 μsec. In design and mode of operation they are so similar to the standard 6SN7 and 6SL7 scaler units that no additional discussion is required.

The circuit for driving a C. S. Co. register is extremely simple in that it requires but a single 6C4 triode. Since no coupling stage is used that would invert the polarity of the signal reaching the grid of the driver stage, it is necessary to secure an inverted signal directly from the final scale of two by a connection to the plate that operates the interpolation light. The circuit shown will drive the register reliably at 40 counts per second.

(c) Model 400 Counter. The Model 400 counter, Fig. 4.7, has been specifically designed for use with a Geiger-Mueller tube of the self-quenching type. It contains (1) a plug-in high-voltage power supply of the r-f type; (2) a discriminator based on a univibrator circuit element; (3) a scale of 64 consisting of six plug-in 6SL7 scaler units; and (4) a driver for a C. S. Co. register. These features of the circuit will now be described in turn.

The design and operation of the r-f power supply are discussed in Chap. 7, Sec. 6.1. Although the high voltage furnished by the supply is not directly stabilized, it will remain constant to 2 per cent or better once the circuit has warmed up. This is due to the fact that the load is constant and the plate voltage furnished the r-f supply is stabilized. The high voltage can be varied in the range of from 400 to 1,500 volts by varying the screen potential of the r-f oscillator. The value of the high voltage impressed on the Geiger-Mueller tube can be read with sufficient accuracy on a panel-type meter, which is provided in the circuit. High-voltage supplies of other types can be substituted for the r-f supply, whose main advantage is one of compactness.

The Model 400 counter is intended to be used with self-quenching Geiger-Mueller tubes that produce negative pulses of several volts amplitude. Suitable Geiger-Mueller tubes are described in "Ionization Chambers and Counters," by Rossi and Staub, National Nuclear Energy Series, Division V, Volume 2. The discriminator used in the counter is essentially a cathode-coupled univibrator (see Chap. 2, Sec. 4.2) and is triggered to its quasi-stable state by any negative pulse of amplitude greater than about 1 volt. A square negative pulse is generated at the plate of T-2 each time it is triggered. When the

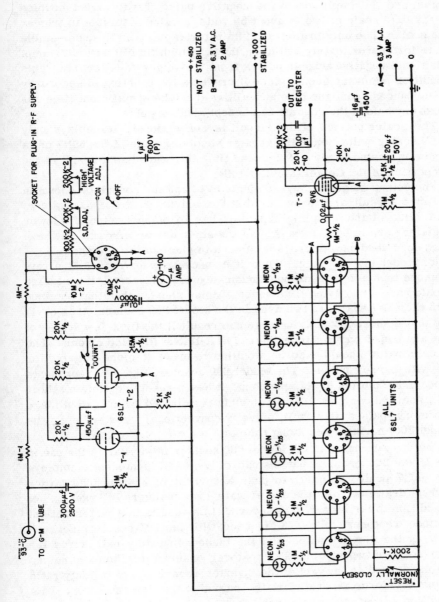

Fig. 4.7—The Model 400 counter.

count switch is closed, the plate-load resistance of T-2 is 10,000 ohms, and the amplitude of the negative pulse that is direct-coupled to the first scale of two is about 50 volts, a value sufficient to trigger the scaler. The univibrator-discriminator remains in its quasi-stable state for approximately 100 μsec, during which time it will not accept additional negative trigger pulses from the Geiger-Mueller tube. This condition is advantageous, since it prevents the counting of secondary disturbances from the tube and allows the tube a sufficient time for recovery before the counter can accept another pulse.

The scaler portion of the circuit is conventional. It employs only 6SL7 scaler units, since the greater resolving time of the 6SN7 units would be wasted in view of the dead time introduced as a result of the properties of the Geiger-Mueller tube.

The output stage employs a single 6V6, and the constants shown in the grid circuit are those suitable for driving a C. S. Co. register. The value of the coupling capacitor has to be increased if slower registers are to be driven. Any of the other driver circuits that have been described can, of course, be used in place of the one shown.

(d) <u>Model 600 Counter.</u> When it is necessary to record at a rate of more than a few thousand random counts per second, the counter should have a resolving time several times shorter than that obtained with the 6SN7 scales of two used in the Model 200 counter. It is obvious that a shorter resolving time can result if the first few scales of two are based on a pentode instead of a triode flip-flop circuit. The discriminator should also be modified to make it more suitable for use with narrow pulses. The Model 600 counter, Fig. 4.8, represents a possible solution to this problem. It has a resolving time of about 0.7 μsec and contains a scale of eight terminated by an output stage producing pulses that will drive a conventional counter (e.g., the Model 200) having a resolving time of 5 μsec.

The discriminator in the Model 600 counter is similar to the one in the Model 200 counter, but instead of two 6AC7 pentodes it employs two 6AG7 pentodes biased to pass a current of 25 ma. The larger current drawn permits the use of plate-load resistors of lower value; in addition to the larger gain secured, this results in a faster action. A diode restorer, tube T-3, is used with the RC-coupling network between the discriminator and the biased inverter that drives the first scale of two circuit. The restorer ensures that uniform pulses are impressed on the grid of the inverter, regardless of the duty ratio of the waveform generated at the output of the discriminator. This condition is necessary since the fast scales of two are much more critical with respect to the form of triggering pulse than are the 6SN7 scales of two, in which larger voltage swings occur.

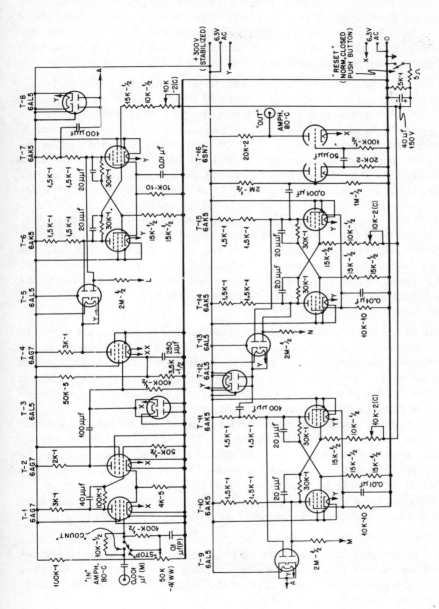

Fig. 4.8—The Model 600 counter.

Familiar diode coupling is used between the plate of the inverter and the first scale of two. Although it is possible to use a coupling of this type between the succeeding scales of two, it is found that the scaler is more stable if a combination of capacitive and diode coupling is used, with a diode restorer on the coupling capacitor.

The maximum rate at which a scale of two of this type can be operated appears to be limited primarily by the time constant present in the resistance-capacitance networks coupling each plate to the opposite grid in the flip-flop. The amount of capacitance present is determined by the existing parasitic circuit capacitance and by the capacitance that must be added in order for each grid to be sufficiently driven by the signal produced at the opposite plate. To reduce the time constant, it is necessary to employ relatively low resistances for the resistive couplings between grids and plates. The extent to which the resistances can be lowered depends on the amount of current and power that one can afford to supply. In the Model 600 counter the current is approximately 5 ma for each resistive path, and the time constant for recovery is estimated to be about 0.5 μsec. The plate-load resistors must, of course, be reduced to as low a value as is consistent with the required stability of the two stable states of the flip-flop.

In order to ensure that the two stable states of each scale of two be equivalent to each other, part of the resistance in one arm of the resistive coupling between tubes is made adjustable. Adjustment is made while using a pulse generator furnishing two narrow pulses whose time separation can be varied at will. A suitable pulse generator for this application is described in Chap. 6.

It is found that the scales of two used in the Model 600 counter require somewhat critical operation. They call for careful adjustment and testing before the performance of any particular unit can be trusted. It would appear that the Model 600 counter represents only a partial solution to the problem of obtaining a reliable counter with a resolving time of less than 1 μsec. Further developmental work should be undertaken to improve fast counters.

The output stage of the Model 600 counter is designed to offer a high-impedance loading to the final scale of two and to deliver large positive pulses to the succeeding counting circuit that continues the scaling operation. The operation of the output stage should be obvious on inspection of the circuit diagram.

The problem of obtaining interpolation indicators with a fast scaler is not so simple as with an ordinary triode scaler. The reason, of course, is that the changes in plate potential are less than the difference between the ignition and extinction voltages of a small neon lamp. It is therefore necessary to use an arrangement of the sort shown in Fig. 4.9, where the cathode bias of the triode amplifiers is adjusted so that the tubes are either conducting or nonconducting and the corresponding neon lamps are either off or on, depending on the state of the scale of two.

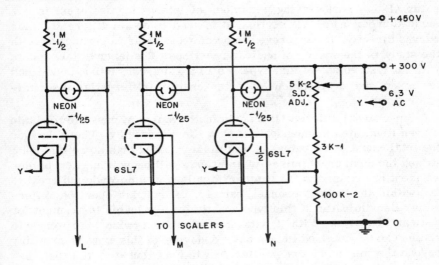

Fig. 4.9—Interpolation-indicator circuit for the Model 600 counter.

Provided that the electrical detector and the pulse amplifier used with the Model 600 counter furnish pulses lasting only a few tenths of a microsecond, it is possible to count 14,000 pulses per second $(0.8 \times 10^6$ pulses per minute) with a 1 per cent counting loss. In actual practice, 10^5 pulses per second have been counted with less than a 10 per cent counting loss.

2.5 **Differential Amplitude Discriminators.** In many experiments in nuclear physics it is important to know the distribution of the amplitudes of pulses coming from an electrical detector. If the source is steady, it is possible to obtain this information by using a single discriminator whose bias can be varied by known amounts. The counting rate is determined for a number of bias settings, and the so-called "integral bias curve" relating counting rate and bias setting (or pulse height) can be plotted directly. When the source is not steady, it is possible to use two discriminators, keeping one of them at a fixed bias setting. The counting rate of the discriminator of variable bias can then be normalized by the fixed-bias counting rate.

A more elaborate type of discriminator results if one simple discriminator is used at fixed bias to secure a normalizing counting rate, while two other simple discriminators having a fixed separation in bias are used with a coincidence circuit to record only those pulses falling in between the two values of bias. This discriminator is the simplest type of differential amplitude discriminator. It is often termed a "single-channel differential discriminator." A discriminator of this sort, having a number of interesting features, is described under (a) of this section. It is used to obtain differential bias curves directly. It has proved to be of great value in connection with the study of the energy of nuclear reactions. The labor of taking data with an instrument of this type — still a time-consuming task — has prompted the development of a ten-channel differential discriminator.

A ten-channel differential discriminator makes it possible to obtain eleven items (ten independent) of data simultaneously. These include the total count of all pulses of amplitude greater than some minimum value; the number of pulses of amplitude falling within each of nine adjacent channels; and the number of pulses of amplitude too great to fall within the highest channel, namely, the surplus count. A differential discriminator of this type constitutes a valuable instrument for nuclear research. With it data that might otherwise take weeks to obtain can be obtained in one day. A device of this sort is probably beyond the means of the smaller institutions, but it is felt that, because of the rapidity with which data can be taken, the cost of a ten-channel differential discriminator, with associated counters, constitutes a worth-while investment where the operating cost of a large accelerator is great. In many cases more accurate data can be taken with a ten-channel discriminator, since conditions tend to remain constant during the short interval required to obtain a complete bias curve.

Several types of ten-channel discriminators have been made, with varying degrees of success. The experiences gained have led to the most recent model, which has operated satisfactorily for several months. It will be described following the discussion of the single-channel discriminator.

(a) A Single-channel Differential Discriminator. This instrument consists of two parts, either of which can be used in combination with other types of circuits for measuring pulse amplitudes. One part provides for the shaping and selecting of pulses from an amplifier, in such a manner as to decrease the probability of error due to the random times of occurrence and the finite duration of single pulses. The other part provides an output pulse for counting only when an input pulse has an amplitude that falls between two definite values. Under certain conditions the combination of the two parts permits pulse-amplitude measurements to be made more accurately and more rapidly than would be possible with a simple amplitude discriminator. We shall first discuss the pulse-shaping part of the circuit and later the differential-discriminator part. Finally a brief account will be given of the adjustment and operation of the complete instrument.

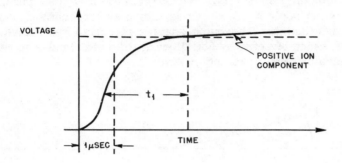

Fig. 4.10 — A possible detector pulse.

The shape of pulses originating in an ionization chamber, or especially in a proportional counter, is not that of an idealized step function, but may have an initial fast rise that tapers gradually into a much slower rise caused by the collection of positive ions. Often various pulses will not have the same shape, which makes it difficult to use a delay-line pulse shaper (see Chap. 3, Sec. 3.2) to obtain a fast recovery of the trailing edge of each pulse. In such a case it is desirable to use a relatively long RC clipping time so that the amplitude of the shaped pulse will not depend so markedly on the rise time. It is then found best to define the "amplitude" of the pulse as its height at some sufficiently long, predetermined time after the start of the initial rise.

In Fig. 4.10 is shown the first part of a pulse that might be observed with an ideal amplifier. It is convenient to use the time t_1 indicated in the figure for establishing the position at which the amplitude is defined. The result one obtains is evidently not sensitive to small changes in t_1. If this pulse is passed through an amplifier having a long RC clipper — say 100 μsec — the peak of the output pulse will essentially have the amplitude that has been defined. If the amplifier should have a 5-μsec clipper, a lower value for the amplitude would be obtained, and this value would be relatively sensitive to variations in pulse shape.

The principal reason for using a short time constant to shape the pulses is that higher average counting rates can be tolerated without a large probability that a pulse will occur before a previous pulse is completely over and thus be observed with the wrong amplitude. Figure 4.11(a) shows a stylized pulse of amplitude e_m. If two such pulses occur in a time short compared with the recovery time of the pulses, the resultant output signal from the amplifier will have the form shown in Fig. 4.11(b). With a conventional discriminator the second pulse would be recorded as having an amplitude e_m' instead of e_m, its true height. The pulse-shaping circuit to be described prevents this sort of error by not allowing the second pulse to reach the discriminator of the counting circuit.

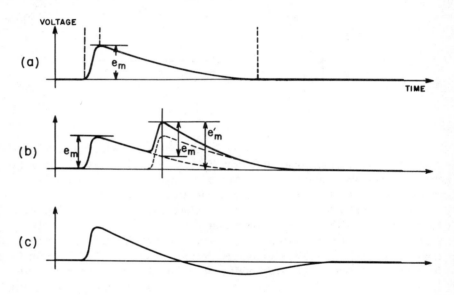

Fig. 4.11 — Input-pulse forms.

A pulse of another type sometimes encountered in practice has the form illustrated in Fig. 4.11(c). Here again an incorrect pulse height will be recorded for a second pulse falling in the trough of the pulse shown. The pulse-shaping circuit to be described does not completely correct for this difficulty. If possible, pulses of this form should be avoided by a proper choice of the amplifier (see Chap. 3, Sec. 3) used with the electrical detector.

The operation of the pulse-shaping circuit, in response to various possible pulse forms, is illustrated in Fig. 4.12. When a single pulse, as shown in (a) occurs, it appears after shaping as in (b). A short time T_1 after the initial rise, the pulse is clamped to a voltage slightly

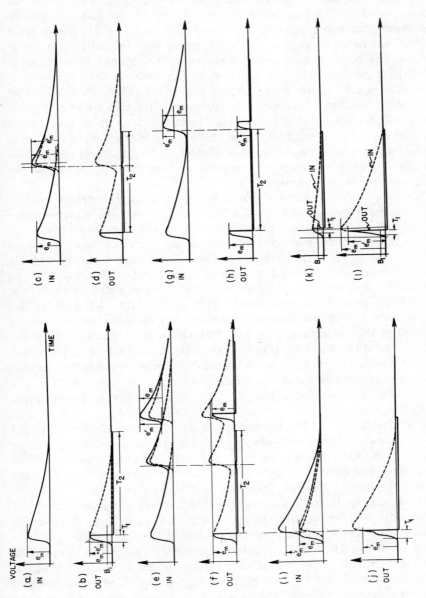

Fig. 4.12 — Possible pulse forms at input and output of gate.

below the zero line and held for a time T_2, after which the clamp is released. The time T_1 is adjustable and is normally set to make the clamping occur shortly after the maximum of the pulse has been reached. The duration of the clamping action, T_2, is also adjustable and should be made as long as the recovery time (or until the pulse is within, say, 5 per cent of zero). Because of the nature of the clamping circuit, if the clamp is released almost immediately the output signal will still remain at zero for the duration of the pulse. This condition should be avoided because there are errors introduced in a manner to be described presently, and also because there is danger that a second pulse, occurring after the short clamped period, may be distorted on account of underswing produced in the pulse amplifier. It is evident that the apparent, or measured, amplitude e'_m in (b) is the same as the defined amplitude e_m.

The next most frequently occurring situation is illustrated in Fig. 4.12(c) where two pulses are so close together that the apparent amplitude e'_m of the second pulse is greater than its true amplitude e_m. When these pulses emerge from the shaping circuit, they have the form shown in (d). Here the first pulse is shaped as in (b), but the second pulse appears as a small bump on the base line and is of an amplitude too small to be counted. The second pulse is therefore discarded instead of being measured incorrectly. As long as the pulses occur in a truly random fashion, this does not affect the data regarding the relative amplitude distribution. It does lower the absolute value of the counting rate observed, but a correction can be made if the times T_1 and T_2 are measured. However, the single-channel differential discriminator is not intended primarily for use in measuring absolute counting rates, but for use in measuring pulse-height distributions.

The elimination of the type of spurious event just described is the main purpose of the pulse-shaping circuit. If the counting rate is so low that this kind of event occurs but rarely, then the other events to be considered here are extremely rare in occurrence. For the sake of completeness, however, they will be discussed.

Occasionally three pulses will occur so close together that all three will overlap as illustrated in Fig. 4.12(e). If the third pulse occurs after the clamp has been released, the output signal takes the form shown in (f), where, as before, the second pulse is not counted, but the third pulse is reproduced with an apparent amplitude e'_m, a little smaller than its true amplitude e_m. If the third pulse had occurred somewhat before the release of the clamp, it would have been discarded along with the second pulse.

In the borderline case where the rise of a second pulse occurs exactly at the time of release of the clamp, the input and output signals take the forms shown in Figs. 4.12(g) and (h). The apparent amplitude of the second pulse may have a value that is any fraction of the original pulse height. The probability that events of this type will occur is very small when the rise time of the pulse is short compared with the recovery time.

Another improbable event, but one of some interest, is illustrated in Figs. 4.12(i) and (j). Here a second pulse occurs during the time T_1 measured from the rise of the first pulse. In such a case the output pulse will have an apparent amplitude between e_m and $2e_m$. Since the probability of this event, though small, is proportional to the time T_1, the value of T_1 should not be made larger than necessary. This type of event is of interest because of the way it affects the data. The other spurious events simply tend to spread the data below the true amplitude, whereas the event illustrated in (i) and (j) causes a spread above the true amplitude, but in a peculiar fashion.

Suppose all pulses lie in a small amplitude range, and the correct differential amplitude-frequency curve has the form shown in Fig. 4.13(a). If one attempted to measure this distribution with a conventional discriminator and with a relatively long clipping time in the amplifier, the distribution shown in (b) might be obtained. The same distribution measured with the pulse-shaping circuit described in this section might have the appearance indicated in (c). Here the straggling at the low amplitude end is due to the effects illustrated in Figs. 4.12(f) and (h), whereas the small peak observed at $2A_0$ shown in Fig. 4.13(c) is due to pulses occurring very close together, as illustrated in (i) and (j). The amplitude of the small peak will be found to vary directly with the value of T_1, whereas the amplitude of the main peak will be independent of T_1, but will, of course, depend on the value of T_2.

For the sake of comparison, Fig. 4.13(d) has been drawn to indicate the sort of distribution that is measured when it is possible to employ only delay-line pulse-shaping. In all the curves a small amount of spread has been indicated to take into account random noise that is present in the output signal of the amplifier. A smaller signal-to-noise ratio would alter the observed curves to a greater extent. A similar effect is produced by variations of the input pulse amplitudes that result from straggling of particle ranges and from thick sources.

In the foregoing discussion it has been assumed that all pulses from the amplifier have essentially the same amplitude, but it is evident that similar conditions exist when a variety of pulse amplitudes are present. There is, however, one difficulty that should be noted in this case. The interval T_1, in practice, is initiated not at corresponding points on pulses of different amplitude, but at a given pulse amplitude set by a simple amplitude discriminator. Figures 4.12(k) and (l) show

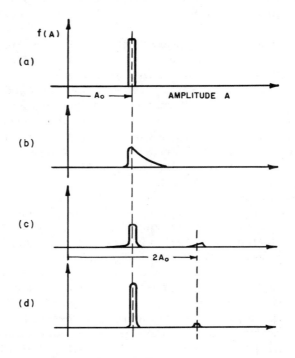

Fig. 4.13—Differential bias curves.

what can occur because of this if T_1 is made too short. In (k) the output pulse from the shaping circuit is shown with T_1 suitably adjusted for a small pulse. This value of T_1, however, may be too short for a large pulse, since the interval T_1 is then initiated at a relatively earlier time. The large pulse is therefore clamped before it reaches its maximum amplitude, as shown in (l). When T_1 is adjusted, care must be taken to make sure that it is long enough to accommodate the largest pulses to be encountered.

The operation of the pulse-shaping circuit in the differential discriminator can be understood by reference to Fig. 4.14. Tubes T-1 through T-14 comprise this part of the circuit. The circuit elements

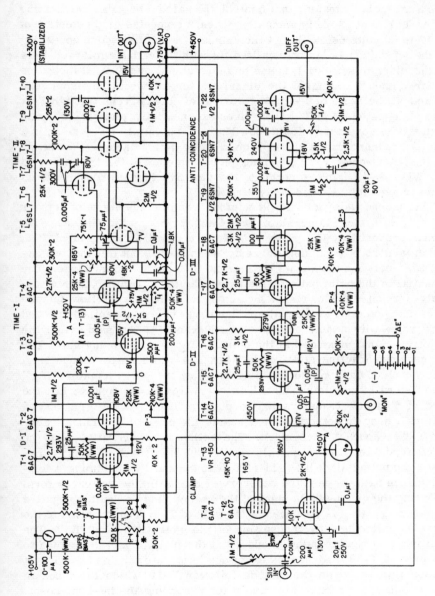

Fig. 4.14 — A single-channel differential discriminator.

employed include a gate (or clamp), an amplitude discriminator, and two time-delay circuits that control the gate. The gate, comprising tubes T-11 and T-12, is normally "open," since the grid potential of T-12 is 20 volts below that of the cathode. A positive pulse appearing at the input "Sig In" is transmitted through the cathode follower T-14 to the discriminator D-I, based on tubes of T-1 and T-2. If the pulse is large enough to trigger the discriminator, the negative signal generated at the plate of T-1 serves to cut off the current through T-3. The plate potential of T-3 then rises exponentially toward +300 volts with a time constant of 100 μsec. The grid potential of T-4 rises in a similar manner, but it starts from a value determined by the setting of the potentiometer "T_1," which serves to control the time interval T_1. When T-4 begins to conduct, the negative signal produced at its plate triggers the second delay circuit.

The second delay circuit is a more complicated form of trigger circuit, with one stable state (see Chap. 2, Sec. 4.2). The negative signal produced at the plate of T-4 is coupled to the grid of T-8, which is normally passing current. When T-8 is cut off, the two capacitors between the plates of T-6 and T-8 begin to discharge. The potential of the point between the two capacitors, however, is immediately prevented from rising by virtue of grid-current flow in tube T-5. The potential at the plate of T-8 then rises exponentially toward +300 volts with a time constant of 500 μsec. At the same time the negative signal produced at the plate of T-5 serves to maintain T-8 in the nonconducting state, even when T-4 is no longer conducting. After a time determined by the setting of the potentiometer "T_2," tube T-6 will start to conduct. The current that was flowing into the grid of T-5 now transfers to the plate of T-6, and the grid of T-5 suffers a drop in potential. As a result, the plate of T-5 rises, causing T-8 to conduct once more. The action is regenerative, and the original stable state is quickly reached. The diode T-7 acts to restore the potential of the grid of T-5 to ground by furnishing a low-impedance path to speed the recovery of charge on the two capacitors.

During the quasi-stable state of the second delay circuit, a negative rectangular pulse is produced at the grid of T-9. The duration of the pulse is controlled by the setting of the potentiometer "T_2." The positive rectangular pulse produced at the plate of T-9 is coupled to the grid of T-12, and serves to "close" the gate for the time T_2. It is also impressed on the cathode follower T-10, which furnishes an output pulse to an external counter for recording the integral count.

The operation of the pulse-shaping circuit may be summarized as follows: An input pulse passes through the gate and triggers the discriminator D-I. A short time T_1 later the gate is closed, and it remains closed for the time T_2, after which it reopens ready to accept subsequent pulses. The resultant pulse form at the cathode of T-14 is that illustrated in Fig. 4.12(b) provided the discriminator bias of D-I is set at a value smaller than the average pulse amplitude (i.e., to a bias of the order of 5 to 10 volts).

Since the gate operates by clamping the input signal through a capacitor, the gating action is effective only if the rate of change of the input signal does not exceed a certain maximum value. For the values of circuit components given in Fig. 4.14, the maximum allowable value is about 250 volts per microsecond.

The counter connected to the "Int. Out" terminal serves to monitor the rate at which incoming pulses occur. The integral counting rate is ordinarily used as a normalizing factor for the counting rate observed in a given range of the differential discriminator.

Some typical pulse forms that occur at various points in the pulse-shaping circuit are illustrated in Fig. 4.15.

Let us now turn to a discussion of the differential discriminator part of the circuit. Since the output pulses from the pulse-shaping circuit have a definite desirable shape and since two pulses are always separated in time by a certain minimum amount, a relatively simple differential discriminator circuit can be employed. Tubes T-15 through T-22 in Fig. 4.14 comprise this part of the circuit. A positive pulse occurs at the "Diff. Out" terminal only when a pulse from the amplifier has passed through the pulse-shaping circuit, and then only when its amplitude is greater than some minimum value E_1 and less than some maximum value $E_1 + \Delta E$. The two quantities E_1 and ΔE can be varied independently.

Reference to Fig. 4.14 will make the operation of the circuit clear. Tubes T-15 and T-16 comprise a simple amplitude discriminator, D-II (see Chap. 2, Sec. 4.3). Tubes T-17 and T-18 constitute an identical discriminator, D-III. By proper adjustment of the variable resistors P-4 and P-5, the two discriminators can be made to trigger when their input grids are at the same potential. It will be seen that the bias voltage of D-III can be made to differ from that of D-II by small fixed amounts, ΔE, determined by a battery and selector-switch arrangement. The bias voltage of D-III will therefore always be ΔE volts greater than that of D-II, whose bias is determined by the setting of the potentiometer P-1. For a given setting of P-1, pulses of amplitude below a certain minimum value will trigger neither discriminator, whereas pulses in a small amplitude interval will trigger D-II but not D-III. Pulses of greater amplitude will trigger both discriminators.

The rest of the differential discriminator is an anticoincidence circuit, which responds only when D-II, but not D-III, has been triggered. Because of the finite rise time of the input pulses, D-II is always triggered before D-III. Hence the anticoincidence circuit must not operate until sufficient time has elapsed to enable D-III to be triggered, if it is going to be triggered. For this reason the circuit

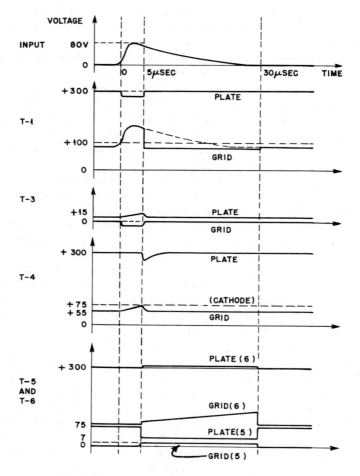

Fig. 4.15 — Pulse forms in pulse-shaping circuit.

has been designed to operate after the input pulse has reached its maximum amplitude. To accomplish this result, the anticoincidence circuit uses pulses obtained from the two discriminators when they are returned to their initial states by the abrupt trailing edge of the input pulse.

The details of the operation are straightforward. When D-II is first triggered, the plate of T-16 rises in potential. The grid potential of T-21, however, can rise only about 7 volts on account of grid-current flow, which changes the charge on the coupling capacitor. If now D-II is triggered to its initial state, without D-III having been triggered, the resulting negative signal at the plate of T-16 will cut off the current through T-21. Since T-20 is normally in a nonconducting state, a positive pulse is produced at the common plate connection, and it is coupled to the "Diff. Out" terminal by the cathode follower T-22. The output pulse can be recorded by the use of a conventional counter.

If both D-II and D-III are triggered by the input pulse, the plates of T-16 and T-18 both rise in potential. Tube T-21 draws grid current as before, as does tube T-19. When the two discriminators return to their initial states, the plates of T-18 and then of T-16 go negative. The negative signal from the plate of T-18 serves to cut off the current through T-19, and the large positive signal produced at the plate of T-19 is coupled to the grid of T-21. When tube T-22 is now cut off by the signal from D-II, there is no positive output signal produced. Indeed, a small negative pulse appears at the output terminal. Since the counter connected there is supposed to count only large positive pulses, no count is recorded. To prevent a count from occurring during the recovery of the anticoincidence circuit, the time constants in the circuit are so chosen that the duration of the positive pulse at the grid of T-21 is always greater than the duration of the negative pulse applied to the grid of T-22. It is evident that the almost vertical return of the pulse provided by the pulse-shaping circuit is essential to the operation of the anticoincidence circuit.

The potentiometers P-1 and P-2 provide a means for controlling the biases of the discriminators. A meter circuit is also included to measure, relative to +105 volts, the bias voltage applied to D-I and to D-II. Since the triggering voltage for the two discriminators can be adjusted by means of P-3 and P-4 to be exactly +105 volts, the meter reading is proportional to the bias, i.e., the pulse height required to trigger the discriminators.

It is perhaps worth while to point out a few details regarding the adjustment and operation of the complete circuit. The only preliminary adjustment that need be made is that of the potentiometers P-3, P-4, and P-5. This can best be done by introducing a small test pulse of fixed amplitude at the input terminal and then observing the signals that appear at the two output terminals. The test pulse should result in a signal at the "Mon." terminal of about 10 volts. The controls P-1 and P-2 are then so adjusted that the meter reads 10 volts with the meter switch in either position. The control P-3 is next adjusted until pulses just begin to appear at the "Int. Out" terminal. Similarly, with the ΔE switch at position 6, P-4 is adjusted until pulses first begin to appear at the "Diff. Out" terminal. The ΔE switch is then placed at position 1, and P-5 is adjusted until negative pulses just appear instead of positive pulses.

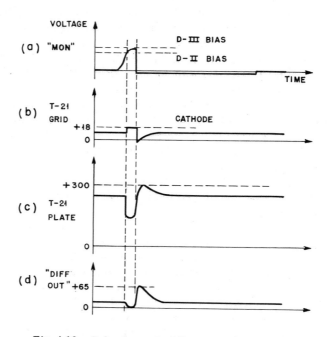

Fig. 4.16— Pulse forms in differential discriminator.

In the actual operation of the circuit with a pulse amplifier and electrical detector, the proper adjustment of the "T_1" and "T_2" controls can be made only with the aid of a sweep circuit containing a circuit for delaying pulses for presentation with a cathode-ray oscillograph. Suitable sweep circuits are described in Chap. 6, Sec. 2.1. The sweep circuit is connected to the "Mon." terminal, and the two time controls are adjusted until the operation of the shaping circuit is similar to that described earlier. These adjustments, of course, should be made after the amplifier gain and the setting of the discriminator bias control P-1 have been determined. The latter control is set so that the pulse-shaping circuit is triggered for the smallest possible pulse size compatible with noise in the amplifier output signal. In any event, the setting of the differential bias (P-1) should never be less than that used for the integral bias (P-2). This restriction should be carefully adhered to; otherwise interpretation of the data will be rendered difficult.

Pulse forms at various points in the differential discriminator, when only D-II is triggered, are shown in Fig. 4.16. Those present when both D-II and D-III are triggered appear in Fig. 4.17.

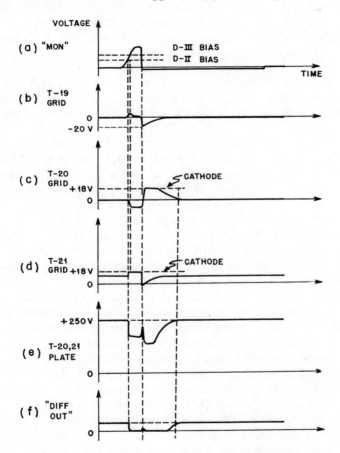

Fig. 4.17—Pulse forms in differential discriminator.

An alternate form of circuit that performs the same function as a differential discriminator is described in Sec. 3.2(a) of this chapter.

(b) A Ten-channel Differential Discriminator. An n-channel differential discriminator serves to sort pulses according to their voltage amplitudes into n − 1 channels of definite width, and to give an indication of the number of pulses of amplitude too great to fall within these channels. In addition it should provide an independent count of the total number of pulses received, to enable a check of the operation of the complete discriminator to be made. The basic design of a discriminator of this sort depends on using n simple discriminators, of the type discussed in Sec. 2.1 of this chapter, with coincidence circuits (see Chap. 2, Sec. 5.2) connected between adjacent discriminators. The bias voltages of successive discriminators in the sequence are set at values that increase in equal steps. If an input pulse has an amplitude sufficient to trigger only the first r discriminators, and not the r + 1 and other discriminators of higher bias, an anticoincidence circuit between the r and the r + 1 discriminator can be arranged to deliver one pulse to a counting circuit. Similar anticoincidence circuits between other adjacent discriminators will fail to respond.

The chief problem in carrying out the design of a multichannel discriminator lies in the time relationships that must exist among the various pulses and signals present in the circuit. The input pulse, coming from an electrical detector through a pulse amplifier, remains at its maximum amplitude for only a short time, perhaps a few microseconds, before it begins to decay to the original base line. If the individual discriminators in the multichannel discriminator are of the Schmitt-trigger-circuit variety, it is necessary to obtain a "count" pulse from the proper anticoincidence circuit during the small interval of time spent by the input pulse at its maximum amplitude, and to avoid coincidence pulses that might be initiated during the rise and decay of the input pulse. It is possible to accomplish this by supplying an accurately timed "registering" pulse to the coincidence circuits, which can be of the sort illustrated in Fig. 2.47(b). The operation of a multichannel discriminator based on this principle is necessarily critical in regard to the delay introduced between the triggering of the discriminator having the lowest bias setting, and the later occurrence of the registering pulse, which is ordinarily initiated by that discriminator. The registering pulse must be of short duration to avoid causing coincidence counts as the input pulse decays, and the input pulses must have reasonably well-defined shapes to ensure that a registering pulse shall always occur at their maximum amplitude. One difficulty with the system suggested here is that the registering pulse may cause a discriminator on the verge of being triggered to trigger, thus producing counts in two adjacent channels. The sum of the counts recorded in individual channels will then not equal the total count.

A somewhat less critical multichannel discriminator results if the trigger circuits used for discrimination are "lock-in discriminators" that can remain in their second state for a time after the input pulse has decayed to its original base line. A delayed registering pulse can then be supplied to the coincidence circuits, and a count can be obtained from the most highly biased channel that has been triggered by the input pulse. A second pulse, delayed with respect to the registering pulse, can be used to reset all the lock-in discriminators simultaneously and thus to clear the way for the next input pulse. The second pulse is termed the "reset" pulse. The ten-channel differential discriminator, which will now be described, is based on this method of operation.

In Fig. 4.18 is shown a block diagram of the complete pulse-height analyzer. The input pulse is impressed simultaneously on ten lock-in discriminators, whose biases increase progressively from discriminator 1 to discriminator 10. Each discriminator has two output leads having steady voltages, whose relative polarities are indicated by plus and minus signs. If a particular discriminator is triggered into its other state, where it will remain for some time, the output voltages have relative polarities indicated by the plus and minus signs in parentheses. When discriminator 1 is triggered, a positive pulse is supplied to the sequence of blocking oscillators and delay lines, which generate the registering and reset pulses. The delays are such that before these pulses appear the input pulse must have risen to its maximum amplitude, triggering all discriminators up to some point, and then decayed to zero. The coincidence circuit in the highest channel reached by the input pulse has two negative input signals entering from the left. All other coincidence circuits have both a positive and a negative input signal. When the registering pulse occurs, a count is recorded only in the one channel that differs from the rest. Soon after the pulse is recorded, the reset pulse returns all discriminators to their original state, thus restoring the circuit to its original condition except for the count that has been recorded in one of the channels.

Any input pulse of amplitude too small to trigger the first discriminator passes unnoticed. If the input pulse is great enough to trigger discriminator 10, it is recorded in the surplus-count channel. The total number of input pulses with sufficient amplitude to trigger the first discriminator, and so to trigger the first blocking oscillator, is recorded by counting the number of registering pulses. If the circuit is working properly, the sum of the counts in the nine channels and the surplus count should equal the total count.

Let us now consider the detailed circuit diagram, Fig. 4.19, which shows the first discriminator, the first coincidence circuit, the circuit for generating the registering and reset pulses, and the connec-

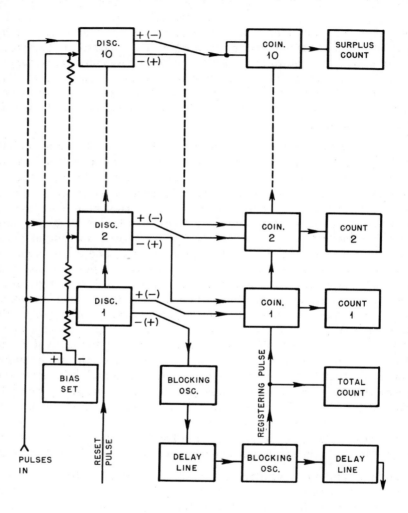

Fig. 4.18—Block diagram of pulse-height analyzer.

tions made to the scale-of-two units used for counting pulses. Additional channels of the discriminator each consist of the portion of the circuit shown within broken lines. A circuit suitable for obtaining a sequence of bias voltages for the ten discriminators is described later.

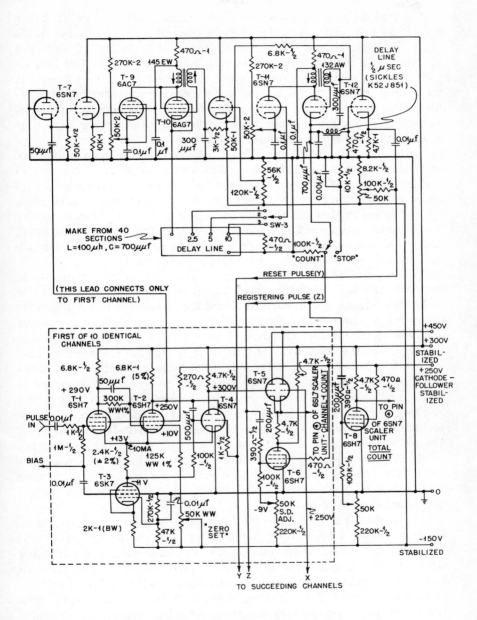

Fig. 4.19—A ten-channel differential discriminator.

The lock-in discriminator for each channel consists of the tubes T-1, T-2, T-3, and T-4, which form a trigger circuit with one stable state. Tubes T-1 and T-2 form a simple discriminator, with T-3 constituting a constant-current source (see Chap. 2, Sec. 3.7) replacing the usual resistive cathode load. The constant-current device in the cathode circuit of the discriminator not only increases the stability of the discriminator but permits the use of larger input pulses without grid current being drawn. The left-hand triode in T-4 is coupled to the discriminator in such a way that if the circuit is triggered by a positive input pulse it will remain in a second quasi-stable state for a relatively long time. The exact duration of the quasi-stable state is of no consequence, since after a maximum time of about 10 μ sec the trigger circuit is reset by a positive reset pulse applied to the grid of the right-hand triode in T-4. A variable resistor, denoted by "Zero Set," is provided to enable the absolute value of the bias setting for each discriminator to be brought into harmony with the absolute value of all the other bias settings.

When a positive input pulse triggers the lock-in discriminator in the first channel, a positive step signal is generated at the plate of T-2. This signal is differentiated, and then passes through a cathode follower and a biased-coupling stage to trigger the blocking oscillator comprising tube T-10. One half of tube T-7 is used for the cathode follower, and the other half for a diode restorer for the negative signal produced when tube T-2 returns to its conducting state. The cathode load of the blocking oscillator consists of a delay line* tapped at 2.5, 5, and 10 μsec. When the pulse produced in the delay line by the blocking oscillator reaches the tap selected by the switch SW-3, the second blocking oscillator, comprising one half of T-12, is triggered. The pulse taken from the cathode circuit constitutes the registering pulse. The same pulse proceeds down a 0.5-μ sec delay line to a cathode follower, from which it emerges as the reset pulse. The left-hand section of tube T-11 serves to provide Class C negative bias for the two blocking oscillators.

It is evident that each time the first discriminator is triggered by an input pulse, a registering pulse and a reset pulse are generated having accurate time relationships with the input pulse and with each other. It is also evident that the input pulse should have decayed to zero, or at least to a value below the bias setting of the first discriminator, before these pulses appear. It is for this reason that several different delay times are provided in the circuit. The shortest

---

*See Chap. 2, Sec. 2.4, for the design of a lumped-parameter delay line.

delay compatible with the input-pulse duration should be used to avoid lengthening the resolving time of the circuit.

To ensure that the pulse from the electrical detector decays rapidly enough, the ten-channel discriminator is always used with an amplifier employing delay-line pulse-shaping (see Chap. 3, Sec. 3.2). Since the lock-in discriminators are not particularly fast, the rise time of the input pulse should be no shorter than perhaps 0.5 μsec. The Model 100 pulse amplifier (see Chap. 3, Sec. 7), modified to have a cathode-follower output stage based on a 6AG7, is a suitable amplifier, especially since it is already provided with connections for a delay-line pulse-shaping circuit.

The coincidence circuit, comprising tubes T-5 and T-6, is of the type shown in Fig. 2.47(a). The connection X leads to the second channel, and connects to the plate of T-2 of that channel. The registering pulse is applied to the grid of T-6. The grid bias of this tube is adjustable in each channel to make it possible to generate a coincidence pulse that is of the correct amplitude to trigger the scaler units (not shown). In the tenth channel, the connection X is made also to the other grid of the coincidence tube T-5 in the same channel, thus terminating the sequence of channels.

The tube T-8 constitutes a stage to couple the registering pulse to a 6SN7 scaler unit, which is the first element in a counter for recording the total count.

The counting circuits employed in the complete pulse-height analyzer are based on the 6SN7 and 6SL7 scaler units described in Sec. 2.2 of this chapter. In channels 1 through 9, three 6SL7 units are needed. For the surplus count (channel 10), one 6SN7 and three 6SL7 units are used to provide for the greater counting rate that may occur there. For the total count, two 6SN7 and three 6SL7 units are necessary. Each scaler is terminated by the register-driver circuit shown in Fig. 4.4, which employs a Mercury register.

An examination of the bias circuit, Fig. 4.20, indicates that it is possible to have a variety of different bias arrangements. With SW-3 open, and SW-1 and SW-4 both in position 1, a current of 10 ma flows through the resistor network. Hence, with SW-2 in position 1, the values of the bias voltages relative to ground are $-10, -20, \ldots, -100$ volts. The entire sequence is reduced in 10-volt steps by advancing the position of SW-2. The maximum possible bias available for discriminator 10 is -140 volts. This limit is necessary since the maximum pulse height from a Model 100 amplifier is about +150 volts and since the discriminators may draw grid current for pulses of greater amplitude. When SW-2 is in position 5, only 1 per cent or less of the pulses should fall in the surplus-count channel. The height of the input pulses can, of course, be reduced by lowering the gain of the amplifier.

If SW-1 is placed in position 2, a current of 5 ma passes through the resistors, and a sequence of 5-volt channels, adjustable with

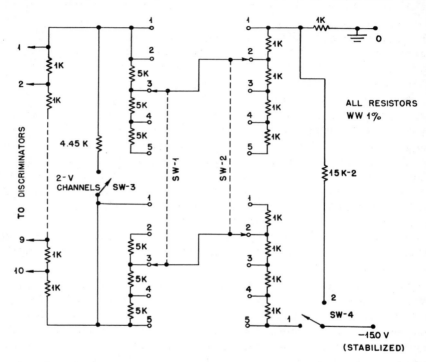

Fig. 4.20—Bias circuit for a ten-channel differential discriminator.

SW-1 and SW-2 to cover the same range formerly occupied by the 10-volt channels, is possible. By closing SW-3, the width of the 5-volt channels is reduced to 2 volts. When SW-4 is in position 2, all discriminators have the same bias applied to their grids. This condition is used to aid in adjusting the "zero set" control provided with each discriminator, since all or none of the discriminators should trigger when the circuit is supplied with test pulses of adjustable amplitude.

The adjustment and testing of the ten-channel differential discriminator are best carried out with the use of the Model 300 sliding-pulse generator, described in Chap. 6, Sec. 3. Pulses from this instrument are fed in through the connection to the preamplifier normally used for the electrical detector. The pulse amplitude is set so that each channel in turn is active, to test the operation of the coincidence circuits, the counting circuits, etc. The pulse generator is then turned to the condition where it generates "sliding" pulses, which are periodically occurring pulses whose amplitudes slowly increase, then decrease, then increase, etc., linearly with time. With the exception of the surplus channel, the various channels of the differential discriminator, if of equal width, receive the same number of pulses for each excursion of the sliding pulser. Hence the equality of channel width can be determined, and the total count can be checked against the sum of the counts in all channels. The latter sum should normally equal the total count exactly, when the apparatus is in adjustment. The fastest random counting rate that should be used with the instrument is about 200 counts per second, with no more than half the counts falling into one channel. The counting loss will then be less than 0.1 per cent.

It is worth noting that it is possible to place an external control on the registering pulse, so that only those pulses are counted which meet other requirements determined by additional equipment.

Since the ten-channel differential discriminator is complex, it is important to design the physical layout so as to provide ready access to all points of the various circuits while the circuit is in operation. Furthermore, since the entire circuit dissipates more than one kilowatt of power, a construction of an open type is desirable. Both these requirements are met if closely associated parts of the circuit are built on long, relatively narrow strips of metal, which can be mounted vertically across a wide relay rack. It is best to mount the power supplies at the bottom of the rack and the amplifier at the top. Succeeding channels of the differential discriminator and associated counting circuits can be arranged between the amplifier and the power supplies.

2.6 Counting-rate Meters. A counting-rate meter is a device in which counting rates are indicated on a pivoted-coil meter whose scale can be calibrated in counts per unit of time. It is often used in portable instruments designed to measure radiation intensity. Also it is particularly suited to obtain a continuous record of the intensity of radiation from a source such as a chain reactor. In this case a pen-recording meter can be used as the indicating device, and a permanent record obtained. A counting-rate meter is necessarily a less accurate instrument than a counter, but it constitutes a useful supplement to a counter for certain types of exploratory work in connection with a new experiment—for setting the bias of a discriminator, for investigating noise, etc.

This section describes a type of counting-rate meter that is capable of considerable accuracy. For an understanding of the operation of the circuit, a brief discussion will first be made of the basic theory of the device. Following this discussion, the circuits of two counting-rate meters will be described. The Model 100 counting-rate meter contains an accurate discriminator and is used in conjunction with a pulse amplifier. Its chief application has been to monitor relatively steady sources of radiation. It contains a "safety" circuit, which operates when the counting rate exceeds full scale by a sufficient amount. The Model 200 counting-rate meter has been designed to operate on pulses supplied by the Model 200 counter, described in Sec. 2.4(a) of this chapter. It is used to supplement the counter in making routine laboratory measurements.

(a) Simple Theory of a Counting-rate Meter. The usual mechanism by which a counting-rate meter operates is very simple. A circuit is so arranged that each pulse to be counted causes a definite amount of charge to be placed on a capacitor in a time short compared with the average spacing of pulses. The charge on the capacitor leaks off through a high resistor, making the average potential across the capacitor proportional to the counting rate. It will be shown that the value of the capacitance determines primarily the fractional probable statistical error in the observed counting rate, whereas the value of the resistance determines the sensitivity of the meter.

Let us consider the basic circuit of a counting-rate meter, Fig. 4.21. It is assumed that each pulse to be counted produces (in a circuit element not shown) a rectangular voltage pulse of the sort illustrated at the left side of the figure. The output impedance of the pulse-producing device is R_1. The height of each pulse, E, is assumed to be the same for all pulses. The duration T of each pulse need not be exactly the same for all pulses provided it is long enough to ensure that the capacitance C_1 becomes fully charged before the pulse ends. We assume that the following inequalities hold for the circuit,

$$\frac{1}{n} \gg T > 5R_1C_1$$

$$E \gg V > E_B \qquad (1)$$

$$C_2 \gg C_1$$

where n is the counting rate. The other quantities are defined in Fig. 4.21. In view of these inequalities, an amount of charge, $q = C_1E$, is deposited on the capacitance C_2 each time a pulse occurs. The average potential V that is developed at the output terminal is clearly

$$V = nqR_2 = nC_1ER_2 \qquad (2)$$

Equation 2 indicates that various ranges of counting rates can be selected by changing accurately measured resistors R_2. The values

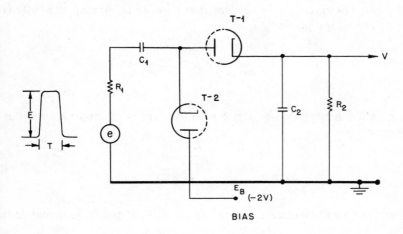

Fig. 4.21—Basic circuit of a counting-rate meter.

for C_1 or E (or both) can be altered slightly until the counting-rate meter is direct-reading on the vacuum-tube voltmeter used to measure the value of V. The small bias placed on the plate of the diode T-2 is necessary to keep the scale linear over the entire range of output voltage, which is usually 1 to 2 volts. If this bias is not present, a small current may flow through the diodes as the result of (1) contact differences of potential and (2) the finite velocity of emission of electrons from the cathodes of the diodes. Such a current is clearly undesirable. It should be noticed that the rectangular pulse used to operate the circuit can be of either polarity, since the two diodes ensure that the correct amount of charge is always transported to the capacitance C_2. The polarity and biasing of the diodes may also be reversed, if this seems desirable. The output signal V will then be negative instead of positive.

Let us next compute the probable error in the observed counting rate. This error is caused by statistical fluctuations in the occurrence of pulses. To make the calculation, it is convenient to use

Campbell's theorem,* which, in one form, states that if the voltage $v(t)$ is induced in a circuit by each event of many that are occurring randomly at the average rate n, then the mean-square fluctuation voltage existing in the circuit is given by

$$(\Delta v)^2 = \overline{[v(t) - V]^2} = n \int_{-\infty}^{\infty} v^2(t)\, dt \tag{3}$$

In the present circuit it is evident that a pulse occurring at $t = 0$ produces the voltage pulse

$$v(t) = \frac{C_1}{C_2} Ee^{-t/R_2 C_2} \tag{4}$$

which, when substituted in Eq. 3 with the limits of integration from 0 to ∞ gives

$$(\Delta v)^2 = \frac{nC_1^2 E^2 R^2}{2C_2} \tag{5}$$

The fractional probable error, from Eqs. 2 and 5, is found to be

$$\epsilon = 0.67 \frac{\Delta v}{V} = 0.67 \frac{1}{\sqrt{2nR_2 C_2}} \tag{6}$$

where the factor 0.67 is used to convert the rms error to the most probable error.

For any given reading of the voltmeter in the counting-rate meter, Eq. 2 shows that the product nR_2 is a constant. A certain value of C_2 therefore corresponds to a definite fractional probable error, regardless of the sensitivity of the counting-rate meter, i.e., the value of R_2. This result makes it convenient to alter the probable error of the instrument simply by switching in different values for the capacitance C_2. The fractional (or percentage) probable error for a full-scale reading can be indicated on the switch in a manner independent of a second switch used to alter the sensitivity of the meter. A control for the probable error is convenient, since the time required for the instrument to respond to changes in counting rate depends on the

*See, for instance, R. H. Fowler, "Statistical Mechanics," 2d ed., p. 778, The Macmillan Company, New York, 1937.

probable error desired for the observed counting rate. When only rough values are wanted, the probable-error setting can be increased so that the response time is less.

(b) Model 100 Counting-rate Meter. The circuit of the Model 100 counting-rate meter is shown in Fig. 4.22. The input circuit consists of a pulse amplitude discriminator whose bias can be adjusted from 0 to 100 volts. The discriminator is very similar to the one discussed in Sec. 2.1 of this chapter. It furnishes positive output pulses that have an amplitude of about 40 volts. These pulses serve to trigger a univibrator pulse-shaping circuit (see Chap. 2, Sec. 4.2). The tube T-3 serves to couple the trigger pulses to the univibrator. It contains a switch in its cathode circuit so that it can be completely biased off in order that the zero setting of the meter may be checked.

The univibrator has a quasi-stable state lasting about 15 μsec, during which time a negative pulse from the plate of T-4 is impressed on the capacitor C_1, whose capacitance can be varied somewhat to bring the calibration of the instrument within the range of control of the potentiometer in the cathode circuit of the univibrator. The operation of the remainder of the circuit should be clear, with the possible exception of the role played by T-8. This tube is used to increase the effective value of the "damping" capacitances determining the fractional probable error. The capacitances are effectively multiplied by the factor $(1 + |G|)$, where G is the gain of the stage between grid and plate.* By this means, large values of effective capacitance can be obtained, without the disadvantage of large leakage currents or of physically large capacitors. In the present circuit the values of the capacitance actually present are multiplied by the factor 14. Equation 6 has been used to compute the values of capacitance necessary to give the percentage probable errors (of full-scale readings) listed in the figure.

The vacuum-tube voltmeter has a sensitivity of about 1 ma per volt. Provision is made to drive an Esterline-Angus recording meter (0 to 1 ma) and a micromax recorder (0 to 5 mv) simultaneously, and also to have an indication of the counting rate on a panel-type meter.

The safety circuit is based on a discriminator employing a 6SU7 double triode. The "Safety Set" control enables the circuit to be adjusted so that it will be triggered when the counting rate is somewhat above full-scale reading—for instance, 1.2 times full-scale reading. The other adjustment available in the trigger circuit controls its hysteresis. Thus one can adjust the hysteresis to make the safety circuit return to normal when the counting rate has dropped to

---

*This method of obtaining high capacitance is briefly discussed in Chap. 2, Sec. 3.8.

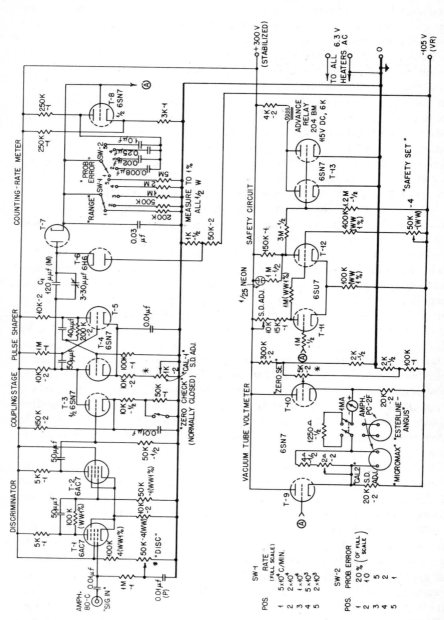

Fig. 4.22 — The Model 100 counting-rate meter.

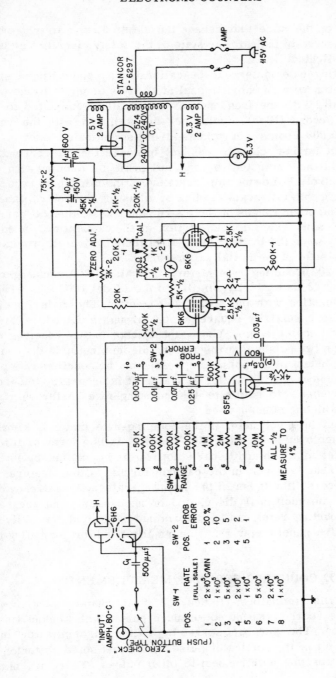

Fig. 4.23 —The Model 200 counting-rate meter.

80 per cent of the value that causes the safety circuit to trigger. A neon lamp serves to indicate the state of the safety circuit. The lamp is normally lighted.

The counting-rate meter can be calibrated by connecting a sine-wave oscillator with an output signal of 10 volts or more to the input of the circuit. With the frequency of the oscillator adjusted to 167 cycles per second (10,000 cycles per minute), and with the range switch at 10,000 counts per minute, the discriminator bias is decreased until further change does not increase the meter reading. The meter is then adjusted to read full scale by manipulating the "Cal. 1" control. Following this adjustment, the micromax recorder can be brought into full-scale reading by adjusting the control labeled "Cal. 2." The other ranges of the instrument should then be correct to a few per cent. The variable portion of the capacitor C_1 need be adjusted only when the instrument is first tested, since it provides a coarse adjustment of the initial calibration.

(c) Model 200 Counting-rate Meter. The Model 200 counting-rate meter, Fig. 4.23, is basically similar to the Model 100. It is always used in conjunction with the Model 200 counter, shown in Fig. 4.5, which supplies essentially square pulses through a cathode follower from the first scaler stage. The counting-rate meter receives one pulse for each two pulses that trigger the discriminator in the counter. Since the height of the pulses impressed on the counting-rate meter varies somewhat from scaler to scaler, it is necessary for accurate measurements to calibrate the counting-rate meter with the scaler with which it is being used.

The vacuum-tube voltmeter in the counting-rate meter is similar to the one employed in the RCA Volt Ohmyst. It is a form of difference amplifier in which additional stabilization is obtained by use of negative-current feedback in the cathode circuit. Other features of the circuit are so like those of the counting-rate meter already described that no additional discussion is necessary. The accuracy with which counting rates can be determined is limited primarily by the inexpensive panel meter that is normally used for indicating the counting rate.

3. COUNTERS FOR TIME MEASUREMENTS

3.1 Time Discriminators. In Sec. 2.2 of this chapter mention was made of pulse sources that do not produce pulses with random times of occurrence. The purpose served by a time discriminator in a counting circuit is the sorting of pulses that meet some criterion in their relation in time with respect to other pulses. There are many varieties of experiments that require some sort of time discrimination, and since the electronic circuits required may be very different according to the nature of the experiment at hand, some attempt will be made to classify the types of problems encountered and to indicate the general methods that can be applied to their solution. Pulses that are to be sorted for time distribution must usually meet certain amplitude requirements. It will therefore be assumed that the time discriminator receives, from an amplitude discriminator, pulses that are all of equal magnitude.

(a) Simple Time Discriminators. Probably the simplest type of time discriminator is the so-called "coincidence circuit."* This discriminator is used to count only those pulses from one source that occur "simultaneously" with pulses from another source. Since the probability of two events (even when connected) occurring within a small time Δt† goes to zero as Δt goes to zero, a simple time discriminator, more precisely, is a circuit that records the occurrence of a pulse from one source falling within some finite time Δt of a pulse from a second source. The value of Δt is known as the resolving time of the time discriminator. Resolving times as short as 10^{-7} sec can be achieved with present techniques.

There are two types of simple time-discriminator circuits of particular interest. In a symmetric discriminator, a count is obtained if a pulse from a source B occurs within a time $\pm \Delta t$ of a pulse from a source A. In an asymmetric discriminator, a count is obtained only when a pulse from source B occurs within a time interval $+\Delta t$ after a pulse from source A. Figure 4.24 illustrates the usual principle of operation of these simple time discriminators. Voltage is plotted vertically against a horizontal time scale. The waveforms indicated are idealized but can be approached in practice.

In Fig. 4.24(a) waveforms are shown that are typical of an asymmetric discriminator. Lines A and B represent the output signal from the sources A and B, respectively. Each pulse from source A initiates in the circuit a rectangular pulse of duration Δt, represented in line A-1. Pulses from source B produce infinitely sharp pulses, represented in line B-1. When the voltages indicated by lines A-1 and B-1 are applied with proper polarity to a coincidence circuit of the type

---

*In this book we have limited the use of the term "coincidence circuit" to those parts of time-discriminator circuits that satisfy the definition given in Chap. 2, Sec. 5.2.

† By the time between two pulses of finite duration we mean the time between corresponding points on the pulses.

described in Sec. 5.2(c) of Chap. 2, the output signal will have the form indicated by line C. It is apparent that the requirements of an asymmetric time discriminator of resolving time Δt have been met.

Figure 4.24(b) indicates the waveforms associated with a symmetric time discriminator of resolving time ±Δt. In this case input pulses from both sources produce rectangular pulses, indicated in lines A-1 and B-1. When the rectangular pulses are applied to a coincidence

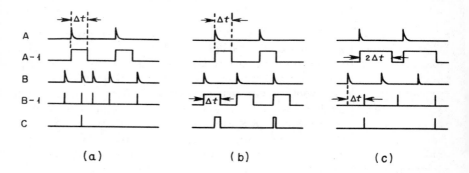

(a)   (b)   (c)

Fig. 4.24—Time-discriminator waveforms.

circuit, the output signal shown in line C is obtained. An alternate scheme for a symmetric discriminator is illustrated in Fig. 4.24(c). Here the pulses from source A produce rectangular pulses of length 2Δt, indicated in line A-1, and the pulses from source B produce sharp pulses delayed by a time Δt, indicated in line B-1. It is evident that the results achieved by the two schemes are the same, provided the ideal waveforms of the figure can be obtained. Since it is not always possible to make the width of the sharp pulses much less than Δt, the scheme represented by (b) is sometimes to be preferred. This scheme can also be used for an asymmetric discriminator if a delay of Δt is introduced in one of the channels. Evidently a number of combinations of the various schemes are possible.

(b) Delay Discriminators. Time discriminators can be made which record only those pulses that occur in a time greater than t and less than t + Δt from another pulse. Provided that t is greater than zero, the two pulses may come either from the same source or from different sources. It is usual to make delay discriminators asymmetric.

Delay discriminators play an important part in modern modulation techniques applied to positive ion accelerators. In this type of application a pulse from a periodic oscillator is applied simultaneously to a modulator of the ion beam and to a delay discriminator. Pulses

from a detector that are delayed because of nuclear processes, diffusion times, or times of flight are also applied to the discriminator,
and they are sorted according to their delay times. It is often convenient to use multichannel delay discriminators, usually with equal
channel widths, Δt_i, arranged such that $t_i + \Delta t_i = t_{i+1}$.

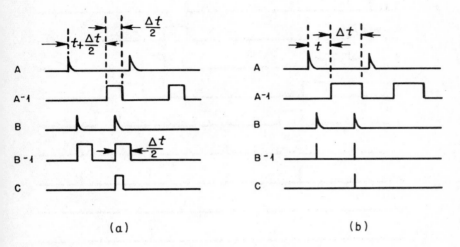

(a)   (b)

Fig. 4.25—Delay-discriminator waveforms.

The idealized waveforms in Fig. 4.25 represent the signals that are
produced in typical delay discriminators performing the same function by two different methods. The input pulses from sources A and B
are represented on lines A and B, respectively. Pulses derived from
these are shown on lines A-1 and B-1. When these two sets of pulses
are applied to a coincidence circuit, the output pulses indicated in
line C are obtained. It is evident for both cases that, when the derived
pulses have the widths and delays indicated, the discriminator will
count each pulse from source B occurring between t and $t + \Delta t$ after
a pulse from source A.

When it is important to take data rapidly, several single-channel
discriminators can be used simultaneously, each with a different
delay time. A multichannel delay discriminator is essentially such
an instrument from an operational point of view, but it may be struc-
turally quite different. Figure 4.26 illustrates the waveforms that
might appear in a four-channel delay discriminator with adjacent
channels of width Δt. Lines A and B represent the input from two
sources. Lines A-1 to A-4 represent waveforms that are produced
with delays of 0, Δt, $2\Delta t$, and $3\Delta t$ from the pulses of line A. Line B-1

represents the sharp pulses derived from pulses of line B. When the signals of lines B-1 and A-1 are applied to a coincidence circuit, the output signal indicated in line C-1 is obtained. Similarly, line C-2 is the output of a coincidence circuit that has inputs B-1 and A-2, C-3

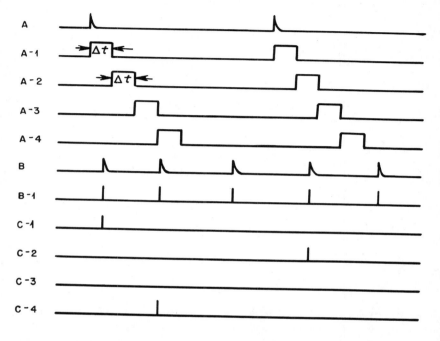

Fig. 4.26—Waveforms of a multichannel delay discriminator.

is the coincidence output of B-1 and A-3, etc. In practice the pulses in line B-1 have a finite width and therefore will count in two channels when they occur right at the boundary between the channels. This is not necessarily disadvantageous, since it means simply that the effective widths of the channels are somewhat larger than they would otherwise be.

The principle of operation of a second type of delay discriminator is illustrated by the waveforms in Fig. 4.27. Here signals are produced whose amplitude is proportional to the time separation between two pulses. These signals are then counted according to their amplitudes.

In Fig. 4.27(a) the waveforms of lines A and B represent input signals from two sources. Each pulse from source A initiates a linearly

increasing voltage signal. The succeeding pulse from source B terminates this signal. It is evident that the amplitude of the saw-tooth
signal so generated will be proportional to the time separation between the two pulses. If it is desired to use this method to measure

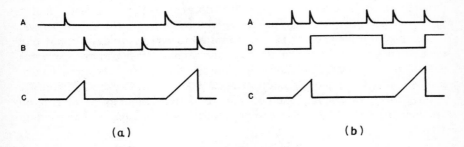

(a)   (b)

Fig. 4.27—Delay-discriminator waveforms.

the time separation between pulses from the same source, a system
of the type indicated in Fig. 4.27(b) can be employed. One pulse initiates the saw-tooth wave and the next terminates it. Since most saw-
tooth-generating circuits require a recovery time before initial conditions are restored, it is usual to provide an interval, represented
by the gate signal in line D, during which time the operation of the
circuit is impossible. The complete discriminator includes not only
the saw-tooth generator but also an amplitude discriminator that can
be either of the simple or of the multichannel variety.

(c) Time-distribution Discriminators. The circuits discussed so
far record a pulse from one source when it happens to occur in a
short time interval Δt related in time to the occurrence of another
pulse, either from the same or from a different source. On account
of the small probability of getting a count in any given interval Δt,
the average counting rates involved are low. It is extremely rare that
more than one count will occur in any given time interval. If it is
desired to measure the probability of obtaining n pulses in a much
longer time interval Δt, possibly delayed with respect to a given
pulse, the scheme indicated in Fig. 4.25(b) can be used. In this case
the output pulses from the coincidence circuit must be counted and
recorded after each operation of the circuit. Alternatively a multichannel counter can be used which records on separate counters the
occurrence of intervals possessing one count, two counts, etc. Similar
data can also be taken by recording the time required for n pulses to
be produced from a source. This method has not been used.

(d) Electronic Time Scales. An electronic time scale is essential to the operation of all time discriminators, since it is necessary for determining the widths and delays of the waveforms produced in the discriminator. Although an LC oscillator has a greater stability than an RC oscillator of comparable complexity, an LC circuit element cannot always be used conveniently to determine the time scale, and it is often found necessary to use RC circuit elements for this purpose.

If one of the sources of pulses supplied to a time discriminator can be controlled, as in modulation experiments, then either a crystal oscillator or an LC oscillator is suitable for setting the time scale. In case a high-frequency oscillation is used as the source of timing, pulses for establishing each channel of a time discriminator can be derived from the high-frequency oscillations by means of a frequency divider.

When a time discriminator must operate on random pulses, a pulsed LC oscillator of the type discussed in Chap. 2, Sec. 3.6, constitutes a possible timing means, but one that is rarely used. If short time scales are involved, delay lines can give good stability. For longer time scales, RC circuits are customarily used in circuit elements such as univibrators, blocking oscillators, and saw-tooth generators to produce the required waveforms and delays. Typical circuits illustrating the application of the principles that have been outlined are given in the following section. Some of the circuits in Chap. 5 have been found useful in time-discriminator applications.

3.2 Several Time-discriminator Circuits. In the foregoing section a general discussion has been given outlining the methods that can be used to study the time distribution of pulses arising in various experiments in nuclear physics. The information sought is usually peculiar to the experiment at hand and requires special circuits that cannot be considered as standard laboratory equipment. The circuits now to be described are for the most part of this sort. On account of limitation in space, it is impossible to describe the experiments for which each time discriminator has been specifically designed. Only sufficient information will be given for an understanding of the purpose served by each circuit.

(a) A Coincidence Gate. The circuit to be described here has been designed for use with an ionization chamber that consists of three adjacent but electrically isolated compartments. A separate Model 100 amplifier (see Chap. 3, Sec. 7) is connected to a collecting electrode in each of the three compartments. Ionizing particles entering the triple ion chamber will produce output pulses from one or more of the three amplifiers. Occasional particles will traverse all three chambers, and so will produce three output pulses simultaneously. It is desired to measure the amplitude of the pulse from the middle chamber, II, when pulses above a certain size come simultaneously from the two outer chambers, I and III. A further condition of measurement is that, if the pulse from chamber III is too large, no measurement shall be made.

The coincidence gate circuit designed to accomplish this measurement is given in Fig. 4.28. Pulses from the three Model 100 amplifiers are fed into the three input connectors. The Model 100 delay-line pulse shaper, shown in Fig. 3.19, is used with each amplifier to secure pulses of suitable shape. In addition, a Sickles No. 12799A delay line is installed between the preamplifier and main amplifier for chamber II to provide a delay of 5 μsec for the pulses originating in this chamber. The form of the various pulses that may exist in the circuit is indicated in the circuit diagram.

An examination of the circuit and of the accompanying waveforms should reveal the manner in which the circuit operates. For instance, a pulse from amplifier I, having a sufficient amplitude, will trigger discriminator I. The positive pulse produced at the plate of T-2 initially fails to reach the coincidence stage T-7 by virtue of the diode clamp in the circuit. As soon as the pulse ends, however, one grid of T-7 is driven negative. The other two discriminators, IIIa and IIIb, are coupled to the coincidence circuit in an analogous fashion. If pulses occur simultaneously in amplifiers I and III, and if they are of a magnitude sufficient to trigger the discriminators I and IIIa but not IIIb, then a positive coincidence pulse is obtained. Any other combination of input pulses fails to call forth a coincidence pulse.

The coincidence pulse from T-7 is used to trigger a univibrator (see Chap. 2, Sec. 4.2) which furnishes an 8-μsec gating pulse to the gating circuit (see Chap. 2, Secs. 5.1 and 5.2) comprising tubes T-12 and T-13. The input "In-II" must be direct-coupled to the cathode-follower output stage of amplifier II, from which a pulse emerges at a time delayed a few microseconds from the start of the 8-μsec gating pulse. The height of the pedestal on which the gated output pulse rests can be chosen by adjusting the grid potential of the right-hand section of T-13. By careful adjustment, the pedestal can be almost removed without cutting off the lower part of the pulse from amplifier II. To aid in making this adjustment, a positive trigger pulse is provided from the univibrator at the start of the gating pulse, to enable the sweep of a cathode-ray oscillograph to be started at this time. The oscillograph can be used to examine the waveform of the output pulse.

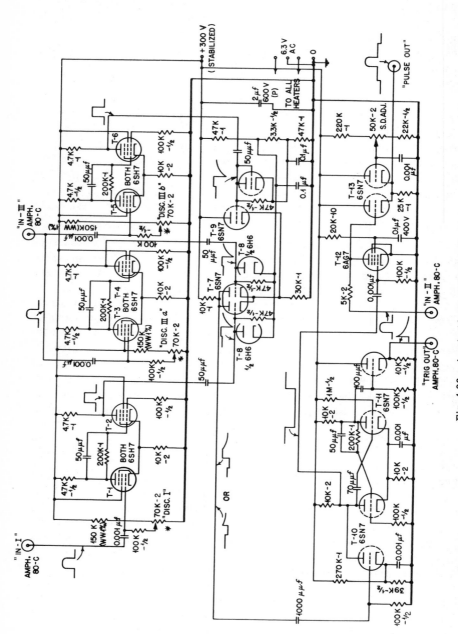

Fig. 4.28 — A coincidence-gate circuit.

It is interesting to note that the three discriminators, together with the coincidence circuit, form the basis of a single-channel differential discriminator that is simpler than the one described in Sec. 2.5 of this chapter. Two cathode followers should be added to these components to couple out positive pulses from discriminator I and from the coincidence circuit. These pulses are then impressed on two ordinary counters, which will record the total count and the differential count, respectively. A differential discriminator of this sort is suitable for use only with delay-line-shaped pulses having a rise time in the range 0.5 to 1 μsec.

(b) A General-purpose Time Discriminator. In Fig. 4.29 is shown the circuit of a time discriminator that can be used either as a simple symmetric time discriminator (or coincidence circuit) based on the principle of operation illustrated in Fig. 4.24(b) or as a delay discriminator based on the principle of operation illustrated in Fig. 4.25(a). The resolving time of the circuit can be selected by the triple-ganged switch SW-1 to be 1, 2, 4, or 5.1 μsec, corresponding to positions 1, 2, 3, or 4 of the switch. The delay in the circuit can be varied continuously from about 1 to 300 μsec by the potentiometer labeled "Delay" (Fig. 4.29).

The circuit contains two conventional amplitude discriminators, each of which triggers a biased blocking oscillator. When the switch SW-2 is in position 1, negative pulses from the blocking oscillators are impressed on the two grids of T-4, which constitutes a coincidence stage. When SW-2 is in position 2, a trigger delay circuit is inserted in channel II, in order that a variable delay shall occur between the pulse entering this channel and the pulse appearing at the grid of the right-hand section of T-4. The duration of the blocking-oscillator pulses impressed on the coincidence stage can be varied by changing the grid capacitors in the three blocking oscillators. The width of these pulses determines the resolving time of the circuit.

Three output connections are provided in the circuit to make it possible to obtain the count in each channel as well as the coincidence count. The pulses that appear at the output connections are negative and have an amplitude of 50 volts or more. Ordinarily they will be coupled to a scaler circuit through an inverting stage, and then through a biased coupling stage such as used in the Model 200 counter shown in Fig. 4.5.

The mode of operation of the delay circuit has already been described in connection with the single-channel differential discriminator, in Sec. 2.5(a) of this chapter. This particular delay circuit has been used because it requires fewer tubes than other suitable circuits

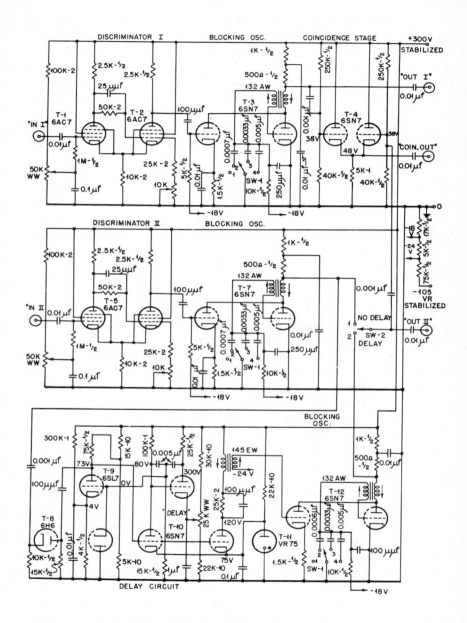

Fig. 4.29 — A general-purpose time discriminator.

that have the necessary stability of operation. A simple delay circuit based on a univibrator is not very satisfactory for two reasons: it is difficult to reduce the delay much below 5 μsec, and the delay time it provides is not very stable.

The time discriminator under discussion has been used in a particular experiment with two self-quenching Geiger-Mueller tubes. Since the output pulse from these tubes is negative and of only a few volts amplitude, it is necessary to incorporate one stage of gain between each Geiger-Mueller tube and the input discriminator.

(c) A Ten-channel Delay Discriminator. The development of the technique of modulating a positive ion accelerator has given rise to an important method of obtaining information regarding nuclear processes that occur delayed in time with respect to the pulses of radiation produced at the target of the accelerator. If the electrical detector used in the setup employs electron collection, it is possible to obtain from it pulses that have a rise time of a few tenths of a microsecond. Hence it is not unreasonable to employ a multichannel delay discriminator in which the channel widths are as narrow as 0.5 μsec. It would be pointless to attempt to use a delay discriminator of this sort if the pulses from the electrical detector had a rise time of many microseconds, even though the pulses could be sharpened later in the circuit. The difficulty in using slow collection lies in the uncertainty in time between the entry of an ionizing particle into the electrical detector and the later occurrence of a very narrow pulse derived from the relatively slow electrical pulse supplied by the detector.

The ten-channel delay discriminator to be described here has been used primarily with a Cockroft-Walton accelerator, but it is suitable for use with any accelerator capable of giving bursts of radiation lasting a fraction of 1 μsec. Since the design of the modulator for the ion beam of an accelerator will depend on the particular accelerator involved, no discussion will be made here of circuits of this type.* In the circuits to be described, provision is made for supplying a narrow blocking-oscillator pulse to the beam modulator, which, in the case of the Cockroft-Walton machine, serves to deflect the beam onto the target during a brief interval of time, accurately located with respect to the triggering pulse supplied to the modulator.

---

*For a discussion of certain methods for modulating accelerators, see Rossi and Staub, "Ionization Chambers and Counters," Chap. 6, National Nuclear Energy Series, Division V, Vol. 2.

As an aid in understanding the role played by various circuits involved in the complete discriminator, let us consider the block diagram shown in Fig. 4.30, which shows the essential parts of the discriminator.

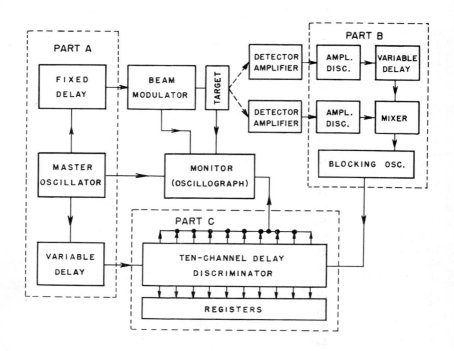

Fig. 4.30 — Block diagram of a delay analyzer.

The master oscillator is a free-running blocking oscillator, which supplies narrow positive pulses through delay circuits to the beam modulator and to the delay discriminator. An undelayed pulse is furnished the monitor for starting the sweep of a cathode-ray oscillograph each time a timing pulse occurs. It is possible to observe on the oscillograph the waveform and the relative timing of the beam-modulating signal and of the target current, as well as the relative timing of the various channels of the delay discriminator. The monitor is an essential part of the setup. Without it the operation of the equipment would be well-nigh impossible.

Radiation from the target (slow and fast neutrons) is intercepted both by a slow-neutron detector and by a fast-neutron detector. The output signals from the detectors are amplified by fast pulse ampli-fiers* and impressed on two conventional amplitude discriminators. The output pulses from the discriminator used with the slow-neutron detector are delayed and mixed with the pulses from the other dis-criminator, which occur only while the beam is on the target. All pulses finally appear as narrow blocking-oscillator pulses. By ad-justing the various delays in the setup, it is possible to have the pulses from the fast-neutron detector fall in the first few channels of the time discriminator, whereas the pulses from the slow-neutron detector occupy the later channels. By this means a control is af-forded for evaluating the significance of the experimental data ob-tained.

The delay discriminator itself consists of a sequence of gating tubes (type 6L7), each tube in turn being sensitive for 0.5 μsec fol-lowing the reception of a trigger pulse from the master oscillator through the variable delay circuit. The pulses that originate in the detectors are supplied to all gating tubes. If a pulse happens to occur when a particular gating tube is sensitive, an output pulse from the gating tube passes to a univibrator that serves to drive a register. Since the probability of obtaining more than one count in any one channel during the resolving time of the register is extremely small, no scaling circuits are required. The portions of the complete circuit designated by parts A, B, and C in Fig. 4.30 will now be discussed in turn.

The circuit diagram of part A is given in Fig. 4.31. The master blocking oscillator has a frequency that can be controlled in the range 50 to 150 kilocycles per second. The bias setting of the discriminator used between the master oscillator and the biased blocking oscillator that supplies pulses to the beam modulator affords a fine adjustment for the relative timing of the pulses delivered to the modulator and to the delay discriminator. A smooth variation in timing of about 0.2 μsec is possible. Since the taps on the lumped-parameter delay line are separated 0.2 μsec in time, a total range of about 2 μsec can be covered continuously in the relative timing of the two output pulses. It is important to be able to control the timing in this way, since it enables one to make the pulses of radiation occur just as the first channel of the delay discriminator becomes sensitive. After securing a series of points on the curve of counting rate against delay, the time at which the pulses of radiation occur can then be moved into

* The Model 50 pulse amplifier, described in Chap. 3, Sec. 7, has been used for this application.

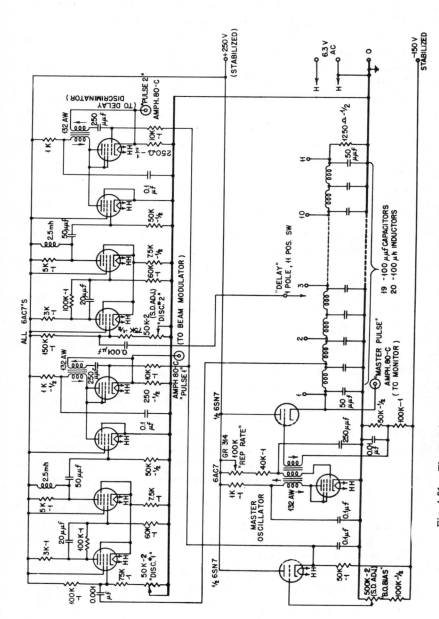

Fig. 4.31—The master oscillator and delay circuits of a ten-channel delay analyzer (see Fig. 4.30, part A).

the center of the first channel. A second series of points will then fall midway in time between points of the first set, affording a practical means of interpolating the data, i.e., of obtaining twice as many points on the experimental curve.

The use of blocking oscillators and of fast discriminators to generate the pulses that control the operation of the entire system results in an exceptionally stable time relationship between the pulses. The amount of "jitter" between the pulses is negligible for all practical purposes. The output blocking-oscillator pulses are about 75 volts high and roughly triangular in shape, with a base 0.2 μsec wide.

The circuit diagram for part B is shown in Fig. 4.32. The two amplitude discriminators are of the type discussed in Sec. 2.1 of this chapter. Each discriminator is coupled to a cathode follower, which is direct-coupled to the grid of a stage that serves both to deliver a trigger to the plate of the biased blocking oscillator, and to furnish a steady positive bias to its cathode. The tapped delay line in the cathode circuit of one of the cathode followers affords a means of introducing a maximum delay of 2 μsec, in 0.2-μsec steps, into one channel. Evidently the blocking oscillator is equally well triggered by a pulse in either channel, so that its output signal contains pulses from both detectors. The recovery time of the blocking oscillator is less than the period of operation of the system (>7 μsec). On account of the low intensity of the radiation, there is a very small probability that counts will be recorded in successive bursts of radiation.

The most important part of the ten-channel delay analyzer is part C, the delay discriminator, the circuit of which is shown in Fig. 4.33. The portion of the circuit included within the broken lines constitutes one of ten channels. The method by which succeeding channels are connected to one another is indicated in the drawing.

Tube T-2 and associated components constitute a biased blocking oscillator that is triggered through tube T-1 by timing pulses coming from the master oscillator circuit (Fig. 4.31). To obtain very narrow pulses (total duration 0.1 μsec), turns have been removed from a 132 AW transformer, leaving two windings of 16 turns each. The additional two-turn coil indicated in the figure is used in the monitoring circuit shown in Fig. 4.34. The two turns are simply wrapped around the outside of the main windings. Positive output pulses are obtained across the 250-ohm cathode resistor of T-2, and are impressed on the first channel of the delay discriminator at point A.

The portion of the circuit comprising tubes T-7 and T-8 serves a similar purpose for pulses coming from the electrical detectors, by way of the discriminator-mixer circuit (Fig. 4.31). The positive output pulses from the blocking oscillator are developed across the 50-ohm cathode resistor of T-8, and are supplied to the grid of T-9

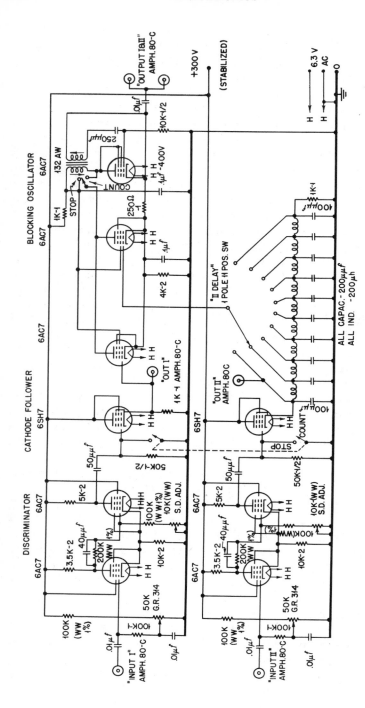

Fig. 4.32 — The amplitude discriminator and delay circuits of a ten-channel delay analyzer (see Fig. 4.30, part B).

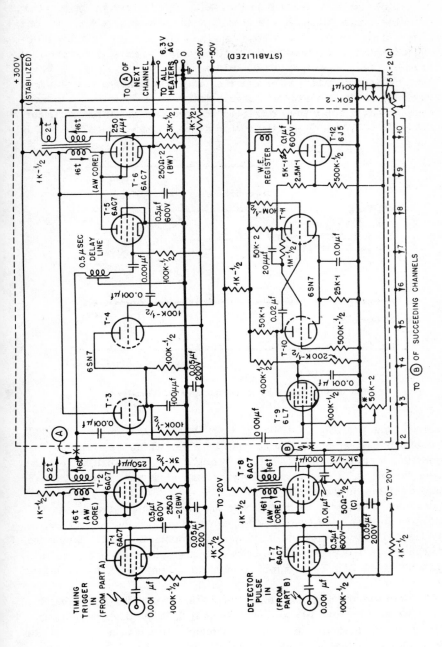

Fig. 4.33—The delay discriminator of a ten-channel delay analyzer (see Fig. 4.30, part C).

in all ten channels, at point B in Fig. 4.33. The far end of the bus that distributes these pulses has a resistive termination, since the long lead is a transmission line whose length is comparable with the electrical wavelengths present in the fast signals and must be terminated to prevent the occurrence of reflections.

A blocking-oscillator pulse entering the first channel at point A is impressed on the grid of the cathode follower T-3, and also passes down a 0.5-μsec delay line to trigger another fast blocking oscillator, based on T-6. The 100-μμf capacitor in the cathode circuit of T-3 is

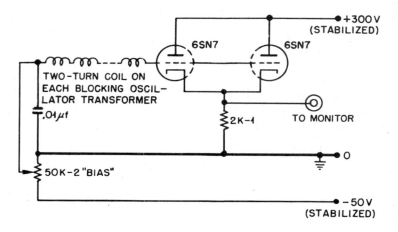

Fig. 4.34—Circuit for monitoring the delay analyzer.

charged to a potential of about 20 volts by the input pulse. One-half microsecond later it is discharged by T-4, which receives at this moment a blocking-oscillator pulse from T-6. A rectangular positive pulse lasting 0.5 μsec is therefore generated at the cathode of T-3. The rise time of the leading and trailing edges of the pulse is about 0.05 μsec. The pulse is impressed on one control grid of the 6L7 coincidence tube T-9, whose other control grid receives all pulses coming from the detectors. If a pulse happens to come during the time in which T-9 is sensitive, a trigger pulse is coupled to the univibrator, T-10 and T-11, which generates a long pulse for actuating the register.

The positive pulse generated at the cathode of T-6 not only serves to discharge the capacitor in the cathode of T-3 but also is coupled to point A of the next channel and so produces the leading edge of the gating pulse in that channel. Evidently the blocking oscillators in successive channels are triggered at 0.5-μsec intervals, and each pulse generated serves to terminate one gating pulse and to initiate another in the next channel.

The delay lines used in the circuit are made from pieces of delay cable manufactured by the General Electric Company (see Table 2.1). Since this cable possesses considerable attenuation, it is found unnecessary to employ terminating resistances at the receiving ends of the delay lines. The rise time of the pieces of cable used (about 7 in.) is less than that of the blocking oscillator pulses that pass down them. As a result there exists no appreciable cumulative scatter in the timing of succeeding channels. In preparing the delay lines, no attempt need be made to ensure that the duration (or width) of each channel is exactly the same as that of all others, since it is better to determine the effective widths of the various channels by actual measurement.

The calibration of the channel widths can be carried out by means of the double pulse generator described in Chap. 6, Sec. 4.3. The separation in time of two pulses furnished by the pulse generator is obtained by the combined use of a tapped lumped-parameter delay line and of a continuously variable delay line. The pulse generator is in reality a secondary standard, which must be initially calibrated, using a crystal oscillator as the time standard. By employing the pulse generator in the manner described in Chap. 6, Sec. 4.3, the effective width of each channel of the delay discriminator can be measured. It is evident that the existence of small gaps or overlaps between adjacent channels is not serious, provided the effective width and relative position of each channel remain constant with time. A calibration of the relative channel widths can also be made by operating the time discriminator from purely random pulses. Then the number of counts in each channel (under normal conditions) is proportional to the channel width. Since the timing in the delay discriminator is determined primarily by delay lines, it has a stability sufficient to meet any practical demand placed on it. Statistical fluctuation in the data will ordinarily give rise to the largest error in an experiment.

Now that the operation of the important parts of the complete delay analyzer has been described, it is well to consider once more the role played by the monitor. The "master pulse" from the master oscillator (part A) is used to trigger the sweep of a cathode-ray oscillograph. Since repetition rates in the range 50 to 150 kilocycles per second are normally used, there is no need to employ a high accelerating voltage for the cathode-ray tube in order to see comfortably repetitive sweeps lasting 10 μsec. The normal sweep circuit in a commercial oscillograph, however, is quite inadequate for an application of this sort, and it is necessary to employ a sweep circuit of the type described in Chap. 6, Sec. 2.1. These circuits have the property that one accurately timed sweep is produced for each trigger pulse received. If the sweep speed is adjusted to be a few microseconds per inch, then the form of pulses existing at various points in the complete delay analyzer can be displayed in a steady pattern.

To monitor the sequence of channels in the delay discriminator, pulses are obtained from each blocking-oscillator transformer by means of a special two-turn coil. All coils are connected in series, and the positive pulses induced in them are impressed on the grid of a biased cathode follower whose output can be connected to one deflecting plate of the cathode-ray oscillograph. The simple circuit used for this purpose is shown in Fig. 4.34. Evidently the pulses that are observed mark the boundaries of the various gating pulses in the discriminator.

Perhaps the most important pulse to present on the oscillograph sweep is that of the target current. The target is connected to ground through a resistor whose value is chosen to give a time constant of a few tenths of a microsecond when considered in connection with the capacitance of the target to ground. A suitable transient amplifier is then connected to the target to enable the target-current pulse to be presented on the oscillograph. The shape of the observed waveform permits one to adjust the beam modulator properly and to see that conditions remain steady during the course of a run. It is obvious that the monitor is practically indispensable in setting the various delay controls in the complete system.

(d) A Distribution Discriminator. In certain experiments in nuclear physics it is necessary to measure a distribution of pulses in time where the time scale is reckoned in milliseconds. Let any pulse from source A, occurring at an arbitrary instant in time, serve as a temporary time origin. It is then desired to count all pulses from source B occurring in an interval of time Δt, starting at a time t_d later than the initial pulse from source A. At the end of the interval Δt another pulse from source A causes the same measurement to be repeated, and so on. The situation is that depicted in Fig. 4.25(b). For a given number of counts from source A, each of which has called forth the counting of pulses from source B in the manner specified, it is possible to determine a curve of total B counts against the delay time t_d. This curve represents the distribution in time of counts from source B relative to counts from source A. If no causal connection exists between the two sources, then the measured distribution will be uniform.

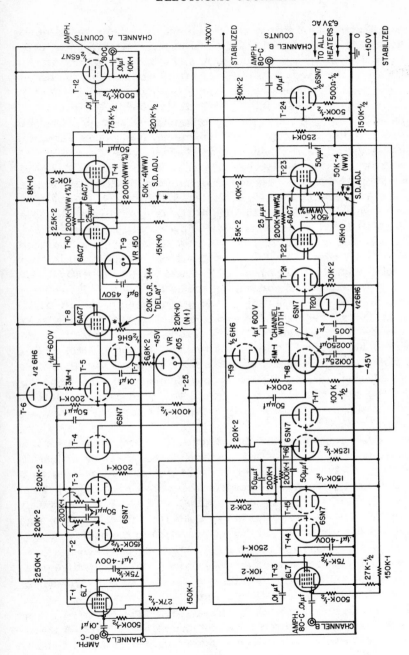

Fig. 4.35 — A distribution discriminator.

A time discriminator that is suitable for making the measurements is shown in Fig. 4.35. The circuit contains a variable trigger delay circuit based on a saw-tooth generator and a discriminator. After a known delay in the range 0 to about 15 milliseconds from the occurrence of a pulse in channel A, a gate is opened allowing pulses in channel B to be counted for 0.5, 1, or 2 milliseconds, as desired. The duration of the gate is accurately determined by another saw-tooth generator and discriminator. Until the circuit has passed through a complete cycle, all pulses occurring in channel A are ignored.

Let us now examine the detailed operation of the circuit. A 30-volt positive pulse (from an amplitude discriminator) that enters channel A triggers the flip-flop (see Chap. 2, Sec. 4.3) based on T-2 and T-3. The gating tube T-1 serves to couple the trigger to the flip-flop. When the flip-flop is in its second stable state, a negative gating signal is supplied to the grid of T-5, which is the clamp in a saw-tooth generator (see Chap. 2, Sec. 3.7). A saw-tooth signal is taken from the potentiometer in the cathode of T-8 and applied directly to the grid of the discriminator comprising tubes T-10 and T-11. After a delay determined by the setting of the potentiometer, the discriminator is triggered, resetting the flip-flop in channel A and triggering another flip-flop in channel B (T-15 and T-16). Channel A is now returned to its original state except that the second control grid of T-1 is biased off by a connection to the flip-flop in channel B. Pulses entering channel A fail to start a second sequence of measurements until the flip-flop in channel B is reset. The dead time so provided enables channel A to recover fully before it is called on to function once more.

When the flip-flop in channel B is triggered, a positive gating pulse is supplied to tube T-13, so that positive pulses entering channel B pass through T-13 and the inverter T-24 and can be counted by a standard counting circuit designed to accept positive input pulses.

The duration of the gating pulse supplied to T-13 is accurately determined by a saw-tooth delay circuit, utilizing tubes T-18 through T-23. The delay circuit is similar in operation to the one in channel A. When the discriminator (T-22 and T-23) is triggered by the saw-tooth voltage signal impressed on the grid of T-22, the positive pulse at the plate of T-23 resets the flip-flop through tube T-17, and the entire circuit is back in its original state.

Each time the discriminator in channel A is triggered, a positive output pulse is provided through the cathode follower T-12. A standard counter therefore can be used to determine the number of counts in channel A that have resulted in gating pulses supplied to channel B.

The scale provided with the potentiometer determining the delay in channel A can be calibrated to make it direct reading. It is also necessary to measure accurately the gate widths provided in channel B. If the power supply used with the circuit is highly stabilized, the timing in the circuit should remain stable to better than 1 or 2 per cent.

Chapter 5

OSCILLOGRAPHS AND ASSOCIATED EQUIPMENT

By William C. Elmore

1. INTRODUCTION

The cathode-ray oscillograph plays an indispensable part in the study of phenomena that occur in times too short to make other means of recording possible. Experience with ordinary cathode-ray tubes, such as the type 5CP11, and with available photographic emulsions and cameras indicates that it is feasible to obtain usable photographs with writing speeds of 15 or more inches per microsecond.* Unfortunately there are no commercial oscillographs available that are really suitable for the majority of research problems where fast single transients must be photographed. Nor are any of them suitable if it is desired to record or observe transients that occur randomly distributed in time, e.g., pulses from an electrical detector exposed to radiation from a radioactive source. The emphasis in the present chapter will be directed toward circuits intended primarily for use in studying single transients. With some changes, however, most of the circuits can be modified for studying signals that occur either regularly or randomly distributed in time.

At least three important types of situations are met in photographically recording or visually observing electrical transients. In the first type, an electrical signal, or trigger, is used to initiate the entire sequence of events, causing both the phenomenon under study to occur and the cathode-ray spot to sweep across the cathode-ray tube at exactly the right moment for recording or observing the electrical signal produced by some aspect of the phenomenon. In the second type, some aspect of the phenomenon itself is used to initiate the sweep at the proper moment so that transients occurring later in time

---

*By using the newly developed type 5RP11 tube with an accelerating potential of 35 kv, writing speeds in excess of 200 in./μsec can be photographed.

can be recorded. In the third type, no previous signals are available to initiate the sweep, so the signal itself must be used as a trigger. To avoid losing a record of the leading edge of the signal, the signal can be passed through a high-fidelity delay line before it reaches the deflecting plates of the cathode-ray tube.

Evidently it is necessary to have a sweep circuit that will respond whenever it receives a suitable trigger. A sweep of this type is often termed a "slave sweep." In some cases it is desirable that the system contain a locking circuit to prevent more than a single sweep from occurring. This is important if the trigger is derived from the phenomenon itself, since trigger pulses following the initial trigger may inadvertently cause additional sweeps and thereby confuse the record. Another important type of circuit is used for delaying triggers in order that the sweep may be started at the correct instant in time. Still another type of circuit is often necessary in order that time fiducials may be placed on the record, either along with the signal being recorded or at an earlier or later time, but on the same piece of photographic film. Therefore circuits must be available either to produce narrow timing pulses, which may be mixed with the signal, or to blank the oscillograph trace at regular known intervals.

This chapter describes a number of practical circuits for accomplishing the various tasks that have been mentioned. Transient amplifiers have already been discussed in Chap. 3.

2. CATHODE-RAY TUBES

The type 5CP11 cathode-ray tube appears to be the most satisfactory tube available for the photography of single transients lasting a few microseconds or longer. When an over-all accelerating potential of 6 kv is used, it is possible to obtain discernible photographic records of traces having a writing speed of 15 in./μsec. In order to achieve accurate measurements of the record with a low-power microscope, the maximum writing speed must be restricted to a few inches per microsecond, and it may be desirable to increase the accelerating potential to 8 kv. To obtain good photographs at maximum writing speed, it is necessary to use a high-quality lens, such as a coated f/1.5 lens, and to employ a fast photographic plate or film, such as Eastman 103-O Spectroscopic, Agfa Triple-S Ortho, or Agfa Fluorapid Blue. A high-energy developer is also essential.

Where the parasitic capacitance of the deflecting plates must be kept low, it is possible to use a 5JP11 cathode-ray tube, in which the deflecting-plate connections are brought out along the neck of the tube. The focus of this type of tube, however, is somewhat inferior to that of the 5CP11, and there is also a greater distortion of the record for large deflections. A 5JP11 tube appears to be definitely inferior to a 5CP11, and its use can be justified only when it is imperative to keep the capacitance of the deflecting-plate connections at a minimum.

A new type of cathode-ray tube that shows great promise is the Du Mont 5RP11. It is possible to operate this tube with an over-all accelerating potential of 35 kv (5 kv preacceleration) and to obtain usable photographs of traces having writing speeds in excess of 200 in./μsec. Because of only a limited experience with this tube, no attempt will be made to evaluate its performance, but there is no doubt that with it one can obtain records of transients too fast to be handled by the amplifiers and sweep circuits described in this book.

2.1 <u>Bias Circuits for Cathode-ray Tubes</u>.* Although sufficient information is given in tube handbooks for the design of suitable bias circuits for various cathode-ray tubes, there are a few points of design that warrant description here. A typical bias circuit for a 5CP11 tube operating at 6 kv is given in Fig. 5.1.

Voltage for the positioning controls in the circuit is obtained from any 300-volt supply used with other circuits associated with the oscillograph. The average potential of each pair of deflecting plates is evidently +150 volts, which, for best focus, should also be the approximate potential of anode 2. The potentiometer denoted by "Aux. Focus" is used to set the potential of this anode. It is always found that at some potential, not necessarily +150 volts, a best focus is obtained. When the potential differs from this value, a weak electrostatic lens of the cylindrical type exists. It can serve to make a first-order correction to a small amount of astigmatism existing elsewhere in the electron-optical system. The auxiliary-focus control is usually of the screw-driver type. It need be altered only when the cathode-ray tube is changed.

A more accurate correction for astigmatism can be made if the average potential of one pair of deflecting plates, in addition to the potential of anode 2, can be varied with respect to the other pair. A circuit for accomplishing this end is shown in Fig. 5.2. Provision for the additional auxiliary-focus control appears to be worth while when a single deflecting plate is used for a signal consisting of pulses of one sign. If the auxiliary-focus controls are adjusted to give best focus when the spot is deflected one-half its maximum excursion in the vertical direction, the spot will have reasonable focus at each end

---

*For a general reference to this subject see O. S. Puckle, "Time Bases," John Wiley & Sons, Inc., New York, 1943.

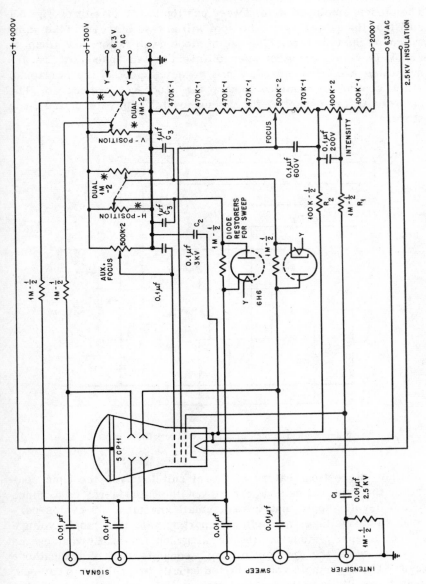

Fig. 5.1 — Bias circuit for a 5CP11 cathode-ray tube.

of its excursion. The result is superior to that obtained when the spot is in best focus at its home position.

The diodes employed in the sweep portion of the circuit of Fig. 5.1 ensure that the cathode-ray tube spot will always start from the same position on the tube face. The use of diode restoration (see Chap. 2, Sec. 5.1) is very convenient when different sweep speeds and recurrence rates are encountered, since no adjustment of the horizontal position control is required to keep the scope trace centered. The capacitors C_3 are essential for the successful operation of the diode restorers.

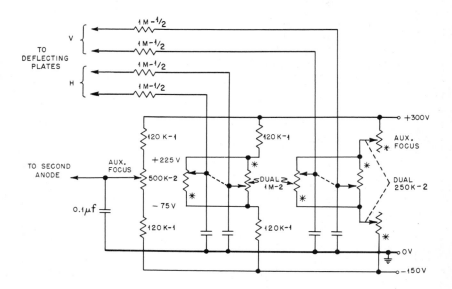

Fig. 5.2 — Method of obtaining two auxiliary-focus controls.

Another interesting feature of the circuit involves the time constants in the grid and cathode circuits of the cathode-ray tube. Since the $-2,000$-volt supply may have a small amount of 60-cycles-per-second ripple voltage, it is often important that this ripple voltage shall not intensity-modulate the oscillograph trace. By making the time constant of the grid circuit R_1C_1 equal to that of the cathode circuit R_2C_2, any ripple voltage is fed equally to grid and to cathode, and as a result there is no variation of the grid-cathode potential difference. For this result to hold, the circuit supplying the intensifier gate signal must have a low output impedance. This is usually the case, since the intensifier gate will normally come from a cath-ode-follower output stage in the sweep circuit. It is often convenient to employ diode restoration for the grid circuit in a manner similar to that shown for the sweep circuit. The heater of the diode can be connected to the supply for the heater of the cathode-ray tube.

If the circuit is to be used for slow sweeps, all the time constants in the circuit must be increased to avoid differentiating the sweep signals, the intensifier gate, and the signals applied to the vertical deflecting plates. If C_1 is changed, thus altering the time constant $R_1 C_1$, a corresponding change must be made in the time constant $R_2 C_2$. For very slow sweeps, the capacitors C_3 may have to be increased. When an r-f high-voltage supply (see Chap. 7, Sec. 6) is used, or the 60-cycles-per-second supply has negligible ripple, the resistor R_2 can be omitted.

In constructing an oscillograph, care must be taken to keep mag-netic fields varying at 60 cycles per second from the region of the cathode-ray tube. Power transformers must be mounted at some dis-tance, and they may have to be oriented in some particular direction to avoid causing a small periodic deflection of the spot. It is cus-tomary to use a magnetic shield of high-permeability material around the cathode-ray tube. To avoid a-c chassis currents, the chassis should not be used as a common connection for heaters of tubes lo-cated near the cathode-ray tube. It is good practice to run all heater leads, including those to the cathode-ray tube heater, as twisted pairs.

The focus and intensity controls should be mounted on an insulating strip, and their shafts should be extended to the front panel with a rod of insulating material.

No trouble has been experienced in operating type 5CP11 tubes at voltages somewhat in excess of the maximum ratings set by the manu-facturer. Several tubes of this type have been operated daily over long periods with 3 kv and 8 kv as pre- and post-deflection acceler-ating potentials, respectively. A greater number of oscillographs have employed accelerating potentials of 2 kv and 6 kv. These are about the maximum potentials that should be used for a type 5JP11, which has a smaller base than the 5CP11.

3. A SWEEP CIRCUIT

This section deals with a sweep circuit intended primarily for use in recording fast single transients. In Chap. 6 three additional sweep circuits are described, and these are particularly suitable for use in testing electronic equipment and in making qualitative observations of amplified pulses from electrical detectors.

It is possible to design sweep circuits in a variety of ways.* The particular circuit described here is perhaps more elaborate than necessary for some applications. No attempt has been made to economize on tubes or parts, as would have to be done if the circuit were to be part of a portable oscillograph. Before describing the circuit, let us consider several properties that are desirable in a sweep circuit of this sort.

A 5CP11 cathode-ray tube having an over-all accelerating potential of 6 kv (2 kv preacceleration) has a deflection factor of about 100 volts per inch. Hence the sweep circuit must be capable of supplying a push-pull linearly increasing deflecting voltage of about 500 volts maximum, in order to deflect the spot all the way across the face of the cathode-ray tube. Although the focus of the tube is usually good only over the middle 3 in. of the trace, it is often convenient to have the trace as long as one tube diameter.

On account of difficulties in photography, a reasonable upper limit to the speed of a sweep is 0.5 μsec/in.† For most applications it is desirable to have a series of definite sweep speeds. The steps in speed can be so chosen that any particular transient will just nicely fit a particular sweep speed. Usually the sweep speeds will form a geometric series. Except for very accurate measurements, each sweep speed can be calibrated once and for all if important circuit voltages are stabilized.

The sweep should start with a delay of only 0.1 or 0.2 μsec after it has received a trigger pulse. Not only must the deflecting signals get under way, but the intensifier-gate signal must rise perhaps +60 volts during the period of delay. Evidently parasitic circuit capacitances must be kept at a minimum to avoid the necessity for drawing excessive currents through the output stages of the sweep circuit. If the sweep circuit is to be suitable for a variety of applications, not too stringent requirements must be placed on the nature of the input-trigger pulse. For this reason the Schmitt trigger circuit (or voltage discriminator) described in Chap. 2, Sec. 4.3(c) makes a convenient input circuit element. The sweep can then be triggered by a positive signal having any sort of waveform, provided its amplitude is greater than a minimum value of a few volts. The discriminator supplies a standard signal to trigger the sweep-generating portion of the circuit, which results in uniformity of performance.

---

*An excellent discussion of sweep circuits is found in O. S. Puckle, op. cit.

†It is found convenient always to express the rate at which the spot traverses the tube in the horizontal direction in so many microseconds or milliseconds per inch. Strictly speaking, this quantity should be termed the "slowness," not the "speed," of the sweep.

The recovery time of the sweep circuit need not be very short, since no demands are ever placed on the circuit for an additional sweep immediately following an earlier one. A recovery time as long as 100 μsec is not at all serious in most instances, since the sweep can then be operated at a recurrence rate of perhaps 1,000 cycles per second for the purpose of measuring sweep speeds, setting trigger delay circuits, etc., with the expectation that the system will behave in an identical manner for a single sweep.

In certain applications, spurious trigger pulses may occur following the initial trigger that starts the sweep. Since the camera shutter cannot be closed before additional sweeps have taken place, it is necessary to be able to lock the sweep so that only a single sweep is possible. The locking circuit may be placed in the sweep circuit proper, it may be a separate circuit, or it may be built into a trigger delay circuit if such a circuit is used. The locking action can last indefinitely, requiring the manual operation of a switch to reset the circuit, or it may last for only a few seconds, during which the camera shutter becomes closed. The latter system has many points in its favor. Being automatic in action, it requires no attention of the operator. Furthermore, if the sweep is inadvertently triggered during preliminary adjustments or tests, it will quickly reset itself to be ready for later operation.

The Model 300 sweep, Fig. 5.3, possesses most of the features that appear to be desirable. Tubes T-1 and T-2 constitute a discriminator circuit that enables the sweep to be started by any positive signal of at least a few volts. The amplitude must be greater than a critical value determined by the potentiometer R_1. The trigger pulse need last a minimum of only a few tenths of a microsecond for reliable triggering. The push-button switch SW-1 initiates a single sweep when it is operated, regardless of the setting of R_1. Sweeps so initiated can be used to aid in adjusting the focus and intensity controls of the cathode-ray tube. Unless diode restorers are used at grids of the intensifier circuit, the correct setting for the intensifier bias control depends on the duty ratio of the intensifier waveform.

The output signal from the discriminator is differentiated by an RC-coupling element and passes to the grid of T-3, where it triggers the flip-flop, tubes T-4 and T-5 (see Chap. 2, Sec. 4.3). The flip-flop used in the Model 300 sweep is unusual in that T-5 is a 6AG7 tube in which the cathode, the grid, and the screen electrodes are used as a triode. When the circuit is triggered, the fast positive gate developed at the plate electrode serves to brighten the trace of the cathode-ray tube. Tube T-6 constitutes a low-impedance output stage for the intensifier gate. When the flip-flop is triggered by the output pulse

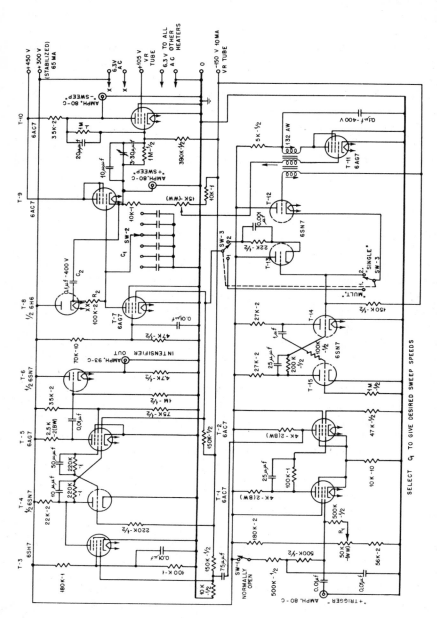

Fig. 5.3—Model 300 sweep circuit.

from the discriminator, the current through T-5 is cut off in less than 0.1 μsec—a time much shorter than the natural flip-over period of a triode flip-flop.

Following the flip-flop come the tubes T-7, T-8, and T-9, which together constitute a saw-tooth generator of the feedback type (see Chap. 2, Sec. 3.7). The grid of the clamp tube T-7 is connected to the grid of T-5, which is at ground potential when the flip-flop is in its normal state. The plate of T-7 is therefore held at perhaps +15 volts, with a current slightly less than 3 ma flowing through the resistor R_2. Since the fast triggering of the flip-flop will cut the current through the clamp in less than 0.1 μsec, the saw-tooth circuit will begin almost immediately to generate a linearly increasing voltage at the cathode of T-9. Some departure from linearity occurs at the start of the signal, since additional current must at once be supplied by the cathode follower T-9 to furnish the feedback current originally passing through the diode T-8 and to charge at a constant rate the capacitive load attached to the cathode of T-9. Trouble from this source becomes annoying only when one attempts to obtain sweep speeds considerably faster than 0.5 μsec/in.*

Tube T-10, with associated components, is a gain-of-minus-one amplifier that inverts the positive saw-tooth signal appearing at the cathode of T-9 (see Chap. 2, Sec. 3.1). The amplifier has an output impedance of approximately $2/g_m$, where g_m is the tube transconductance, and it is biased to deliver a large negative output signal.

In order that the circuit shall automatically restore itself to its original state following each operation, a fraction of the positive saw-tooth signal is taken from the potentiometer forming part of the cathode resistor of tube T-9 and is used to trigger the flip-flop back to its original state. Since it is desirable to cut off the beam current of the cathode-ray tube in a very short time at the end of each sweep, it is necessary to drive the grid of T-5 momentarily positive, so that its plate is rapidly reduced in potential. This operation is performed by the regenerative amplifier T-11 and the cathode follower T-12. Normally the currents through T-11 and T-12 are cut off by the negative biases in the circuit. During the progress of each sweep, however, the grid of T-11 has impressed on it a positively increasing saw-tooth voltage. When the tube finally reaches the conducting region, a violent

---

*Some compensation for nonlinearity at the start of the sweep is afforded by placing a low resistance of a suitable value in series with each of the capacitors C_1. The presence of this resistance causes the grid signal at T-9 to jump in potential when the current through the clamp tube is cut off, so T-9 will start more rapidly to supply the extra current required by the circuit conditions that have been pointed out.

regenerative amplification occurs and a narrow pulse of perhaps 200-volt amplitude is produced across the windings of the blocking-oscillator transformer. Provided the switch SW-3 is in the multiple-sweep position, this pulse passes to the cathode follower T-12, which drives the grid of T-5 positive, thus restoring the flip-flop to its normal state and abruptly ending the intensifier gate. The circuit then passes through a period of recovery while various charges in the circuit redistrubute themselves.

If the switch SW-3 is in the single-sweep position, the resetting pulse triggers the univibrator, tubes T-14 and T-15, and at the same time passes through the cathode follower T-13 to reset the flip-flop as before. Now, however, the sweep cannot be triggered, since the grid of T-14 is at ground potential, securely holding the grid of T-5 at ground potential through the cathode follower T-13. At the end of the flip-over period of the univibrator (about 3 sec for the circuit constants shown), the sweep circuit is again ready for operation. The univibrator, however, requires an additional recovery time of about 1 sec before it is ready to operate again with a locking period of 3 sec. If it appears desirable, the circuit of the univibrator can be altered to make it a flip-flop, in which case the circuit requires manual resetting. It is found that the locking action of the univibrator is sufficient to prevent additional sweeps, but not sufficient to prevent the brightening of a very short length of trace at its starting end. Ordinarily no trouble is caused by this defect in the locking mechanism. It could be remedied by using a negative signal from the univibrator to gate the suppressor of T-3 (replacing the 6SH7 by a 6AC7 or a 6SJ7). Possibly it would be more desirable to replace this tube by either a 6L7 or a 6AS6, and to gate the second control grid—for instance, by connecting it in parallel with the grid of T-15.

Values for the capacitors C_1 are not shown, since it is intended that they be selected to suit the requirements of a particular type of experiment. If sweep speeds slower than 100 μsec/in. are required, it is desirable to switch the resistors R_2 along with the capacitors, using values as high as several megohms for slow sweeps. It may be desirable to increase the value of C_2. Equation 32 in Chap. 2 can be used to determine a suitable value for this capacitance. For fast sweeps, the capacitors C_1 are conveniently made ceramic trimmer capacitors.

It will be noticed that output tubes T-9 and T-10 receive their plate voltage from a 450-volt supply bus, which makes it possible to develop output signals that are sufficient to deflect the spot all the way across the cathode-ray tube. This plate supply does not need to be stabilized on account of the considerable degeneracy existing in both the cathode follower and in the gain-of-minus-one amplifier.

4. TIME-MARKER GENERATORS

Time-marker generators of two types will be described in the present section. Circuits of one type are used to generate narrow pulses or pips at a known repetition rate, for mixing with another signal as it is presented on the screen of a cathode-ray tube. Mixing is usually accomplished by feeding the signal to one deflection plate of the tube and by feeding the timing marks to the opposite plate. Circuits of a second type are used to mix narrow blanking signals with the intensifier gate that comes from the sweep circuit. In both types of circuits the timing marks can be either related or unrelated in time to the trigger pulse, which bears a definite time relation to the sequence of events that are being studied. If the particular transient under study must be related in time to other events not appearing in the record, it is usually necessary to secure timing marks from a pulsed LC oscillator started by a trigger pulse that constitutes the primary time fiducial. In some cases it is necessary only to establish a local time scale for the transient presented on the cathode-ray tube. Hence a continuously running crystal oscillator can be used as the source for timing marks.

4.1 Pip Generators. The Model 3 marker generator, Fig. 5.4, is a circuit designed to accept a fast positive input trigger of 35 volts or more and to proceed to generate thereafter a series of pips spaced 2 μsec apart for a period of 100 to 200 μsec. If the input trigger constitutes the primary time fiducial of the oscillograph recording system, then the position in time of each one of the timing pips can be measured with respect to it. The circuit therefore provides an absolute time scale for calibrating cathode-ray oscillograph traces, even though the start of the trace has been intentionally delayed with respect to the primary trigger.

Let us now consider the operation of the circuit. The positive input trigger, in conjunction with the coupling stage T-1, serves to trigger the univibrator circuit comprising tubes T-2 and T-3 (see Chap. 2, Secs. 4.2 and 4.4). The trigger pulse must have a short rise time so that fast triggering of the univibrator results, and the negative gate at the plate of T-3 drops 150 volts in potential in about 0.1 μsec. The duration of the gate is determined by the time constant RC associated with the univibrator, and to a lesser extent by the static bias voltage at the grid of T-3. If the bias is too small, the univibrator may run free and multivibrate. This condition can be corrected by

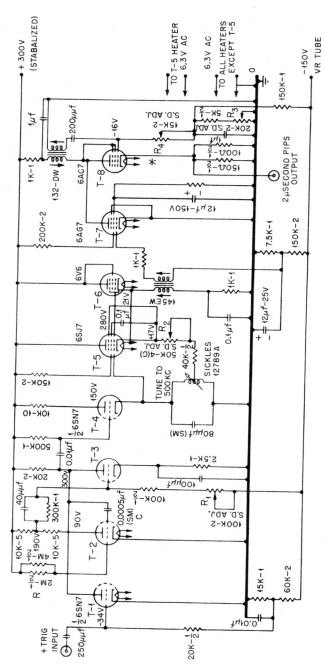

Fig. 5.4 — Model 3 marker generator.

adjusting the variable portion of R_1, which also serves to control the duration of the gate in the range 100 to 200 μsec.

Tubes T-4 and T-5 constitute a pulsed LC oscillator (see Chap. 2, Sec. 3.6). The oscillator is tuned by varying the position of the slug in the tapped inductor, Sickles No. 12789A. It is necessary to remove some turns from the inductor to reduce its inductance from 1.5 to 1 mh, in order to make it tune to a frequency of 500 kilocyles per second with the capacitance that is present. A fixed capacitance less than 80 $\mu\mu$f is undesirable, since too great a fraction of the total capacitance is then furnished by stray circuit capacitance, which may be subject to variations. The screen of the 6SJ7 oscillator tube is tied to its cathode through a capacitor, for the purpose of minimizing changes in oscillator frequency when the tube is replaced. The variable resistance in the cathode of T-5 serves to adjust the steady-state amplitude of oscillation in order to make it equal to the initial amplitude produced when the steady current through the inductance is cut off by the gating signal.

The sinusoidal signal from the oscillator passes to a cathode follower that has a blocking-oscillator transformer in its cathode circuit. The transformer is so connected that its output signal is maximum and positive when the sinusoidal signal from the oscillator is zero but is increasing negatively. The signal from the transformer serves to trigger the blocking oscillator T-8, with T-7 used as a coupling stage [see Chap. 2, Secs. 4.2(c) and 4.4(c)]. The bias resistor R_3 must be set to prevent the blocking oscillator from running free. The grid resistor R_4 must also be adjusted to prevent instability of operation. If its value is too large, the blocking oscillator will tend to be triggered at some subharmonic of 500 kc/sec. The normal output pips have an amplitude of about 75 volts and are roughly triangular in shape, with a width of 0.1 μsec at the base.

If the circuit is allowed a warm-up period of perhaps 20 min, the day-to-day variations in frequency will amount to 0.1 per cent or less, assuming normal variations in ambient temperature. Over a period of months the stability is good to 0.5 per cent. The spacing of the first few pips may not be exactly 2 μsec, owing to unavoidable transient effects, but the shift is normally less than 0.1 μsec. There is an inherent delay of about 0.3 μsec between the initial trigger and the appearance of the first pip.

A very simple marker generator, which has a stability of perhaps 5 per cent, is shown in Fig. 5.5. This unit can be built with a sweep circuit to give pips that are spaced 2, 5, and 10 μsec apart and are synchronized with the sweep. It consists of a blocking oscillator [see Chap. 2, Sec. 4.2(c)] whose repetition frequency is determined in

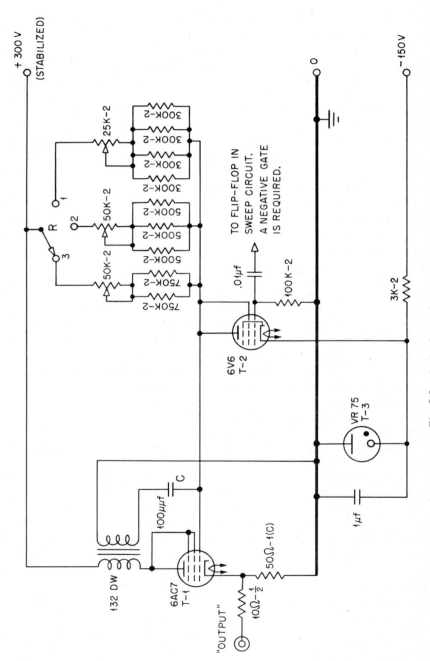

Fig. 5.5 — A simple marker generator.

part by the capacitor C and by one of the resistor combinations R. Normally the tube T-2 serves to bias off the oscillator by holding the grid of T-1 considerably below ground potential. When the grid of T-2 receives a negative gate — for instance, from the flip-flop in the sweep circuit — the grid of T-1 starts to rise exponentially toward the plate-supply potential, and blocking oscillations take place. The variable portions of the resistors R allow the frequency of oscillation to be set at definite values. Evidently the time marks generated by the circuit will always fall at the same point on the cathode-ray tube trace.

4.2 Blanking Generators. Instead of using narrow pips to establish a time scale on an oscillograph trace, it may be desirable to blank the trace at regular intervals of time so that it presents the appearance of a dashed line. This method is advantageous if the two vertical deflection plates are connected to a push-pull amplifier and if it is inconvenient or undesirable to mix timing pips with the signal being amplified. It is usually found convenient to make the blanked portions of the trace occupy about 10 per cent of the entire trace.

Designing a circuit that will produce narrow negative pulses superposed on the positive intensifier gate supplied by the sweep circuit presents some problems. The simplest solution is to mix the blanking pulses and intensifier gate at the cathode-ray tube itself. The usual intensifier gate is therefore furnished to the control grid, and narrow positive pulses are furnished to the cathode. This system unfortunately leads to trouble in the case of the 5JP11 tube, whose cathode is tied to one side of its heater. Partly for this reason the blanking marks in the two circuits to be described here are mixed with the intensifier gate.

The Model 100 blanking-marker generator, Fig. 5.6, contains both a pulsed LC oscillator, which produces blanks spaced 5 μsec apart, and a continuously running crystal oscillator, which is normally used for blanks spaced 10, 5, 2, or 1 μsec apart. The crystal oscillator, comprising the 6SN7 T-1 and T-2, employs the plug-in units described in Chap. 2, Sec. 3.6(c) and illustrated in Fig. 2.24. The univibrator and pulsed LC oscillator comprising the 6SN7's T-3 through T-8 are so similar to the circuit elements used in the Model 3 marker generator that no additional discussion need be given them here. The sinusoidal output of either oscillator can be selected by switch SW-1 for the purpose of generating narrow negative pulses superposed on the positive intensifier gate supplied by the sweep circuit.

The method of generating the blanking marks is somewhat cumbersome and could probably be simplified. The sinusoidal signal is first passed through two stages of a distorting amplifier utilizing

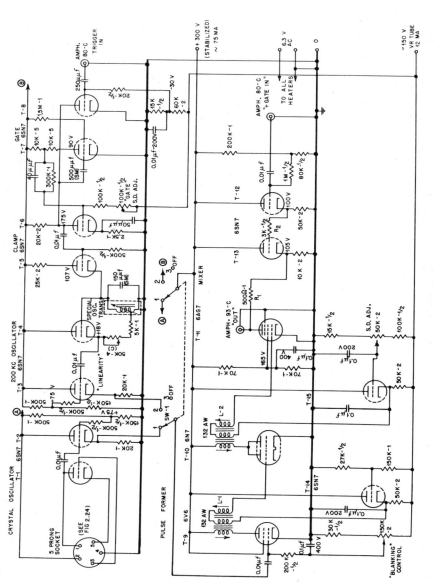

Fig. 5.6 — Model 100 blanking-marker generator.

tubes T-9 and T-10 with blocking-oscillator transformers for interstage coupling and for delivering the distorted output signal. The
operation of the amplifier may be explained as follows: Tube T-9 is
normally biased off so that it passes current only at the peak of the
input sine-wave signal. Because the transformer L-1 has no resistive
load across its secondary, the signal appearing there corresponding
to one current pulse possesses a positive and a negative peak, since
it is roughly proportional to the time derivative of the current pulse
through the primary winding. The positive peak has approximately
half the width of the current pulse through T-9. This process is repeated with tube T-10 and transformer L-2, and a still narrower positive pulse is obtained along with a negative pulse and minor oscillations of lesser amplitude. The final positive pulse is then used to
drive the grid of the tube T-11 positive.

The intensifier-gate signal passes through the two cathode followers
T-12 and T-13, and, if no signals reach the grid of T-11, it emerges
from the circuit little altered in shape, although diminished about 15
per cent in amplitude. However, each time the tube T-11 has its grid
driven positive, a negative pulse of perhaps 50-volt amplitude is superposed on the intensifier-gate signal. To limit the grid current
drawn by cathode follower T-13 when its cathode is driven negative,
the resistors R_1 and R_2 are placed in the circuit. Grid current is not
drawn by T-12. This permits the use of capacitive coupling of the input intensifier signal and explains the need for two cathode followers.
Since both tubes T-10 and T-11 draw grid current during the operation of the circuit, their negative grid bias is supplied by the cathode
followers T-14 and T-15.

The width of the blanking marks is controlled by the grid bias furnished to tube T-9. This bias must be adjusted to conform to the amplitude of the sinusoidal wave supplied by the pulsed LC oscillator or
by the particular plug-in crystal oscillator unit being used in the circuit. It is found that for frequencies in the range 100 kilocycles per
second to 1 megacycle per second the length of the blanking marks
can always be adjusted for optimum definition.

In certain applications of the blanking-marker generator, the pulsed
LC oscillator has been used in setting the delay between a pulse constituting the primary time fiducial and a second, delayed, pulse that
serves to trigger the sweep. The pulsed LC oscillator is started by
the primary trigger, and as the delay of the sweep trigger is increased from zero the blanking marks move contrary to the direction
of motion of the sweep trace. The magnitude of the delay is obtained
by counting the number of marks that pass a given point on the trace.
The generator may then be switched to a crystal oscillator while the

transient is being recorded, if this procedure appears desirable. If it is necessary to establish an absolute time scale when the crystal is used, the primary trigger can be passed through a delay line of known delay and presented, along with the blanking marks, on the sweep it initiates.

Let us now turn to the consideration of another blanking-marker generator, the Model 200, having the circuit shown in Fig. 5.7. The purpose of this circuit is somewhat similar to that of the Model 100, but it is of more recent design and possesses a number of improvements over the older circuit. The timing in this circuit is based on a 1-megacycle-per-second crystal oscillator. Circuits are provided that enable blanking marks to be placed on four independent intensifier gate signals. The blanking marks are spaced either 1 μsec or 5 μsec apart. It is possible to have both sets of blanking marks present at the same time to aid in relating traces that appear on separate oscillographs having sweeps that start with various time delays. The 1-μsec marks can be used for relative time measurements on each trace, while the 5-μsec marks enable the various records to be interrelated, provided trigger delay circuits used for starting the sweeps are accurate to 1 or 2 μsec, in order to enable the 5-μsec marks to be identified. The circuit also provides an accurately timed trigger at a repetition frequency of about 1 kilocycle per second to serve as a primary time fiducial in setting various trigger delay circuits and in selecting proper sweep speeds. Although the frequency of this trigger signal is not an accurate subharmonic of the crystal frequency, each trigger pulse occurs accurately located in time with respect to one of the 5-μsec blanking marks. The relative variation in timing is only a few hundredths of a microsecond.

Let us now consider the operation of the circuit. The oscillator tube T-1 furnishes Class C current pulses to a point on a 500-ohm lumped-parameter delay line of total delay 0.5 μsec. If a pulse occurs at the left-hand end of the line at t = 0, then, depending on the position at which the cathode of T-1 is connected to the line, i.e., at

$$n = 0, 1, \ldots , 5,$$

the same pulse appears at the right-hand end at $t = (5-2n)10^{-7}$ sec. Hence, by selecting n, the time between the two pulses can be varied over a range of 1 μsec, which is, of course, the time between successive pulses coming from the oscillator. The purpose of the delay line in the circuit is as follows: It is desirable that the position of each of the blanking marks spaced 5 μsec apart should lie midway between two marks spaced 1 μsec apart. Since there are unknown inherent

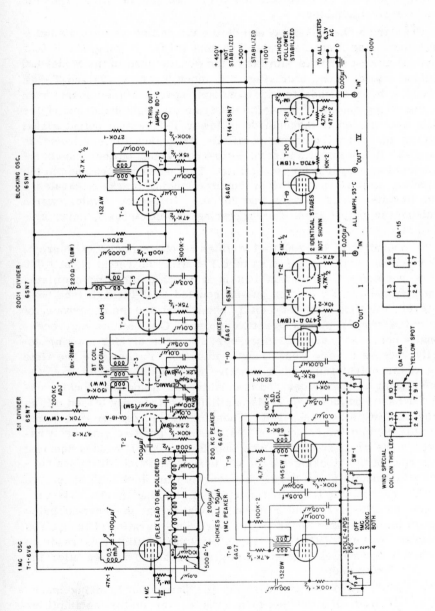

Fig. 5.7—Model 200 blanking-marker generator.

delays in various parts of the circuit, the tap on the delay line can be used to adjust the relative position of the two sets of marks when the circuit is first adjusted.

Pulses from the left-hand end of the delay line pass to a single-stage distorting amplifier, tube T-8, and thence to the grids of four identical mixing circuits similar to the circuit used in the Model 100 blanking-marker generator (Fig. 5.6, tubes T-11, T-12, and T-13). Provision is also made to add in pulses, spaced 5 μsec apart, from the distorting amplifier T-9. Pulses from the right-hand end of the delay line are fed to the cathode follower T-2, whose output signal triggers the 5-to-1 blocking-oscillator frequency divider based on tube T-3. By means of a special 8-turn coil wound on the transformer, a positive output pulse is obtained. This pulse is furnished to the distorting amplifier T-9 for producing blanking marks separated 5 μsec in time. It also passes to a 200-to-1 frequency divider, which furnishes an output pulse for triggering sweep circuits, delay circuits, etc.

The operation of the 200-to-1 divider is of considerable interest. The blocking oscillator based on tube T-5 will run free at about 1,000 cycles per second. The exact instant at which it blocking-oscillates is determined by the trigger pulses coupled to it through tube T-4. However, the time lock between its oscillation and the occurrence of one of the trigger pulses is not very good. Oscillations may occasionally occur as much as 1 μsec late, since the divider must necessarily receive a very weak trigger impulse. To improve the time lock of the output triggers, a negative gate signal is taken from the plate circuit of the divider and is used to gate a second blocking oscillator based on tube T-7. This oscillator is normally biased off, as is the coupling stage, tube T-6. When a suitable negative gate signal is impressed on the cathode of T-6, the next positive trigger it receives at its grid, somewhat less than 5 μsec later, causes the fast triggering of the blocking oscillator, tube T-7, which therefore supplies a fast output pulse having an accurate time lock with the pulses directly responsible for the production of blanking marks. The circuit of the 200-to-1 divider is so arranged that the current pulse through the tube lasts for about 10 μsec. This duration of the gate is necessary to ensure that the output blocking oscillator is ready to accept trigger pulses that ordinarily occur about 5 μsec after the divider is triggered.

The switch SW-1 serves to select the particular blanking marks that are desired. If either set is not wanted, the distorting amplifier for that set is biased off. During operation of the amplifiers, grid bias is obtained by virtue of grid-current flow. Grid bias for the four tubes T-10, T-13, T-16, and T-19 is also obtained by grid-current flow. These tubes must be biased off if no blanking marks at all are wanted.

The reliability of the circuit is excellent. The 5-to-1 frequency divider is very stable in operation. It is extremely simple to check its operation when the circuit is in use, since one can observe the 1-μsec and the 5-μsec marks simultaneously.

5. TRIGGER DELAY CIRCUITS

It is often necessary to delay the start of the sweep of an oscillograph with respect to a trigger pulse occurring earlier in time. In some instances it may be necessary to record a transient lasting only a few microseconds but occurring perhaps 100 μsec after the last signal that can serve as a reliable trigger pulse. In other instances, several oscillographs may be used to record different phases of some phenomenon. Each oscillograph may require a different speed for its sweep, and each sweep may have to be started with a trigger having a predetermined delay with respect to the primary trigger that is available for the recording system.

If sweeps as short as a few microseconds are used, it is clear that a trigger delay circuit should be reliable to a fraction of a microsecond. Since the circuit will normally be used in conjunction with a time-marker generator of the sort described in the last section, it is not imperative that the delay control of the circuit possess an absolute calibration, although this feature is certainly desirable. For flexibility in operation and for ease in setting delays, it is almost necessary to have a continuous range of delays available from a minimum delay of a fraction of a microsecond to the maximum required delay. The two delay circuits to be described here have a maximum delay in the range 100 to 200 μsec. By making minor changes in the circuits, the maximum value can be increased by a factor of perhaps 10, or even more.

The Model 50 trigger delay circuit, Fig. 5.8, requires a fast positive input trigger of 25 volts or more and gives out a delayed trigger having an amplitude in excess of 100 volts and a rise time of about 0.2 μsec. The minimum delay of the circuit is less than 1 μsec, and the maximum delay is 200 μsec. Provision is made for aligning a linear delay control so that it is direct reading from a few microseconds to 200 μsec.

The basic operation of the complete circuit can be outlined as follows: An input buffer-amplifier stage T-1 couples the input trigger to a univibrator gate circuit utilizing the 6SN7 tube, T-2 and T-3, described in Chap. 2, Sec. 4.2(b). The gate signal from the plate of

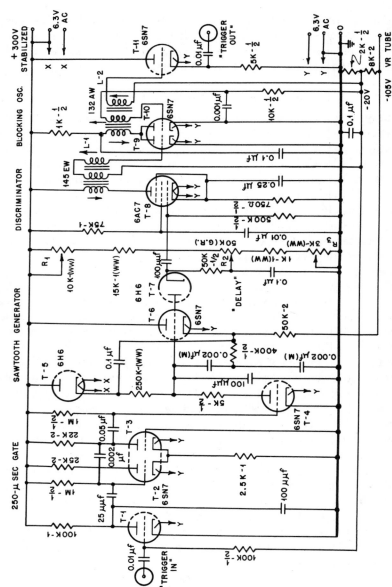

Fig. 5.8 — Model 50 trigger delay circuit.

T-3 cuts the current of the clamp T-4, which is part of a compensated saw-tooth generator (see Chap. 2, Sec. 3.7). The linearly increasing voltage signal generated at the grid of T-6 is connected to the plate of the diode T-7, which constitutes a voltage discriminator. When the potential of the diode plate reaches that of its cathode, a linearly increasing signal is impressed on the grid of the amplifier T-8, which has the blocking-oscillator transformer L-1 in its plate circuit. The signal across the secondary of L-1 is roughly proportional to the time derivative of the linearly increasing current signal through the primary, and therefore has a fairly steep wavefront. This signal is coupled through T-9 to trigger the blocking oscillator based on T-10. The positive pulse developed across the tertiary winding of the transformer L-2 is coupled through the cathode follower T-11 to serve as the delayed output trigger.

The stability of a delay circuit of this type is very good provided the power-supply voltage is well stabilized and provided stable circuit components are used in positions where a change in value could alter the delay. The delay-control potentiometer R_2 can be made direct reading by adjusting the two variable resistors R_1 and R_3. Perhaps the weakest point in the circuit involves the stability of the starting voltage of the linear saw-tooth signal generated at the grid of T-6. This is determined by the voltage at which the plate of T-4 resides when grid current is flowing through the 1-megohm resistor to the plate-supply bus. A change in this voltage may occur when T-4 is replaced.

Let us next consider the Model 100 trigger delay circuit, Fig. 5.9, which is considerably more elaborate than the delay circuit just described. The Model 100 circuit requires a trigger greater than a few volts, and it then generates one "immediate" trigger and three delayed triggers whose delays can be independently controlled in the range 0.5 μsec to perhaps 200 μsec. The output triggers are pulses which rise somewhat more that 50 volts in a few tenths of a microsecond and decay exponentially with a time constant of 10 μsec. The circuit contains a thyratron relaxation oscillator to serve as a trigger source for testing purposes.

Let us now trace the sequence of events that occur through the circuit, first assuming that the switch SW-1 is in position 1. A positive input pulse arriving at the input connection labeled "Single" triggers the discriminator comprising tubes T-1 and T-2 (see Chap. 2, Sec. 4.3). The positive output pulse from the discriminator then triggers the flip-flop based on T-4 and T-5. The flip-flop furnishes a gate to a saw-tooth generator (see Chap. 2, Sec. 3.7), whose starting voltage is definitely determined, since the clamp T-6 and the diode T-7 hold

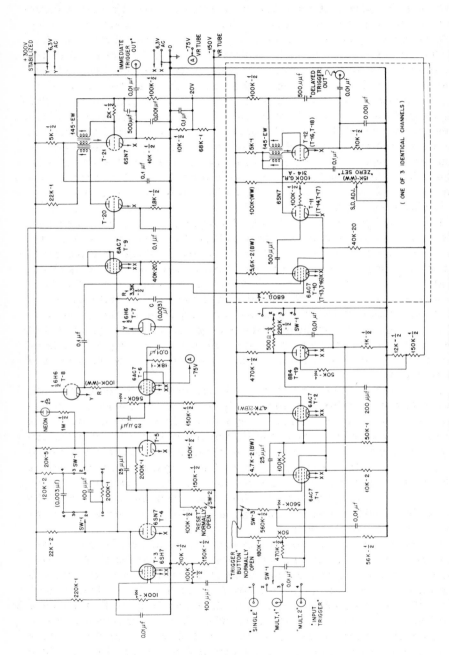

Fig. 5.9—Model 100 trigger delay circuit.

the potential of the grid of T-9 very close to ground potential. As soon as the current through the clamp tube is cut, the current of 3 ma flowing through R transfers from the clamp tube to the resistor R_1 and starts charging the capacitor C. The sudden flow of current through R_1 causes the grid of T-9 to rise about 10 volts in potential in a little more than 0.1 μsec. Since the subsequent flow of current through R_1 remains substantially constant, the resistor plays no role in the operation of the circuit other than to generate a step at the beginning of the saw-toothed waveform.

The step-and-saw-toothed waveform is now taken from the cathode of T-9 and direct-coupled to three identical discriminator channels which independently generate output trigger pulses when the voltage impressed on each of them reaches a sufficiently high value. Each channel is seen to consist of a circuit element that combines some of the features of a Schmitt trigger circuit, a univibrator, and a biased blocking oscillator. The voltage level at which the blocking oscillator is triggered is determined by a potentiometer furnishing grid bias to T-11. After all three of the discriminators have been triggered, the voltage signal from T-9 continues to increase until it is stopped by grid-current flow. The circuit is now locked against the occurrence of additional output triggers excited by later input triggers. To reset the circuit, the flip-flop must be returned to its original state by manual operation of the push-button switch SW-2. A neon lamp connected in the plate circuit of T-5 indicates when the circuit is ready for operation.

The remainder of the circuit consists of a thyratron relaxation oscillator T-19 and a circuit to supply an immediate output trigger. The thyratron oscillator runs free at about 1,000 cycles per second when the switch SW-1 is in position 2. It furnishes triggers to the discriminator for the purpose of generating the various output pulses for testing purposes. The immediate-trigger circuit consists of a blocking oscillator, T-21, which is triggered when the current through T-20 is cut off by the triggering of the flip-flop. The inherent delay between an input trigger and an immediate output trigger is about 0.3 μsec.

When the switch SW-1 is in position 2, 3, or 4, the flip-flop circuit becomes a univibrator generating a gating signal for the saw-tooth generator. The gate should be perhaps 25 per cent longer than the maximum delay of the circuit. Both the length of the gate and the slope of the saw-tooth waveform must be adjusted to have suitable values when the circuit is first tested. The values of the capacitors which in part determine these quantities and which should be altered, if necessary, are enclosed in parentheses in the diagram.

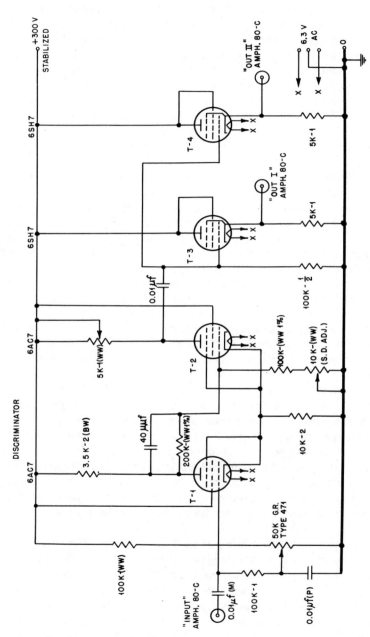

Fig. 5.10 — A trace-brightening circuit.

The recovery time of the circuit, when it is used at a repetition rate, is about 500 μsec. Hence delays obtained by the circuit are independent of the repetition rate up to nearly 2,000 cycles per second. Careful measurements show that an increase in delay of a few tenths of a microsecond can be expected when the repetition rate is increased from a few cycles per second to 1,000 cycles per second, which is the maximum recommended rate. After warming up, the circuit will maintain a given delay — for instance, 100 μsec to a few tenths of a microsecond.

6. A TRACE-BRIGHTENING CIRCUIT

A cathode-ray oscillograph and a continuously moving film camera are sometimes used to record pulses from an electrical detector exposed to radiation. This method of recording is advantageous if it is necessary to obtain an accurate pulse-height distribution from a source that is weak and subject to variations in intensity. In such a case the enhanced accuracy of the method overshadows the disadvantage that it is necessary to spend considerable time in taking data from the film.

To secure good records, the exposure of the moving film to the cathode-ray spot in the absence of a pulse must be approximately equal to the exposure realized during a pulse. Since there may be a factor of 10^4 between the writing speeds for the two types of exposure, it is necessary to brighten the trace during the occurrence of a pulse. Otherwise the film is almost completely fogged by light scattered from the bright, undeflected spot.

A simple yet very effective brightening circuit is shown in Fig. 5.10. The circuit consists of a pulse-height discriminator (see Chap. 2, Sec. 4.3) based on two 6AC7 tubes, together with two cathode-follower output stages whose inputs are connected in parallel. A positive gate signal is produced at the plate of T-2 whenever the input pulse exceeds a minimum value determined by the bias setting of the discriminator. Therefore each pulse as it occurs generates a standard intensifier gate, which lasts only for the length of time spent by the pulse above the bias setting of the discriminator. Ordinarily the bias is set to prevent the discriminator from being triggered by noise peaks. The output pulse from the second cathode follower provided in the circuit can be connected to a counter for recording the total number of pulses that are photographed. The circuit can be used with any cathode-ray oscillograph that provides access to the intensifier grid.

Chapter 6

TEST AND CALIBRATION EQUIPMENT

By William C. Elmore

1. INTRODUCTION

The circuits described in this volume require, for the most part, special equipment in order to be adequately tested. The simplest tests usually involve measuring various circuit voltages and, with the aid of an oscillograph, observing the waveforms of signals that exist at various points in the circuit. To test many of the circuits, pulses bearing a definite time relation to the start of the sweep of the oscillograph must be provided. One purpose of this chapter is to describe pulse generators and sweep circuits suitable for general laboratory testing.

A problem likely to arise concerns the calibration of circuits used for measuring the amplitude of pulses or for setting the time scale in an experiment. Where an accurate pulse-height calibration must be made, it is necessary to have available a voltage pulse generator that delivers pulses of standard shape and of known amplitude. For calibrating time scales, equipment of various types may be needed, depending on the problem at hand. Probably the most accurate time calibration can be achieved with a circular-sweep oscillograph whose timing is based on a crystal-controlled oscillator. Often it is more convenient to employ a double-pulse generator, by means of which the separation of two pulses can be accurately controlled. Several circuits for carrying out amplitude and time calibrations will be discussed in the following sections. In addition, there will be brief discussions of some commonly used procedures both for general circuit testing and for carrying out the calibrations that can be made with the equipment described.

2. LABORATORY OSCILLOGRAPHS

With the possible exception of a test meter (such as the RCA Volt Ohmyst), a good cathode-ray oscillograph is perhaps the most useful piece of test equipment in a laboratory where electronic instruments for studies in nuclear physics are being designed, tested, and serviced. But for the majority of applications that are of interest, none of the oscillographs that were commercially available in 1946 met the requirements for a suitable instrument of this type. The disadvantage of the conventional oscillograph, of course, lies in the sort of sweep circuit that is used—one based on a thyratron relaxation oscillator. Although a thyratron sweep circuit may be suitable for examining the waveform of a periodic phenomenon such as a sine wave, it is of little help in examining pulses which may last a few microseconds and which may occur with a frequency of a few hundred to a few thousand or more per second.

An oscillograph for general laboratory use evidently should be based on circuits of the type described in Chap. 5. In particular, the oscillograph should have a slave sweep with a series of definite sweep speeds, so that one knows at all times the time scale of the waveform under observation. Also it should accept either positive or negative trigger signals of arbitrary waveform for the purpose of initiating the sweep. To meet the need for a suitable oscillograph, it has been customary to use a commercial instrument and to supplement it with a so-called laboratory sweep circuit. This improvisation may eventually become unnecessary with the advent of adequate oscillographs on the market.

The commercial oscillographs that have proved to be the most generally useful are Models 208 and 241 manufactured by Du Mont. These instruments, when supplemented by an external sweep circuit, are suitable for the majority of tests. It will be found, however, that very little use is ever made of the amplifiers in a conventional oscillograph or of the thyratron sweep circuit. This is due to the fact that the signal levels encountered in trigger circuits and at the output of pulse amplifiers are so high that it is best to use direct or capacitive coupling to one deflecting plate of the cathode-ray tube. For the sake of economy it would appear desirable to construct an oscillograph incorporating only the important bias controls, together with one of the sweep circuits about to be described.

When it is desired to use a Du Mont Model 208 oscillograph for general laboratory testing, it is convenient to bring connections from the deflecting plates and from the amplifier, which are at the rear of the instrument, to a panel located above the front of the instrument. In addition, it is necessary to make an internal connection to the intensifier grid of the cathode-ray tube. The customary method of making these modifications is indicated in Fig. 6.1. An examination of the connections shows that the oscillograph can be operated normally by connecting certain pairs of the pin jacks together, or by either capacitive or direct connection to any of the four deflecting plates. When the capacitive connection is used, the positioning controls are made operative by connecting the proper pairs of pin jacks together.

In the case of the Model 241, connections to the deflecting plates are available on the front of the oscillograph—one of them direct and the other capacitive. This arrangement is not so flexible as the modification proposed for the Model 208, and it is often desirable to modify the Model 241 to obtain a greater number of possible connections.

The rise time of the vertical-deflection amplifier in the Model 208 is about 1.5 μsec, and that of the Model 241 about 0.2 μsec. The Model 241 has a low-gain amplifier for the intensifier grid—the so-called Z-axis amplifier. When the oscillograph is used with an external sweep circuit, it is desirable to by-pass this amplifier so that access to the control grid (through a suitable blocking capacitor) is possible.

When examining the pulse forms of signals in a trigger circuit, it is often desirable to avoid loading the circuit with the capacitance associated with the lead to the deflecting plate of the cathode-ray tube. To reduce this capacitance, it is convenient to have available a compact, portable cathode-follower stage that is always ready for use by connecting a power plug to a stabilized d-c power supply located at the test bench. For high-level operation, the cathode follower can be based on a 6AG7 tube (triode-connected) that draws 30 ma from a 600-volt supply (+300, 0, −300 volts). If the grid of the 6AG7 tube is at ground potential, either capacitive or direct connection can be made to the circuit under study. Direct connection can be used, for instance, to examine the d-c levels reached by the grid in a trigger circuit of the multivibrator type.

2.1 General-purpose Sweep Circuits. Let us now consider several sweep circuits that are suitable for supplementing ordinary commercial oscillographs. The first circuit to be described, the Model 220 test unit, is designed for use with either a Model 241 or a Model 224A Du Mont oscillograph. In addition to a sweep circuit, the Model 220 contains a pulse generator for testing amplifiers, and a high-fidelity delay line, which can be used with the oscillograph amplifier

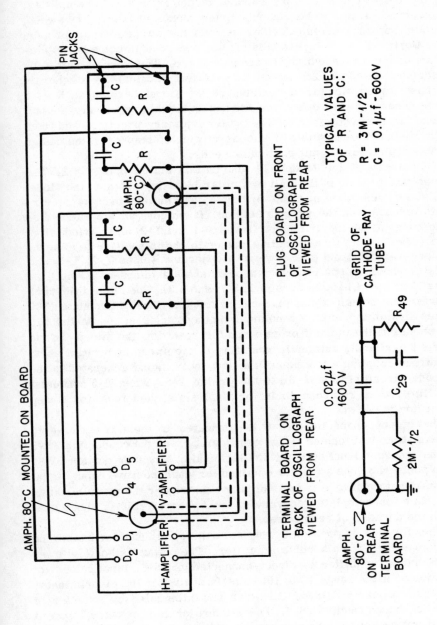

Fig. 6.1—Method of modifying a Du Mont Model 208 cathode-ray oscillograph.

for the purpose of examining random pulses from a pulse amplifier. The second circuit to be described, the Model 50 laboratory sweep, contains several useful devices besides the sweep circuit proper. It is worth while to discuss this circuit even though some of its elements do not represent most recent practice. The third circuit to be described, the Model 260 sweep, is excellent in design for a general-purpose sweep circuit. It contains no additional devices such as a pulse generator or a delay line for use in examining random pulses. These three sweep circuits illustrate customary practice, and from them it should be possible to choose circuit elements for the design of a sweep circuit to suit particular needs.

The circuit of the Model 220 test unit is shown in Fig. 6.2. The sweep circuit used in the unit is similar in basic design to the Model 300 sweep described in Chap. 5, Sec. 3, and to the other sweep circuits discussed in the present section. It employs an amplitude discriminator as an input element (tubes T-1 and T-2) and a triode flip-flop (tube T-4) to furnish gating pulses to the intensifier grid of the cathode-ray tube and to a saw-tooth generator (tubes T-7, T-8, and T-6B), whose output is inverted by a gain-of-minus-one amplifier (tube T-9) (see Chap. 2, Secs. 3.1, 3.7, and 4.3). The chief difference between the design of the present circuit and that of the Model 300 sweep lies in the more economical methods used in the Model 220 for obtaining the intensifier gate and for resetting the sweep. In the Model 220 circuit, automatic resetting of the sweep is brought about by direct-coupling a fraction of the saw-tooth signal generated in the cathode circuit of tube T-6B to the grid of T-5. When T-5 conducts, the flip-flop is returned to its original state, and thus the sweep excursion is ended.

The output connection TS-6 is connected to the intensifier-grid (Z-axis) terminal located on the oscillograph, and the connection TS-5 to the horizontal-deflecting-plate terminals. When the switch SW-1 is in position 3, one sweep is obtained for each positive input signal of sufficient amplitude (5 volts or more) to trigger the discriminator. The time for complete recovery of the sweep circuit is about one-tenth the duration of each sweep.

When SW-1 is in position 2, the test unit can be used for examining random pulses from a pulse amplifier. The output cathode follower of the pulse amplifier is direct-connected to TS-1. Input pulses (of amplitudes in the range 10 to 100 volts) first trigger the discriminator and then appear—delayed 2.2 μsec and attenuated by a factor of 100—at the connector TS-2. The attenuation is necessary, since it would not be possible to connect the delay line, whose impedance is 500 ohms, directly to the amplifier without causing its output stage to

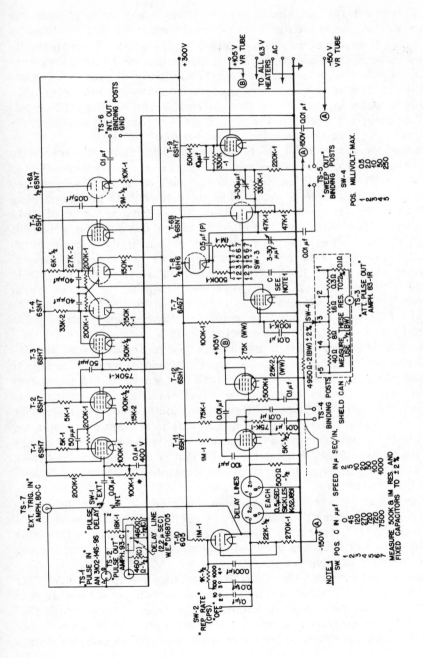

Fig. 6.2.—Model 220 test unit.

overload on large signals. A connection is made from TS-2 to the
Y-axis amplifier of the oscillograph, and the gain of this amplifier is
adjusted to accommodate the amplitude of the pulses it receives. By
adjustment of the bias setting of the discriminator in the sweep circuit, the shape of pulses originating in an electrical detector, including the leading edge, can be examined without the sweep's being triggered by noise signals. Since the rise time of the oscillograph amplifier is about 0.2 μsec and the fastest sweep speed is 2 μsec/in., the
test unit is not suitable for examining very fast pulses.

When the switch SW-1 is in position 1, the thyratron relaxation
oscillator, T-10, causes the sweep to recur at a frequency selected
by switch SW-2. Positive pulses at the cathode of T-10 are delayed
1 μsec by a delay line and applied to the grid of T-11 for the purpose
of generating standard testing pulses. Each time the grid of T-11
receives a positive pulse, its plate is abruptly reduced in potential.
The potential of the plate then recovers exponentially to the positive
supply potential. Tube T-12, which is essentially a cathode follower,
is completely cut off for a period of about 100 μsec, since its grid is
coupled to the plate of T-11. Negative pulses having the waveform
shown in the drawing and a maximum amplitude of 25 volts can be
obtained from TS-4. Similar pulses attenuated for testing pulse
amplifiers are available at connector TS-3.

It should be recalled that the various test pulses available are delayed 1 μsec with respect to the start of the oscillograph sweep. It
is therefore possible to examine both the waveform of the direct
pulses on the oscillograph and the waveform of the pulses that have
passed through a pulse amplifier under test. Since the attenuator
called for in the circuit diagram is accurate to at least 5 per cent, the
gain of the amplifier can be determined to this accuracy by comparing the height of the direct pulses with that of the output pulses from
the amplifier. A more accurate pulse generator is described in Sec.
3 of this chapter.

The Model 220 test unit has been designed primarily for semiportable applications. It should prove useful for general testing in a
nuclear physics laboratory when pulse amplifiers having a rise time
of 0.5 μsec or longer are involved. The circuit is not intended for use
in electronics development work.

Let us next consider the Model 50 laboratory sweep, Fig. 6.3. This
circuit contains a sweep circuit similar to but somewhat simpler than
the Model 220 test unit. In addition it contains a high-level pulse
amplifier incorporating a high-fidelity delay line, to be used in examining random pulses of (either positive or negative polarity) on the

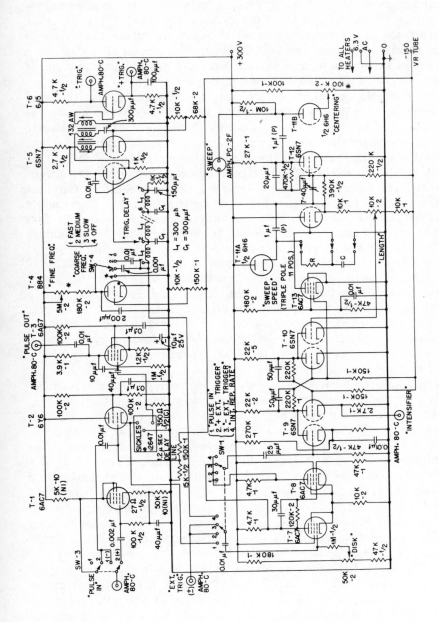

Fig. 6.3—Model 50 laboratory sweep circuit.

oscillograph screen. The amplifier is intended to be coupled capacitively to a deflecting plate of the cathode-ray tube. If the parasitic capacitance of the connecting lead is kept low, pulses having a rise time of about 0.2 μsec can be examined. The circuit also contains a source of repetitive trigger pulses that can be delayed a maximum of nearly 2 μsec with respect to the start of the sweep.

The operation of the sweep circuit is so similar to that of sweep circuits already described that only a few novel features need comment here. The discriminator (tubes T-7 and T-8) can be biased to accept either positive or negative trigger pulses. A positive trigger pulse for the flip-flop is obtained from either the plate of T-7 or the plate of T-8 by means of the trigger selector switch SW-1. An intensifier-gate signal of about 25-volt amplitude is obtained from the cathode circuit of the left-hand tube of the flip-flop. The rise time of the gate is about 0.5 μsec. This rise time is ample in view of the fact that the fastest linear sweep that can be generated with the remainder of the circuit has a speed of a little less than 1 μsec/in. (when the circuit is used with a cathode-ray tube having a deflection factor of 45 volts per inch). A direct connection to the X-axis deflecting plates of the cathode-ray tube can be used, since a centering control and a diode restorer are provided in the circuit itself. Unfortunately this scheme causes some defocusing of the cathode-ray tube spot unless the average potential of the deflecting plates provided by the sweep happens to have the correct value. This problem is discussed more fully in Chap. 5, Sec. 2.

The amplifier incorporating the 1.2-μsec delay line employs tubes T-1, T-2, and T-3. Tube T-1 is a phase inverter (see Chap. 2, Sec. 3.2). It is used only when negative pulses are being examined. The necessity for this stage arises from the asymmetrical biasing given tubes T-2 and T-3 in order that high-level input pulses (maximum amplitude about 50 volts) may be accommodated. Tube T-2 is a cathode follower having a 1.2-μsec delay line (350-ohm characteristic impedance) as its cathode load. Tube T-3 is a voltage-fed-back stage (see Chap. 2, Sec. 3.1) with a gain of a little less than 4, biased to deliver large negative output signals. Positive signals at the cathode of T-2 are used to trigger the sweep, thus enabling the delayed signals to be viewed in their entirety on the oscillograph screen. The over-all gain of the amplifier for positive pulses is about 2.5.

The remainder of the circuit consists of a thyratron relaxation oscillator, a tapped delay line having a delay of about 0.3 μsec per step, and a blocking-oscillator trigger generator. Pulses from the cathode of the thyratron serve to start sweeps, and the delayed output pulses are used to trigger various circuits under test. The waveforms of signals initiated in this manner can be examined in their entirety. The blocking-oscillator output pulses are not suitable for testing pulse amplifiers.

The values of R and C required to obtain various sweep speeds can be estimated from the approximate relation $dV/dt \approx 530/RC$ volts per second. The circuit is ordinarily used with either a Model 208 or a Model 241 Du Mont oscillograph, both of which have a deflection factor of about 45 volts per inch. A useful sequence of sweep speeds is the following: 0.5, 1, 3, 10, 30, $\cdots$, 3×10^4 μsec/in. The sweep speed 0.5 μsec/in. results in some nonlinearity of operation unless all important parasitic capacitances in the circuit are kept at a minimum by careful layout and wiring. The values of the resistance R are usually chosen in the range of several megohms, except for the faster sweep speeds, for which it is convenient to employ ceramic trimmer capacitors (4 to 30 $\mu\mu$f) and to choose values of resistance that bring the sweep speeds into the range of control afforded by the capacitors. The minimum resistance that should be used is about 100,000 ohms.

The Model 260 sweep circuit, Fig. 6.4, has been designed for use primarily in the development and testing of electronic instruments of the sort described in this volume. It is an excellent sweep circuit, incorporating all features that have proved most useful. Although it is intended for use with a conventional laboratory oscillograph, the sweep voltages and the intensifier gate are large enough to drive a cathode-ray tube having an over-all accelerating voltage as high as 6 kv.

The circuit employed in the Model 260 sweep differs but little from that of the Model 300 sweep described in Chap. 5, Sec. 3. Since the latter circuit has been discussed, it is necessary here only to point out the additional provisions that have been made to adapt Model 260 for use in an electronics laboratory. The bias of the discriminator in this sweep can be set to permit the use of positive or negative input triggers—a provision also made in the Model 50 laboratory sweep. The amplifier stage, T-6, can be used to insert blanking marks on the sweep. For this purpose an external marker generator based on a pulsed LC oscillator is suitable (see Chap. 2, Sec. 3.6; Chap. 5, Sec. 4; and Fig. 5.4). The circuit includes diode restorers for the sweep and an auxiliary-focus control to permit the average potential of the X-axis deflecting plates to be set for the best condition of focus (see Chap. 5, Sec. 2). The diode restorers on the sweep serve to maintain a steady pattern, whose horizontal position is independent of the repetition frequency (even when random or single events are observed). This is obviously a desirable feature in the checking of apparatus used in nuclear experiments.

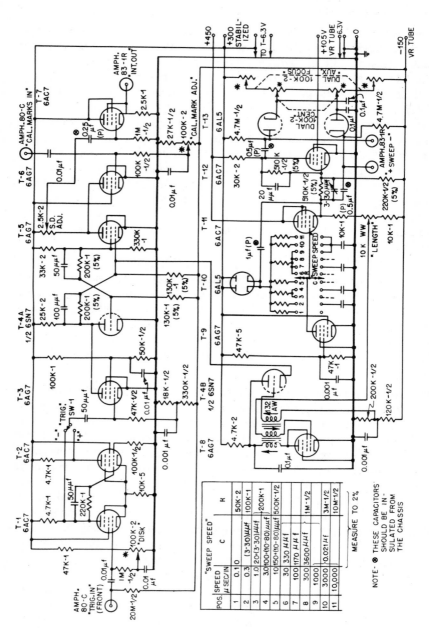

Fig. 6.4—Model 260 sweep circuit.

A set of values for the resistance R and capacitance C, to give sweep speeds ranging from 0.1 μsec/in. to 0.01 sec/in., are included in Fig. 6.4. In order to realize good performance for the fastest sweep speed, it is imperative that parasitic capacitance in the circuit be minimized and that low-capacitance cables be used to connect the sweep circuit to the oscillograph.

It is also desirable to install a diode restorer for the intensifier grid of the cathode-ray tube in the oscillograph itself. On account of the high negative voltage involved, it is not practical to include this diode restorer with the sweep circuit.

3. VOLTAGE PULSE GENERATORS

The testing and calibration of amplifiers and of amplitude discriminators require the use of pulse generators that furnish, at a convenient repetition rate, a series of pulses of known amplitude and of standard shape. Two different methods can be used to establish the amplitude of the pulses. Either the pulses can be generated by an electronic circuit and their amplitude measured with an accurate peak-reading voltmeter, or a known current through a known resistance can be abruptly cut off by electronic means so as to give pulses of accurately known amplitude. A consideration of the relative merits of the two systems favors the second method. Its advantage is that an accurate d-c milliammeter or voltmeter is all that is required to measure pulse heights. It is even possible to employ a standard cell with a potentiometer to establish the initial potential from which the pulses are being generated.

The most desirable shape for pulses intended to be used in testing and in calibrating amplifiers of all types is indicated in Fig. 6.5. Each pulse has a short rise time (about 0.05 μsec), followed by a flat top lasting about 100 μsec. The trailing edge of the pulse should have a relatively long decay time. This is necessary because pulse amplifiers are ordinarily biased to deliver an output signal of one polarity, and also because they contain a differentiating element for converting step waves into narrow pulses. If the trailing edge of the test pulses has a short rise time, a large output pulse of opposite sign will be produced by differentiation, and the output stages of the amplifier will then be overloaded on account of asymmetric biasing.

For certain applications it is important that the duty ratio of the pulses be small — usually 1 per cent or less. (Duty ratio is the ratio of the area A to the area A + B, in Fig. 6.5.) This requirement arises, for instance, in the calibration of an amplitude discriminator through an RC network. If the pulses impressed on the discriminator are

rectangular in shape and of duration τ, a simple analysis shows that
the effective pulse height at the grid of the discriminator is low by
the fractional amount

$$\frac{e^{\tau/RC} - 1}{e^{T/RC} - 1}$$

where T is the time between pulses and RC is the time constant of
the coupling network (a series C and a shunt R).

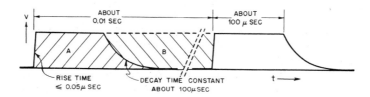

Fig. 6.5 — A pulse waveform suitable for calibrating and testing pulse amplifiers.

Occasionally it is desirable to have pulses of special shape in order
to test particular equipment. A useful shape of pulse is one having
an adjustable linear rise instead of a very abrupt rise — a so-called
"trapezoidal" pulse.

The following section describes several pulse generators that can
be used for calibrating and testing various electronic circuits.

3.1 <u>Pulse Generators for Accurate Amplitude Calibrations</u>. Let
us first consider a pulse generator for calibrating an amplitude discriminator of the type occurring in the counters described in Chap. 4,
Sec. 2.4. The Model 50 pulse generator, Fig. 6.6, has been designed
specifically for this purpose. It generates flat-topped pulses having
a duration of about 200 μsec and occurring at a rate of 25 pulses per
second, which makes the duty ratio 0.5 per cent. The pulse height
can be read by an accurate external voltmeter. It is necessary, of
course, to correct in the usual manner for the resistive loading of
the voltmeter. Pulse heights in two ranges, 0 to 10 volts and 0 to 100
volts, are provided.

The operation of the circuit should be clear on examination of Fig.
6.6. The thyratron T-1 constitutes a relaxation oscillator of fixed
frequency. It furnishes negative trigger pulses to the univibrator [see
Chap. 2, Sec. 4.2(b)] based on the 6SN7 tube, T-2. The univibrator, in

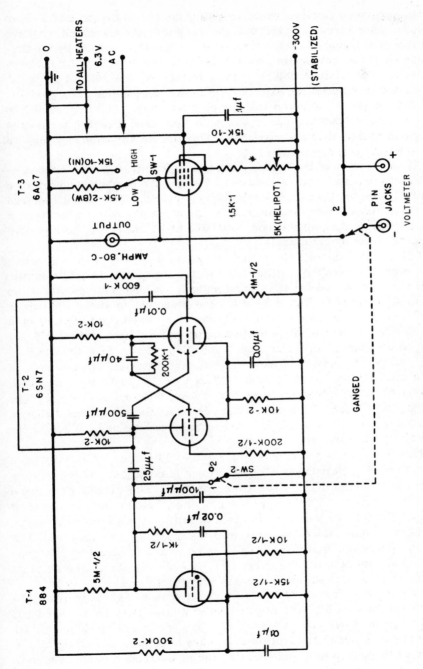

Fig. 6.6—Model 50 pulse generator.

turn, furnishes suitable negative gating pulses to the grid of T-3, in whose plate circuit is located the resistor across which positive pulses are produced each time the tube current is cut off by the thyratron and the univibrator. Switch SW-1 serves to select the range of pulse heights desired. SW-2 serves to turn off the relaxation oscillator and to connect the external voltmeter across the plate resistor of T-3. It should be noted that the positive supply bus is grounded to the chassis so that the output pulses are obtained directly across the resistor where they are produced. This device is ordinarily used in an accurate pulse generator.

The rise time of the output pulses is determined by the time constant of the plate-load resistance of T-3 and the parasitic capacitance that happens to shunt it. A particularly short rise time is not required in the calibration of discriminators. In using the pulse generator, a correction of the pulse height may have to be made for the resistive loading of the discriminator.

Let us next consider the Model 100 pulse generator, Fig. 6.7, which has been designed for calibrating and testing high-gain pulse amplifiers requiring fast negative input signals. It generates pulses of the form illustrated in Fig. 6.5, at a repetition rate of about 150 pulses per second. The pulses are negative. By varying the setting of a potentiometer and of a step-attenuator, pulses from 4 to 1,000 mv can be obtained at an impedance level of 150 ohms. Low-level pulses are obtained by the use of external resistance-capacitance attenuators with attenuating ratios of either 10 to 1 or 100 to 1. By using both attenuators, the minimum pulse height available is 4 microvolts. The output impedance of the attenuators is about 100 ohms shunted by a capacitance of 200 $\mu\mu$f for the 10-to-1 attenuator, and by 0.002 μf for the 100-to-1 attenuator.

The rise time of the pulses generated is 0.06 μsec. The flat region at the top of each pulse is about 100 μsec in duration, and the trailing edge decays with a 100-μsec time constant. The circuit provides a positive trigger pulse occurring 0.5 μsec before each calibrating pulse. The trigger pulse can be used to initiate the sweep of an oscillograph on which the output pulses of the amplifier are observed. The pulse generator, therefore, can be used to aid in adjusting compensating elements in a pulse amplifier, in order to obtain the shortest possible rise time without transient overshoot.

Before the operation of the circuit is discussed, some of the difficulties of generating fast negative step pulses free from overshoot will be pointed out. The most satisfactory method of producing a fast step pulse of accurate amplitude appears to consist in cutting off the current through a tube and securing the pulse from a series resistor

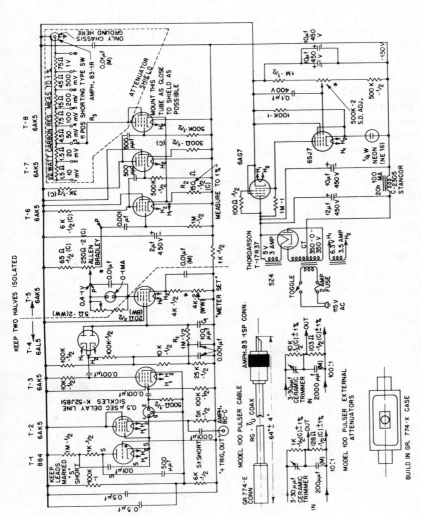

Fig. 6.7 — Model 100 pulse generator.

of suitable value. The advantages of this method are (1) that the signal voltages before and after the step are very definite, and (2) that pulses free from minor oscillations are obtained, provided no undesirable transient effects are encountered at the time the current is cut off. The method is particularly satisfactory for positive step signals, since the tube whose current is cut off can be a pentode in which the screen grid prevents a capacitive feed-through of the grid signal to the plate (where the output signal is generated). If negative pulses are taken from the cathode, there is almost certain to be a small amount of overshoot at the end of the step rise on account of capacitive feed-through from grid to cathode. The method described for generating negative pulses also suffers from the disadvantage that a relatively large cathode resistor cannot be used to stabilize (by negative current feedback) the current through the pulse-generating tube. In order to obtain good negative pulses, it is possible to generate positive pulses and then invert them by a very stable gain-of-minus-one amplifier having good transient properties. This is the method adopted in the Model 100 pulse generator.

Turning now to a discussion of the circuit, Fig. 6.7, we note that the thyratron T-1 serves both to set the repetition rate and to furnish fast positive pulses from its cathode for the purpose of generating the leading edge of the test pulses. The cathode follower T-2 serves as an output stage to provide pulses for triggering the sweep of an oscillograph. Pulses from the cathode of the thyratron traverse a $0.5\text{-}\mu\text{sec}$ delay line and are impressed on the grid of T-3, which normally passes no current. Each positive pulse received by the grid causes a fast negative pulse to be generated at the plate. This pulse is used to place a negative charge on the capacitor C_1, thereby cutting off the current through T-5 and generating at its plate a positive pulse of the form shown in Fig. 6.5. The diode T-4 serves two purposes: (1) It is so biased that only the steepest portion of the pulse generated at the plate of T-3 is coupled to capacitor C_1. This device ensures that the current through tube T-5 will be cut off in a very short time (a few hundredths of a microsecond). (2) The diode makes it necessary for the negative charge placed on the capacitor C_1 to escape through the resistor R_1, ensuring that T-5 remains cut off for some time and that the trailing edge of the pulse generated at the plate of T-5 has a $100\text{-}\mu\text{sec}$ decay constant. The diode also serves to disconnect the tube T-5 from the thyratron circuit, so that transient oscillations do not appear at the output.

The amplitude of the pulses generated in the plate circuit of T-5 can be varied by varying the position of the contact on an Allen-Bradley 250-ohm carbon potentiometer. The central portion of a potentiometer of this make is linear enough to permit the use of a dial for reading directly in fractions of 1 volt if readings are restricted to the range 0.4 to 1 volt. It is not possible, of course, to employ a precision wire-wound potentiometer on account of the large parasitic inductance it possesses. In the present circuit the plate current of T-5 is adjusted to about 4 ma by varying the cathode resistance. The angular position of the dial on the potentiometer and the value of the plate current are varied until the d-c voltage between the point P and the ground-supply bus agrees with the reading of the dial. The resistance shunting the meter is then adjusted to make the meter read full scale. In subsequent use of the instrument it is only necessary to set the meter reading at full scale by slightly adjusting the cathode resistance of T-5. It is found that an absolute accuracy of a few per cent can be achieved by this method. Relative pulse heights have a somewhat greater accuracy. Greater accuracy can be obtained by comparison of the steady potential at the plate of T-5 with a standard null potentiometer.

The positive pulses generated in the plate circuit of T-5 are inverted by means of a three-stage feedback loop of the type discussed in Chap. 2, Sec. 3.5. Here the current signal in the resistor R_2 is stabilized, and so, therefore, is the current through R_3. If $R_2 = R_3$, the gain of the inverter will be given very nearly by $-1/[1 + (1/\mu_1)]$, where μ_1 is the grid-to-screen amplification factor of tube T-6, as measured with the plate voltage and current held constant.*

Since $\mu_1 \approx 30$ for a type 6AK5 tube, the gain will be a few per cent less than unity when $R_2 = R_3$. To correct for this discrepancy, the value of R_2 can be selected to give an exact (unity) phase inversion when the switch SW-1 is in position 8. The maximum pulse height available for the other positions of the switch is indicated on the circuit diagram. In all cases the output impedance is 150 ohms. In constructing the attenuator, considerable care must be taken to keep parasitic inductance and capacitance at a minimum. The only ground to the chassis is made at the signal-output connector.

The chief difficulty in constructing a pulse generator for pulses having a fast step rise lies in avoiding small transient oscillations superposed on the output signal in the vicinity of the step. In the circuit under consideration there is danger that oscillations produced when the thyratron fires will couple into the signal-carrying leads. To avoid interactions of this sort, short leads and good shielding are

---

* This result is evident from an inspection of Eq. 25 in Chap. 2, which holds for the case where the output signal is taken from the cathode of the third tube of the feedback loop.

necessary. It should be kept in mind that the transients present possess important frequency components as high as 10 megacycles per second.

The 10-to-1 and 100-to-1 external attenuators are the resistance-capacitance type discussed briefly in Chap. 2, Sec. 2.2. They can be constructed in small metal cases with mating coaxial connectors on opposite ends of the case. It is best practice to place the external attenuator at the input of the amplifier being tested. Since the capacitance of the coaxial cable between the pulse generator and the external attenuator constitutes a capacitive load in parallel with the 150-ohm output resistance, the capacitance must be kept less than 100 $\mu\mu f$ if the rise time of the output pulses is to be kept as short as 0.06 μsec.

The Model 100 pulse generator, in addition to being used for testing and adjusting pulse amplifiers designed for negative input signals, finds considerable application in setting the bias of discriminators used in counting pulses from an electrical detector of radiation. The pulse generator is connected to the preamplifier of the pulse amplifier, in place of or in parallel with the electrical detector. The gain of the amplifier and the bias of the amplitude discriminator are then adjusted until the counting rate is about one-half the maximum rate for a desired magnitude of input pulses. The same condition can easily be returned to for measurements at subsequent times, with the assurance that if no change has occurred in the electrical detector, counting will be done at the same point on the bias curve that was used in earlier measurements. By a comparison technique, the pulse generator can be used to measure the effective pulse heights produced by various radiations and by amplifier noise (see Chap. 3, Sec. 6). In a certain sense, a pulse generator of this type assumes the same role for pulse amplifiers that a standard signal generator (producing sinusoidal waves) assumes for radio-frequency amplifiers.

The Model 300 pulse generator, Fig. 6.8, illustrates the design of a simple pulse generator that is suitable for testing and calibrating transient amplifiers requiring high-level pulses. The output connector can be placed, by means of a switch, SW-2, either in the plate circuit or in the cathode circuit of two 6Y6 tubes connected in parallel. An output current as high as 100 ma can be cut off in perhaps 0.05 μsec. If an external resistance of 200 ohms is connected at the end of a coaxial cable, step pulses of 20-volt amplitude are generated each time the circuit receives an input-trigger pulse. The output pulses last either 100 or 300 μsec, depending on the position of switch SW-1. By means of taps on the load resistor, pulses at lower levels can be

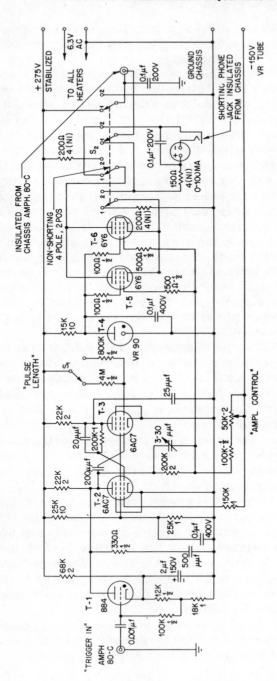

Fig. 6.8—Model 300 pulse generator.

obtained. If an attenuation greater than 10-to-1 is required, a low-impedance ladder attenuator should be used to avoid the difficulties arising from parasitic inductance.

The operation of the circuit is so straightforward that it is necessary to point out only a few interesting features. When the thyratron T-1 is fired by the application of an external trigger pulse, it serves not only to trigger the univibrator (tubes T-2 and T-3), but to cut off the current through the output tubes (see Chap. 2, Sec. 4.2). The thyratron is then extinguished by tube T-2 of the univibrator, which reduces the potential of the plate of the thyratron below the potential of its cathode. The circuit can be used at a moderate repetition rate or it can be employed for producing single step waves, to be used for calibrating a single-sweep oscillograph with its accompanying transient amplifier. Although a panel-type meter is incorporated in the circuit, provision is made for using an accurate milliammeter when calibrations are being made. The negative step signal secured at the cathodes of the 6Y6 tubes has a small amount of overshoot caused by capacitive feed-through of the thyratron pulse. It will be noticed that either the positive supply bus or the zero supply bus is grounded to the chassis, depending on whether positive or negative output pulses, respectively, are wanted.

The Model 100 sliding-pulse generator, Fig. 6.9, has been designed for testing and calibrating multichannel differential discriminators of the type described in Chap. 4, Sec. 2.5. It supplies pulses whose amplitudes are equal to a given positive reference voltage. Reference voltages of two sorts are available in the instrument. One is a fixed potential determined by the setting of a linear dial. It is adjustable from 0 to 50 volts. The other is a symmetric, linear, saw-toothed wave whose slope is adjustable from 0 to 2 volts per second and whose amplitude is adjustable from 12 to 60 volts. A register records each cycle of the saw-toothed wave.

The output pulses have the general form shown in Fig. 6.9 at the "Pulse Out I" connector. The amplitude E is equal to the reference voltage to within ± 0.01 volt for amplitudes between 0 and 50 volts. Both positive and negative pulses are available at high level, and attenuated negative pulses are available at a 50-ohm impedance level, with attenuation factors of 10^{-2}, 3×10^{-3}, 10^{-3}, 3×10^{-4}, and 10^{-4}. The repetition rate of the pulses is continuously adjustable in the range 1 to 200 pulses per second.

The operation of the circuit can be best understood by considering separately the pulse generator and the generator for symmetric saw-toothed waves used when sliding pulses are wanted.

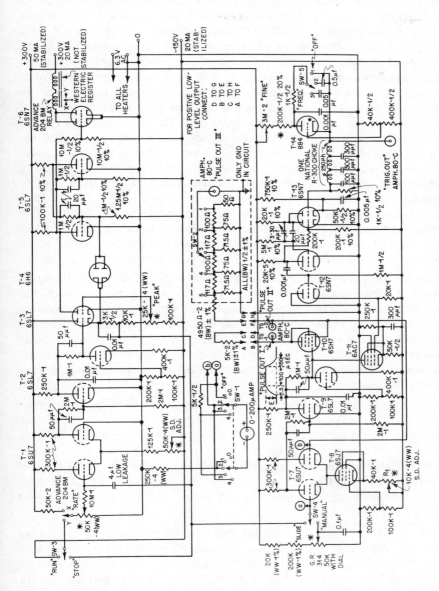

Fig. 6.9—Model 100 sliding-pulse generator.

Let us assume that switch SW-3 is in the "Stop" position, and that SW-4 is in the "Manual" position. A steady reference potential is then supplied to the grid of the left-hand section of T-7, which with tube T-8 constitutes a stable difference amplifier (see Chap. 2, Sec. 3.3). The other grid of the difference amplifier is connected to the cathode of T-10. Since the potential of this cathode determines the exact amplitude of the output pulses, it is desired to keep its potential accurately equal to the reference voltage. This end is attained (to within ± 0.01 volt) by means of a d-c amplifier connecting the output of the difference amplifier to the grid of T-10. The resulting circuit possesses a considerable amount of negative feedback. If, for instance, the cathode potential of T-10 is momentarily high, an amplified negative signal returns to the grid and restores the cathode potential to an equilibrium value. A capacitance of 0.01 μf is used to load the plate circuit of the left-hand section of T-9 in order to prevent high-frequency regenerative oscillations from occurring. The right-hand section of T-9 affords a means of coupling the output of this stage to the grid of T-10 with practically no loss in gain, since T-9 acts as a constant-current device of very high source impedance.

An output pulse of accurate amplitude is obtained each time the tube T-11 receives a positive pulse at its grid, thereby cutting off the current through T-10. The d-c amplifier, which normally maintains the bias of T-10 at the correct value, loses control during the interval of time in which an output pulse is generated. The maximum repetition rate is so low, however, that potentials in the circuit have completely recovered their proper values between the generation of successive pulses.

The signal impressed on the grid of tube T-11 is produced by tubes T-12, T-13, and T-14. Thyratron T-14 determines the frequency of operation and supplies an external trigger for starting the sweep of an oscillograph that can be used for monitoring the multichannel differential discriminator under calibration. It also serves to trigger a univibrator [see Chap. 2, Sec. 4.2(b)] through a 1-μsec delay line. The univibrator than supplies a rectangular positive pulse to the grid of tube T-11.

The method of attenuating the negative output pulses should be clear on inspection of the circuit diagram. By making the changes in connections indicated there, attenuated positive pulses can be obtained instead of the negative pulses that are normally required by a pulse amplifier.

The meter in the circuit, together with switch SW-1, is used for making semiquantitative observations of the operation of the circuit. The switch should normally be left in the "Off" position.

In position 1, the meter reads 50 volts full scale and indicates the reference voltage applied to the difference amplifier. In position 2, the meter reads the voltage at the cathode of T-10, i.e., the output-pulse height. It should not be used in this position when manual control is used, since the resistance of the meter destroys the calibration of the potentiometer dial. In positions 3 and 4, the meter reads 1 volt full scale and measures the difference between the reference and the output potentials. The reading has meaning only if the thyratron is biased off by placing SW-5 in the "Off" position. The meter is used in these positions to aid in adjusting and checking the pulse generator.

To adjust the pulse generator, the meter switch is placed in position 3, the thyratron is biased off, and the reference-voltage potentiometer is set at zero. The cathode resistor (R_1) of the difference amplifier is then varied until the meter just reads zero when this point is approached from a positive deflection. If this setting is made properly, it should be possible to increase the reference voltage to 50 volts without the meter's deflecting more than ± 0.01 volts for any intermediate value. With careful setting, the deflection should increase linearly from 0 to 0.01 volt as the reference voltage is increased from 0 to 50 volts.

The portion of the circuit just described evidently serves to generate pulses whose amplitude equals the value of a steady reference potential. To generate sliding pulses, it is necessary only to supply a reference potential of suitable waveform. Let us therefore consider the operation of the remainder of the circuit that is used to generate this waveform.

If switch SW-3 is in the "Run" position and the relay contacts are in the Y position, a negative potential is impressed on the 10-megohm resistor connected to the grid of the left-hand section of tube T-1. This signal is amplified by a d-c amplifier similar to the one employed in the other portion of the circuit. The negative input signal appears as a positive signal, much amplified, at the cathode of the left-hand section of T-3. From a point on the cathode-load resistor of this tube a 4-μf low-leakage capacitor is connected to the input grid. This portion of the circuit constitutes a stabilized integrating circuit of the type described in Chap. 3, Sec. 10.5. The negative step signal applied to the input of the integrating circuit therefore results in the generation of a linearly increasing voltage at the cathode of the left-hand section of T-3. When this signal has reached an amplitude determined by the setting of the potentiometer labeled "Peak," the flip-flop based on T-5 is triggered into its other stable stage, cutting off the current through tube T-6 and opening the relay. The relay contact X is thereby closed. This substitutes an equal and opposite positive potential for the negative potential formerly applied to the integrating circuit. The integrated output signal is now a linearly decreasing voltage. When it has reached approximately ground potential, the diode T-4 serves to trigger the flip-flop to its original state, closing the relay and causing the cycle to repeat. The slope of the saw-tooth can be varied from 0 to 2 volts per second by adjusting the potentiometer labeled "Rate." The maximum value of the saw-toothed wave can be controlled in the range 12 to 60 volts by the potentiometer labeled "Peak." The minimum value is constant at −3 volts. The saw-toothed wave should always be stopped by throwing SW-3 to the "Stop" position when the slope of the saw-toothed wave is negative. If this is done, the wave will continue to its minimum position and be stopped there. The register in series with the relay records the total number of complete cycles. The wave generated by the circuit has slopes that are constant to 0.5 per cent. Switch SW-4 serves to connect the pulse generator to the saw-toothed-waveform generator.

The sliding pulser is used to calibrate a multichannel differential discriminator in the following way: The attenuated output pulses are coupled to the pulse amplifier, and various adjustments are made until about 25 pulses occur in all channels of average width for one excursion of the saw-toothed wave. The peak control is then adjusted so that there is a small interval (say 25 pulses) in which the pulse height is beyond the limit of the most highly biased channel. The total number of counts obtained in each channel can then be obtained for several (5 to 10) saw-tooth cycles. By this means the relative width of each channel in the differential discriminator is measured. When the instrument is used in the "Manual" condition, a convenient pulse generator exists for testing various channels in the differential discriminator.

3.2 Trapezoidal Voltage Pulse Generators. To test the performance of differentiating circuits and to investigate the distortion produced by an amplifier to the leading edge of a fast pulse, it is convenient to have pulse generators available that generate a step pulse having a linear rate of rise and then a subsequent flat top. For want of a better name, the term "trapezoidal" has been applied to this shape of pulse. Two generators of trapezoidal pulses are described in the present section. One of them is particularly suited to generating pulses of relatively fast rise, and the other is suited to generating pulses of slower rise.

The Model 150 trapezoidal-pulse generator, shown in Fig. 6.10, has been used to calibrate the pulse amplifier and oscillograph employed in an investigation of the fast collection of electrons in an electrical detector. Various times for the complete rise of the linearly increasing voltage at the leading edge of the pulse can be selected in

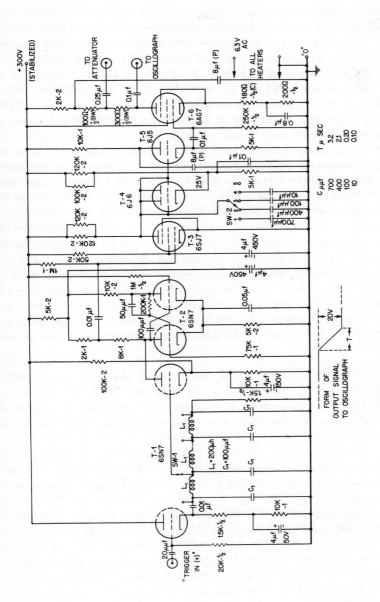

Fig. 6.10—Model 150 trapezoidal-pulse generator.

the range from a few tenths to several microseconds. Values other than those indicated in Fig. 6.10 can be obtained by choosing different values of capacitances to be selected by switch SW-2. A negative output pulse of 20-volt amplitude is provided for direct connection to the plate of a cathode-ray oscillograph. The same pulse at a 5-volt level is provided for connection to an external, ladder-type attenuator (not shown), which supplies a signal to the preamplifier of the pulse amplifier. The direct pulse and the output pulse of the amplifier can be compared on the oscillograph screen. Switch SW-1 provides a range of delays to enable the pulses to be located at a convenient place on the sweep of the oscillograph.

Each pulse is produced in response to an input trigger, which, after passing through the lumped-parameter tapped delay line, serves to trigger the univibrator [see Chap. 2, Sec. 4.2(b)], based on tube T-2.

A negative gate from the univibrator cuts off the current through the clamp T-3. The current originally flowing through T-3 now starts to charge one of the capacitors C, and the potential applied to the grid of the cathode follower T-5 increases almost linearly until the diode T-4 prevents any further increase. The signal from the cathode follower is impressed on the grid of the amplifier stage, T-6, at whose plate the signal indicated in the drawing is generated. The top portion of the pulse lasts for about 50 μsec, depending on time constants in the univibrator. The shape of the trailing edge of the pulse is of no consequence, since it will never occur on the fast oscillograph sweeps that are used to view the leading edge.

The circuit of a second trapezoidal-pulse generator is shown in Fig. 6.11. This circuit has been designed to produce pulses of the general form illustrated in the figure. The time T is approximately 10 μsec. Other values of T can be obtained by altering the RC time constants in the circuit. The curvature at the start and at the end of the linear rise lasts about 0.2 μsec.

The multivibrator based on T-1 furnished a square-wave signal, which is applied to the suppressor of T-3. The suppressor is prevented from going positive by the diode restorer T-2. The tube T-3, with accompanying circuit components, constitutes a generator of negative saw-toothed waves. When the suppressor is negative 100 volts or more, current to the plate is cut off, although both grid and screen current are flowing. As soon as the suppressor is brought to ground potential, current flows to the plate, but the plate potential can drop only by virtue of current flowing through R to the grid side of the capacitor C. The circuit element is evidently a simple form of integrating circuit, and the plate signal is proportional to the integral of the voltage applied to the grid through the resistor R; that is, it is a linearly decreasing voltage.

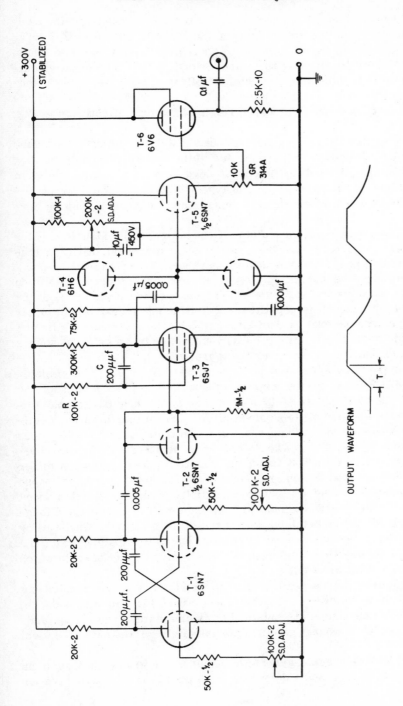

Fig. 6.11—Model 10 trapezoidal-pulse generator.

The double diode, T-4, serves to limit the excursions of the saw-toothed wave applied to the grid of the cathode follower, T-5. The amplitude of the output signal is controlled by the setting of the potentiometer constituting the cathode load of T-5. The negative output signal is furnished by the cathode follower, T-6. The three potentiometers in the circuit labeled "S.D. Adj." (screw-driver adjustment) are varied until the waveform is of the type illustrated in Fig. 6.11.

The trapezoidal-pulse generator under discussion afford a means of testing special circuits used for differentiating signals lasting about 10 μsec. It has been discussed here mainly as an illustration of one method of generating a useful type of signal. It would not be difficult to design a more flexible instrument for general testing purposes.

3.3 A General-purpose Pulse Generator. The Model 2 pulse generator, Fig. 6.12, has been designed as a general utility instrument for use in electronics development work. It provides both positive and negative pulses lasting 1, 10, or 100 μsec, of amplitude variable from about 1 to 75 volts. The pulses have a rise time of the order of 0.1 μsec. The repetition rate of the pulses can be set either by a thyratron relaxation oscillator, which offers frequencies from 1 cycle per second to 10 kilocycles per second, or by an external source of signals that serve to trigger the thyratron.

The pulses are generated across the variable plate-load resistor of the 6AK5, T-4, whose current is cut off for the duration of the pulse. When switch SW-3 is in position 1, the negative signal impressed on the grid of T-4 comes directly from the thyratron oscillator, which employs a 0.5-μsec delay line to produce 1-μsec pulses (see Chap. 2, Sec. 2.4). When SW-3 is in position 2 or 3, the univibrator based on tube T-3 furnishes negative gating pulses of either 10- or 100-μsec duration, respectively. The leading edge of these pulses has a fast rise since it is essentially formed by the thyratron. The univibrator serves simply to keep the tube T-4 cut off for a longer time than can be obtained with the thyratron circuit. The trailing edge of the pulses generated is not so fast as the leading edge, but this is of no practical importance for the majority of uses to which the pulse generator is put.

The positive pulses generated at the plate of T-4 are coupled out by the cathode follower, T-5, which has a very low output impedance. Negative output pulses are obtained from the plate of the voltage fed-back stage, T-6, whose gain is approximately −1 (see Chap. 2, Sec. 3.1).

This particular pulse generator would be of greater utility if an additional thyratron and a delay line were added to the circuit in order

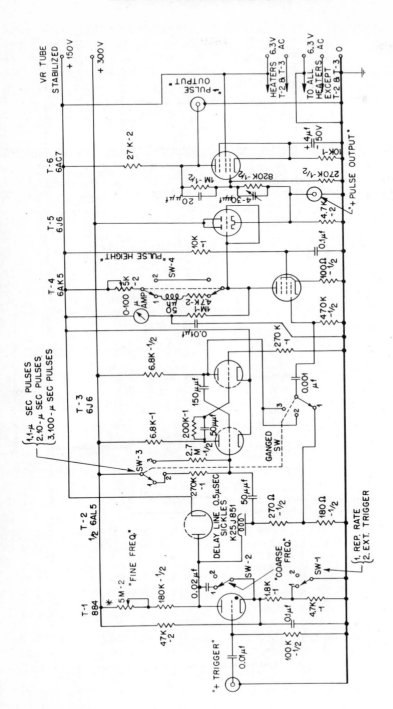

Fig. 6.12—Model 2 pulse generator.

to provide a trigger pulse occurring perhaps 1 μsec before each output pulse. Such a trigger would enable the sweep of an oscillograph
to be started early for the purpose of examining waveforms excited
in a circuit under study. The same result, of course, can be obtained
if a multiple trigger generator is available for starting the sweep and
later triggering the pulse generator, or if the sweep circuit itself
supplies a delayed output pulse for triggering the pulse generator.

4. EQUIPMENT AND METHODS FOR MAKING TIME CALIBRATIONS

The most accurate source of signals for making time calibrations
of electronic devices is an oscillator based on a piezoelectric (quartz)
crystal. In order to make effective use of the timing afforded by a
crystal-controlled oscillator, equipment is required that permits the
simultaneous comparison of standard time signals with the signals
coming from the circuit under calibration. For many purposes a
cathode-ray oscillograph affords the most convenient means of relating the two sources of signals. The standard time signals can be used
either to blank the trace of a linear sweep at regular intervals or to
place narrow "pips" on the sweep. A time scale is thereby provided
for any waveforms appearing there. The Model 200 blanking-marker
generator, described in Chap. 5, Sec. 4.2, is suitable for making time
calibrations of this sort.

When using a linear-sweep oscillograph to make very accurate time
calibrations, it is best not to rely on the linearity of the sweep for
interpolating between timing marks but to bring various points on the
sweep to a standard position by means of the horizontal positioning
voltage. If this voltage is measured by a voltmeter of good precision,
then interpolation can be made in terms of voltage readings, which
results in an improved accuracy. It is not difficult to achieve an
accuracy of ± 0.01 μsec with a good laboratory sweep circuit, such as
the Model 260 sweep, described in Sec. 2 of this chapter. If a suitable
source of time signals based on a crystal oscillator is not available,
it is possible to use a pulsed LC oscillator whose frequency can be
monitored by means of a circular-sweep oscillograph, in which the
timing is based on a crystal oscillator.

When relatively long times must be measured with a greater accuracy than can be obtained with a single linear sweep, the most
convenient time calibrator is a circular-sweep oscillograph based on
a cathode-ray tube having a central electrostatic deflecting electrode
whose action is independent of the usual four electrostatic deflecting
plates, which are now used to produce the circular sweep. A circular-
sweep calibrator having two cathode-ray tubes with a 1-μsec and a

10-μsec circle, respectively, will be described later in the present section.

To measure the timing in a single or a multichannel time discriminator of the types described in Chap. 4, it is more convenient, and probably more accurate, to employ a double-pulse generator which furnishes two pulses whose separation in time can be accurately controlled. The double-pulse generator is first calibrated with a linear or a circular-sweep oscillograph, and then used as a secondary standard for calibrating the time discriminator.

When only moderate accuracy is required, a pulsed LC oscillator constitutes a convenient source of timing marks for the routine calibration of sweep speeds. The frequency of an oscillator of this type is, of course, more subject to thermal drifts and to variations in supply voltage than is the frequency of a crystal-controlled oscillator. It has the great advantage that the sequence of timing marks produced has an accurate time lock with respect to an initiating trigger pulse, which is also used to trigger the sweep. This means that the timing marks will always fall at the same position on each sweep, even though the repetition rate of the trigger pulses is subject to variation. A convenient sweep-speed calibrator based on a pulsed LC oscillator will be described following the description of the circular-sweep calibrator.

4.1 A Circular-sweep Calibrator. A circular sweep on a cathode-ray tube screen is produced if two sinusoidal voltages differing in phase by 90 deg are applied to the two pairs of deflecting plates. The amplitudes of the voltages must be adjusted to give equal deflections along the X and Y axes. The cathode-ray spot then makes one complete revolution in a circular path for each period of oscillation. If a trigger pulse is generated at a low repetition rate, but always at a standard angular position of the rotating spot, then the timing of subsequent pulses initiated by the trigger can be measured on the circle. Pulses can be presented either by blanking the trace or by deflecting the trace with an axially located deflecting electrode in the cathode-ray tube. The type 3DP1 cathode-ray tube contains such an electrode for applications in which the second method of indication is used. The circular-sweep calibrator to be described here contains two tubes of this type, to provide both a 1-μsec and a 10-μsec circle for making time measurements. The basic circuit used is somewhat similar to that of the Model III Range Calibrator, manufactured by the F. W. Sickles Company, which is intended for calibrating and checking radar systems.

In order to avoid ambiguities in timing, it is customary to employ an intensifier gate that lasts for slightly less than one revolution of

the circle. The delay between the trigger pulse supplied by the calibrator and the gate is made adjustable, so that a signal occurring
several periods later than the trigger can be located in time with
respect to the trigger by counting the number of times the bright
portion of the circle must be revolved before the delayed pulse appears on the circle. The angular position of the signal with respect
to the position of the trigger pulse completes the measurement of the
time between the trigger and the delayed signal it initiates. The calibrator is normally used at moderate repetition rates since the low
intensity of the cathode-ray spot precludes operation with single
circular sweeps.

A circular-sweep calibrator ordinarily contains the following circuit elements: (1) a crystal-controlled oscillator, together with networks for controlling the phase, amplitude, and d-c level of two
balanced sinusoidal waves that are applied to the two pairs of deflecting plates of the cathode-ray tube; (2) a frequency divider for producing trigger pulses at a low repetition rate but with an accurate time
lock with respect to the fundamental time scale supplied by the oscillator; (3) an intensifier-gate circuit that serves to brighten the trace
for about one revolution following each trigger pulse; and (4) a variable delay circuit for allowing a known time to elapse between each
trigger and the occurrence of the intensifier gate. The circular-sweep
calibrator to be described here contains additional circuit elements
required for the generation of both a 1-μsec and a 10-μsec circle,
with all timing based on a 1-megacycle-per-second crystal-controlled
oscillator.

The circuit of the circular-sweep calibrator is shown in Fig. 6.13.
Tube T-1 and associated components are the constituent parts of
a 1-megacycle-per-second crystal-controlled oscillator. The plate
load of T-1 consists of a phase-shift network (Sickles No. 12907),
which supplies proper sweep voltages to the cathode-ray tube. By
varying the setting of the three air capacitors, it is possible to control
the shape and radius of the Lissajous figure produced on the cathode-
ray-tube screen.

From the cathode circuit of T-1, pulses are obtained to drive the
10-to-1 blocking-oscillator frequency divider based on tubes T-4 and
T-5. The method of operation of the frequency divider is of considerable interest. Each time it is triggered, the grid of T-4 is temporarily
biased off by negative charge on the grid capacitor, and, in addition,
a transient oscillation is excited at the cathode. The grid potential
then starts to recover exponentially toward the plate-supply potential,
and the cathode potential executes an oscillation made up of two components — one of frequency 150 kilocycles per second and the other of
frequency 250 kilocycles per second. These two components conspire

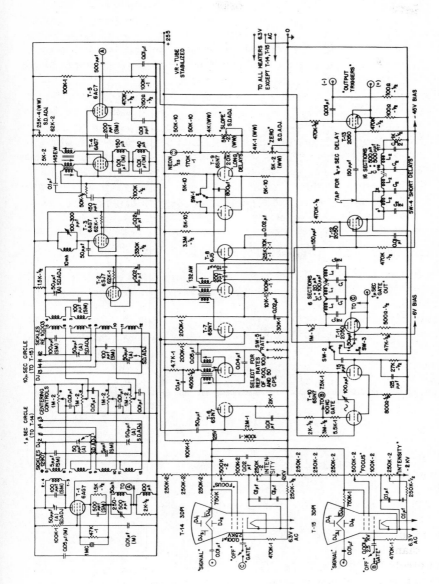

Fig. 6.13—Circular-sweep calibrator.

to reduce the cathode potential to a minimum value 10 μsec after the blocking oscillator has been triggered. The reduction in cathode potential, together with the rising grid potential, strongly tends to favor the selection of every tenth trigger pulse from the trigger pulses (spaced 1 μsec apart) impressed on the divider. The dividing factor (10) is very stable against reasonable changes in supply voltage when the variable resistor in the grid circuit of T-4 is set in the middle of the range in which the circuit divides properly.

Pulses spaced 10 μsec apart are supplied by the frequency divider to the grid of T-3, which has, as a plate load, a parallel resonant element tuned to 100 kc/sec. By this means the narrow blocking-oscillator pulses are converted into a nearly sine-wave oscillation, which is coupled to the grid of T-2. The 100-kilocycles-per-second oscillation is thereby supplied to the phase-shift network (Sickles No. RE 10003), which produces sweep voltages for the cathode-ray tube having the 10-μsec circle. This particular network has been designed for a somewhat lower frequency than 100 kilocycles per second. It is therefore necessary to decrease the values of the fixed capacitors in order to make the network tune to 100 kilocycles per second. The modified values are shown in the diagram.

The tubes T-6, T-7, T-12, and T-13 are employed to obtain output triggers at a relatively low repetition rate but with an accurate time lock with respect to the time scale afforded by the two circular sweeps. Tubes T-6 and T-7 make up a frequency divider in which the dividing factor can be selected by switch SW-5 to be approximately 200, 1,000, or 2,000. The blocking oscillator based on T-6 is triggered by one of the pulses spaced 10 μsec apart. It then furnishes a negative gating pulse, lasting about 15 μsec, to the cathode of the left-hand section of T-7, so that the second blocking oscillator is triggered by the next one of the pulses occurring every 10 μsec. By this means an accurate time lock is obtained between the input and output pulses of the divider.

Each time the thyratron T-12 is fired by one of the pulses from the frequency divider, a sequence of pulses delayed in 0.5-μsec steps is made available by virtue of the tapped delay line constituting the cathode load of T-12. One of these pulses, selected by switch SW-4, can be used to trigger either or both of the two circuits that generate intensifier-gate signals. The thyratron T-13 is fired about 0.25 μsec later than T-12. This delay enables the intensifier-gate signals for each circle to reach their final values before the output-trigger pulse is generated. The output-trigger pulse can therefore be viewed on each circle for the purpose of establishing the time origin. A thyratron is used for the output stage, since it is important to produce very narrow pulses at a low-impedance level. The output pulses rise about 100 volts in 0.05 μsec and decay with a 0.1-μsec time constant. Narrow pulses are necessary if full advantage is to be taken of the timing afforded by the 1-μsec circle.

Tube T-9 and associated components constitute a univibrator delay circuit (see Chap. 2, Sec. 4.2) covering the range from about 5 to 200 μsec. The delay provided by this circuit can be selected by the potentiometer labeled "Long Delays." By means of the controls labeled "Zero" and "Slope," the dial of the delay control can be made direct reading over the useful range of operation. The neon lamp in the bias circuit tends to compensate partially for variations in delay caused by changes in plate-supply voltage and in heater voltage. Values of resistance in the bias network are selected empirically to give the best possible compensation. The delay circuit is operative when switch SW-1 is in position 1. Postion 2 is used when no delay is desired—for instance, when one wishes to have the 10-μsec circle brightened during the first revolution of the spot, so that the output-trigger pulse is included on the circle.

The univibrator delay circuit is not satisfactory for delays shorter than about 5 μsec. To remedy this defect, the tapped delay line in the cathode circuit of T-12 is used when delays in the range 0 to 8 μsec are desired. The two sources of delayed pulses can be selected by switches SW-2 and SW-3.

The intensifier-gate signal for the 10-μsec circle is generated by the univibrator based on T-10. On account of the short duration of the gate required for the 1-μsec circle, it is not possible to employ a similar circuit element here. Instead the thyratron T-11, in conjunction with an open-circuited delay line (see Chap. 2, Sec. 2.4), is used to generate a rectangular gating signal lasting somewhat less than 1 μsec. In order that the timing afforded by the 1-μsec circle may be determined when the gate occurs delayed with respect to the output trigger, a connector is provided so that the 1-μsec gate can be presented on the 10-μsec circle. By this means the exact number of revolutions of the spot of the 1-μsec circle, elapsing between the output trigger and the occurrence of the gate, can be obtained by measurements made on the 10-μsec circle. This provision is convenient, since the control for long delays is too coarse for an accurate count of the revolutions of the 1-μsec circle while the delay control is being advanced. The gap in the coarse delay control for short delays also tends to complicate matters and makes it desirable to be able to observe the 1-μsec gate on the 10-μsec circle.

The great utility of a circular-sweep calibrator is based on two factors: (1) The time scale is furnished by a crystal-controlled oscillator whose stability can be very high. (2) The error made in measuring the time between the trigger pulse supplied by the calibrator and any pulse or waveform initiated by it in equipment undergoing calibration is a constant independent of the total time. The absolute error made depends chiefly on the linearity of the circular sweep. Errors due to nonlinearity of the sweep will not be discussed here, but an account of them can be found in the Radiation Laboratory Series of the Massachusetts Institute of Technology.* In the case of the circular-sweep calibrator that has been described, the absolute error in time for the 10-μsec circle is about $\pm 0.1 \mu$sec, and for the 1-μ sec circle, about ± 0.02 μsec.

As an example of how the calibrator is used, suppose one wishes to calibrate the delay-control dial of one of the trigger delay circuits described in Chap. 5, Sec. 5. The positive output trigger of the calibrator is connected to the trigger delay circuit, and the delayed output pulse is connected to the deflecting electrode of the cathode-ray tube having the 10-μsec circle. The delay control of the trigger circuit is set to zero, and switches SW-1 and SW-2 are both thrown to position 1. The output pulse from the trigger delay circuit should now appear on the circle displaced a small angle from the position that the trigger from the calibrator occupies when it is presented on the circle. If the delay control of the circuit under calibration is advanced, the output pulse will rotate in the direction of rotation of the sweep, i.e., clockwise. Before the delay has reached 10 μsec, the pulse reaches the end of the intensifier gate. Switch SW-1 is then thrown to position 2, and the control for long delays is set to the minimum delay position (about 5 μsec). As the delay of the pulse is increased, the intensifier gate can now be delayed so that the pulse always appears on the circle. Evidently it is a simple matter to obtain a calibration of the trigger delay circuit by relating the readings of the delay-control dial with times determined by the calibrator. If more accurate values of the delay are required, essentially the same method can be employed with the 1-μsec circle. Here, however, more care must be taken to keep track of the number of revolutions through which the pulse passes as its delay is increased. The switch SW-3 will normally be used in position 2 for delays less than 8 μsec, and switch SW-4 will be used to advance the delay of the intensifier

*McGraw-Hill Book Company, Inc., New York.

gate. For longer delays, SW-3 is thrown to position 1, and the control for long delays is used. If the pulse is presented on both circles at once, it will rotate ten times on the 1-μsec circle while it rotates once on the 10-μsec circle.

For some applications it is desirable to incorporate a one- or two-stage wide-band amplifier in the calibrator so that low-level pulses can be observed on the cathode-ray-tube screens. The deflection factor for the axial electrode of the 3DP1 is about 550 volts per inch.

4.2 A Sweep-speed Calibrator. Two time-marker generators based on pulsed LC oscillators have already been described in Chap. 5, Sec. 4. The circuit shown in Fig. 6.14 is intended for similar applications, but owing to its greater utility for making routine calibrations in an electronics laboratory it is discussed in this chapter. The calibrator, in response to a fast positive input trigger of 25-volt amplitude, or more, generates simultaneously three sequences of narrow positive pulses spaced 0.5, 1, and 5 μsec apart, respectively. Each sequence of pulses lasts about 150 μsec.

The first portion of the calibrator is very similar to the Model 3 marker generator (Fig. 5.4), and contains a univibrator gate circuit, a pulsed LC oscillator having a frequency of 2 megacycles per second, and a blocking oscillator to furnish positive output pulses spaced 0.5 μsec apart. Tube T-3, which clamps the oscillator and provides for a storage of energy in the oscillator tank coil, passes a steady current of about 35 ma. A current of this magnitude is necessary in view of the small inductance required for the oscillator inductor. (See Chap. 2, Sec. 3.6, for a discussion of pulsed LC oscillators.)

The blocking oscillator based on tube T-7 not only furnishes output pulses at a 2-megacycle-per-second frequency but also serves to trigger the blocking oscillator based on tube T-9 at a frequency of 1 megacycle per second. A similar arrangement is used to produce output pulses at 200 kilocycles per second. In each of the blocking-oscillator frequency dividers, two adjustments are provided, one controlling the grid bias and the other the grid-circuit time constant. The grid bias must be adjusted to prevent the blocking oscillators from running free. The time constant is then adjusted until a stable frequency division of the proper magnitude is obtained. The stability of the circuit is comparable to that of the Model 3 marker generator.

4.3 Double-pulse Generators. The calibration of various sorts of time discriminators is best made with a double-pulse generator that provides pulses of a form similar to those with which the discriminator will be used. When the shape of the two pulses is not very important, the trigger delay circuits described in Chap. 5, Sec. 5, can

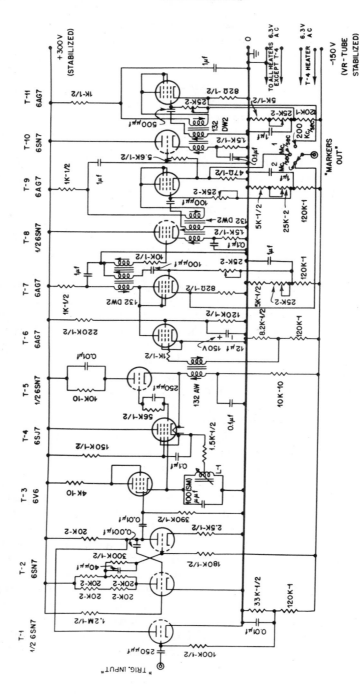

Fig. 6.14—Sweep-speed calibrator.

be used to supply two pulses whose time separation can be varied. In these circuits the delay between an input trigger and a delayed output trigger is obtained by use of a saw-tooth generator that is direct-coupled to a stable amplitude discriminator. This principle of operation is particularly suitable for double-pulse generators where relatively long times occur between the two pulses, i.e., times greater than a few microseconds. For closely spaced pulses it is more satisfactory to base the timing on delay lines, which may be either of the tapped lumped-parameter type or of the continuously variable type (see Chap. 2, Sec. 2.4). A combination of delay lines of the two types is a particularly useful means of covering continuously a range from zero to several microseconds.

Two double-pulse generators will be described here. One of them is suitable for covering the range from a few microseconds to 10 milliseconds. It has been used to calibrate the distribution discriminator described in Chap. 4, Sec. 3.2(d). The other generator is, strictly speaking, a trigger delay circuit covering the range from a few tenths of a microsecond to 5 μsec. It has been used to calibrate the ten-channel delay discriminator described in Chap. 4, Sec. 3.2(c).

Figure 6.15 shows the circuit of the first double-pulse generator. The apparent complexity of the device arises from the fact that it contains circuits required for calibration purposes. Additional equipment needed includes a stable sinusoidal-signal generator to furnish timing, and a conventional laboratory oscillograph to aid in making the dial that controls the separation of the two pulses read directly in time. The double-pulse generator proper will be described first, and then the circuits required for calibrating the delay control.

The basic rate of occurrence of the pairs of pulses is determined by the multivibrator based on T-1. Frequencies from about 10 to 30 cycles per second can be obtained by adjusting the "Rate" control. The multivibrator serves to trigger the univibrator based on T-2 [see Chap. 2, Sec. 4.2(b)]. The univibrator furnishes a gating signal to the cathode of the left-hand section of T-3 just long enough to select one trigger from the Schmitt trigger circuit comprising tubes T-5 and T-6 [see Chap. 2, Sec. 4.3(c)]. Three gate lengths can be selected by SW-1. They are suitable for input frequencies of 1, 10, or 100 kilocycles per second supplied by the external oscillator. It should be noted that the Schmitt trigger circuit generates one narrow positive pulse for each oscillation of the input sine wave. The blocking-oscillator transformer in the plate circuit of T-5 serves to differentiate the square-wave signal present there and to supply it to the grid of the left-hand section of T-3 and to the grid of T-7B. The output signal from T-7B is used in calibrating the instrument.

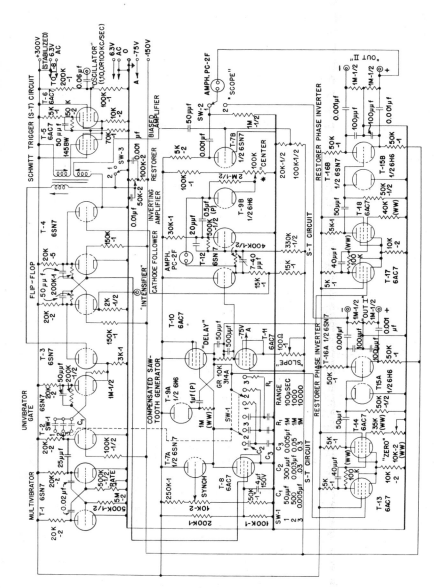

Fig. 6.15—Double-pulse generator for time calibrations in the ranges 0 to 0.1, 1, and 10 milliseconds.

The gated trigger pulse causes the flip-flop [Chap. 2, Sec. 4.3(b)], tubes T-3 and T-4, to pass to the state where the right-hand half of T-3 is conducting. A negative gating pulse is thereby supplied to the compensated saw-tooth generator (see Chap. 2, Sec. 3.7), which proceeds to produce a linearly increasing voltage at the cathode of T-10. This signal first triggers the simple amplitude discriminator based on tubes T-13 and T-14, producing positive and negative output pulses at the plate and cathode, respectively, of T-16A. It then triggers a similar circuit element producing a second pair of pulses at tube T-16B. The delay between the two sets of pulses is controlled by the potentiometer labeled "Delay" located in the cathode circuit of T-10. This potentiometer varies the d-c level but not the slope of the saw-tooth signal applied to T-17. This condition is the result of using a constant-current tube, T-11, as the remainder of the cathode load of T-10 (see Chap. 2, Sec. 3.7). The slope of the saw-toothed wave is controlled by varying the magnitude of the constant current by changing the cathode resistor of T-11. This adjustment is used to make the "Delay" control direct reading.

In order to measure the separation of the two output pulses in terms of the fixed frequency that furnishes the fundamental time scale, the saw-toothed wave is supplied to tube T-12, which generates a push-pull voltage for driving the sweep of an oscillograph. An intensifier-gate signal for the oscillograph is obtained from tube T-3. Each time the flip-flop is triggered, a sweep is produced having an accurate time lock with the input sine wave. The sweep is terminated automatically by the return of the flip-flop to its original state. This occurs when the right-hand section of T-4 begins to conduct because a portion of the saw-toothed wave is applied to its grid. The entire circuit is then restored to its original state.

To calibrate the delay control, the connection labeled "Scope" is made to the Y-deflecting plates of the oscillograph, and switch SW-2 is thrown to position 2. The dial of the delay control is set at zero, and the two output pulses observed on the oscillograph will usually not coincide but can be made to coincide by varying the "Zero" potentiometer in the grid circuit of T-14. Switch SW-2 is then thrown to position 1, and the sequence of pulses derived from the input sine wave and the delayed pulse (still at zero delay) can be seen. By varying the "Synch." control, the output pulse can be made to fall on one of the timing pulses. The delay control is now advanced so that it reads 10. If the delayed output pulse does not fall on the next timing pulse, the "Slope" control is varied until it does. If the delay control is set in turn on 20, 30, ... , 100, the delayed pulse should fall on the second, third, ... , tenth timing pulse, respectively. Any small progressive error can be corrected by further adjustment of the "Slope" control. The double-pulse generator is now calibrated so that it is direct reading on the "Delay" dial. It is necessary to go through this procedure each time the frequency of the timing oscillator is changed. The circuit has been designed to use frequencies of 1, 10, or 100 kilocycles per second, giving ranges of 10^2, 10^3, or 10^4 μsec, respectively, over which the separation of the two output pulses can be continuously varied. The switch SW-1 selects not only the proper slope for the saw-tooth wave for each of these ranges but also a suitable length for the gating pulse supplied by the univibrator (tube T-2).

The output pulses have a rise time of a few tenths of a microsecond and a decay time constant of perhaps 5 μsec. It is desirable to lengthen the decay constant of the pulses if they are to be used with a pulse amplifier having a long rise time. The first of the two pulses is obtained at the connectors labeled "Out I," and the second at the connectors "Out II."

The double-pulse generator can be used to determine the width and the position of a channel in a distribution discriminator. The first pulse is used to initiate the operation of the discriminator. The second pulse can then be varied in time to locate the boundaries of the time channel, as indicated by the occurrence or lack of occurrence of counts in the channel.

The second double-pulse generator to be considered here has the circuit shown in Fig. 6.16. This instrument has been specifically designed for calibrating the ten-channel delay discriminator described in Chap. 4, Sec. 3.2(c). It is necessary to refer to the discussion there in order to explain its purpose. It will be recalled that the delay discriminator is used with an accelerator that is modulated at a high repetition rate (in the range 50 to 150 kilocycles per second). A master oscillator serves the purpose of triggering both the modulating circuit and the delay discriminator. To measure the widths in time of the various channels in the discriminator, it appears best to make use of trigger pulses coming from the master oscillator. By delaying these pulses by a variable but known amount and applying them to the delay discriminator in place of pulses normally originating in the electrical detector of radiation, the delay discriminator can be calibrated. Since the delay discriminator is capable of recording pulses only at a very low repetition rate (it contains no scaling circuits), it is necessary to select only a few of the available pulses for calibration purposes.

The circuit of Fig. 6.16 therefore serves the double purpose of selecting pulses at a low repetition rate and of delaying the pulses it selects by a known but variable amount. The output pulses are obtained from a blocking oscillator. They are about 0.1 μsec wide at

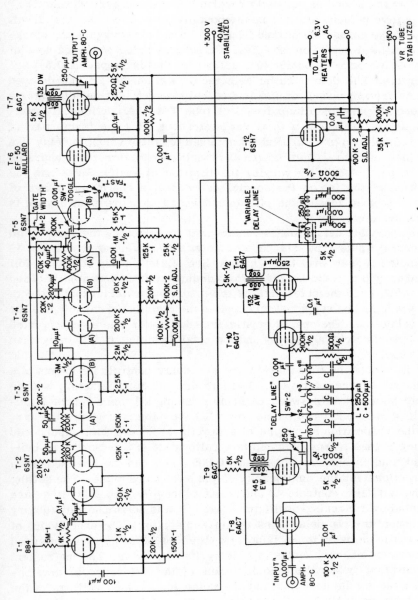

Fig. 6.16 — Pulse generator for time calibrations in the range 0 to 5 μsec.

their base and have an amplitude of about 100 volts, i.e., they are similar to the pulses normally received by the delay discriminator.

Positive pulses from the master oscillator are fed into the circuit through the connector marked "Input." Each pulse triggers the blocking oscillator based on tube T-9. Pulses generated at the cathode of this oscillator are coupled to a delay line that is tapped at 0.5-μsec intervals. The delay can be selected by switch SW-2. The delayed pulses are impressed on the grid of T-10, which is used to trigger a second blocking oscillator based on tube T-11. A continuously variable delay line having a total range of about 0.5 μsec forms part of the cathode load of T-11. Pulses obtained from the variable delay line are then used to trigger the final blocking oscillator that generates the output pulses. By varying the position of switch SW-2 and the position of the tap on the special delay line, a continuous range of delays from a few tenths of a microsecond to more than 5 μsec is made available.

The variable delay line is constructed by removing the turns from a General Radio type 314 potentiometer and rewinding it with No. 34 enameled copper wire (see Chap. 2, Sec. 2.4). A strip of copper foil equal in width to the height of the winding strip is mounted between the winding and the outer strip of the insulating material that protects the winding. The copper strip supplies the distributed capacitance for the delay line. The characteristic impedance of a line so constructed is approximately 500 ohms, and the total delay is slightly more than 0.5 μsec.

It is necessary to calibrate the two delay controls by means of a standard source of timing. Perhaps the most satisfactory source would be a circular-sweep calibrator having a 1-μsec circle as described in Sec. 2.1 of this chapter. It is possible, however, to carry out the calibration by means of a fast linear sweep with superposed timing signals. Data obtained in a calibration of this sort have indicated that an accuracy of about ± 0.005 μsec can be realized when corrections for the nonlinearity of the sweep are made. The setting of the two delay controls is independent since the two delay lines are isolated by a blocking-oscillator stage. (It was not found satisfactory to connect the two delay lines directly in series.) The exact value of the minimum delay is not important when the pulse generator is used to measure channel widths in a delay discriminator. The instrument is therefore best calibrated in terms of the difference in time between the minimum delay and the delay for various settings of the two delay controls. The calibration is recorded as a table of values for switch SW-2 and as a graph for the variable delay line.

Let us now consider the portion of the circuit used for selecting pulses. The repetition rate is set by the thyratron relaxation oscillator based on tube T-1. The oscillator runs free at about 5 cycles per second and furnishes trigger pulses to the flip-flop [see Chap. 2, Sec. 4.3(b)] utilizing tubes T-2 and T-3. When the flip-flop is triggered, a negative gating signal of about 20-volt amplitude is impressed on the cathode of T-4A, which cuts off the current through T-3A, allowing the three common cathodes to drop to ground potential. The next delayed blocking-oscillator pulse appearing at the grid of T-4A triggers the univibrator comprising tubes T-4B and T-5A. As soon as the univibrator is triggered, tube T-3B becomes conducting and triggers the flip-flop back to its original state, preventing later blocking-oscillator pulses at the grid of T-4A from affecting the operation of the univibrator. The univibrator supplies, through the cathode follower T-5B, a positive gating pulse to the suppressor of tube T-6. The duration of the univibrator gate can be adjusted by the control marked "Gate Width" in order that the output blocking oscillator may be triggered only by the next pulse occurring at the grid of T-6, but not by later pulses. The complexity of the circuit has been shown to be necessary. If precautions are not taken to make sure that a pulse to be gated cannot fall at the edge of a gate, "jitter" (small time fluctuations) will result.

A Mullard tube, type EF-50, has been used for T-6, since a tube of this type has a good suppressor-control characteristic. A type 6AS6 tube can be substituted for the EF-50. (The type 6AS6 was not available when the circuit was designed.)

It is evident that output pulses are obtained at a rate set by the thyratron relaxation oscillator. However, the circuit used to select pulses does not interfere in any way with the timing afforded by the delay lines. When the pulse generator is being calibrated—for instance, by means of a circular-sweep calibrator—the pulse-selecting portion of the circuit can be made inoperative by throwing switch SW-1 to position 2.

4.4 A Simple Counter Chronograph. One method much used for measuring the time between two pulses consists in presenting the pulses on the sweep of an oscillograph, together with timing marks, and obtaining a photographic record from which the desired information can be read. For those types of experimental work where it is desirable to know the time separation immediately, a counter chronograph constitutes an alternative method of measurement that has many points in its favor. Not only is the answer immediately available, but the method is capable of greater accuracy when the times to be measured are long compared with the resolving time of the counter used.

A counter chronograph usually contains a gating circuit that is turned on by one pulse and turned off by the second pulse. During the interval of the gate, pulses of a standard frequency are allowed to reach a counting circuit (scaling circuit) of the general type described in Chap. 4. It is possible to build counter chronographs for frequencies as high as 3 megacycles per second, the limitation in frequency resting principally in the scaling circuit. In the present section a very simple counter chronograph will be described. It is suitable for use with a counter having only a moderate resolving time, such as 5 μsec.

The circuit of the counter chronograph is shown in Fig. 6.17. It has been designed to accept negative pulses having an amplitude of a few millivolts or more. The pulses to be calibrated can come from an electrical circuit, a photocell, some sort of electromagnetic pickup, or an acoustic pickup. The first pulse, or "Starting Trigger," is amplified by a two-stage amplifier whose gain is approximately 10,000. It is used to trigger the flip-flop based on tubes T-5B and T-6A. The flip-flop furnishes a gating signal to the gating tube T-7. The "Stopping Trigger" passes through a similar path and returns the flip-flop to its initial state, thus terminating the gating signal. No provision has been made to lock the circuit against subsequent trigger pulses.

The source of timing must be supplied by an external sinusoidal-signal generator whose output signal has an amplitude of at least 10 volts. Tube T-8 is an amplifier stage whose output signal is so large that the grid of T-7 draws grid current and automatically biases itself to the proper operating condition. When the positive gate is impressed on T-7, a series of negative pulses, one for each oscillation, are produced at its plate. These pulses are coupled to an external counting circuit that records the number of oscillations of the input sine wave occurring in the interval between the starting and stopping triggers. This particular counter chronograph has been used with frequencies of 100 kilocycles per second and below.

5. SOME USEFUL TESTING AIDS

In this section the circuits of a multiple-trigger generator and a low-range capacitance bridge will be described. These two devices have been chosen for discussion here from among a number of special testing circuits that have proved useful in electronics development work.

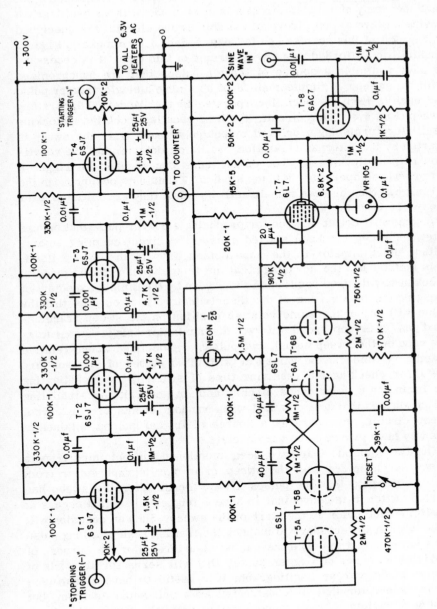

Fig. 6.17—Counter chronograph.

5.1 A Multiple-trigger Generator. It has already been pointed out that the study of trigger circuits is best made with an oscillograph having a slave sweep. (Several suitable sweep circuits are described in Sec. 2.1 of this chapter and in Chap. 5, Sec. 3.) To make full use of possibilities afforded by a sweep circuit of this type, it is necessary to have available a source of trigger pulses that are synchronized with the sweep. A simple method of obtaining a single trigger pulse for each sweep has been incorporated in the Model 50 laboratory sweep (Fig. 6.3). This circuit, it will be recalled, contains a blocking oscillator furnishing a delayed output pulse each time the sweep is started by the internal relaxation oscillator determining the repetition rate of the sweep. The output pulse can be used to trigger a circuit whose operation is being studied. Transients occurring in the circuit can then be seen in their entirety since they are initiated after the sweep is under way.

A somewhat better scheme for producing a trigger pulse that occurs after the sweep has been started consists in direct-coupling an amplitude discriminator to the saw-toothed wave of the sweep itself. This method has the advantage that the trigger pulse can be made to occur at any desired position on the sweep by the simple expedient of changing the bias setting of the discriminator. It is obvious that the pulse will fall at the same relative position on the sweep trace regardless of sweep speed. If two discriminator-trigger generators are used on the sweep signal, two pulses are obtained whose relative spacing in time can be varied at will. Two pulses of this sort are useful for checking the resolving time of scalers, for investigating the timing in a coincidence circuit, and, in general, for simulating the conditions that are obtained when random events are observed. Sweep circuits incorporating a source of trigger pulses obtained in this way have proved to be very useful.

The two methods that have been mentioned for obtaining trigger pulses synchronized with the sweep of an oscillograph suffer from the disadvantage that the pulses always occur after the sweep has started. Often it is convenient to have a trigger pulse that occurs at a definite time prior to the start of the sweep. Such an occasion will arise when it is necessary to inspect the trailing edge of a long pulse while using a fast sweep to reveal its structure. For the purpose of providing a source of trigger pulses that will serve for all sorts of studies made with an oscillograph, it is useful to have a multiple-trigger generator that is constructed as a unit separate from, but used in a variety of ways in conjunction with, the sweep circuit. A multiple-trigger circuit of this sort, Fig. 6.18, will now be described.

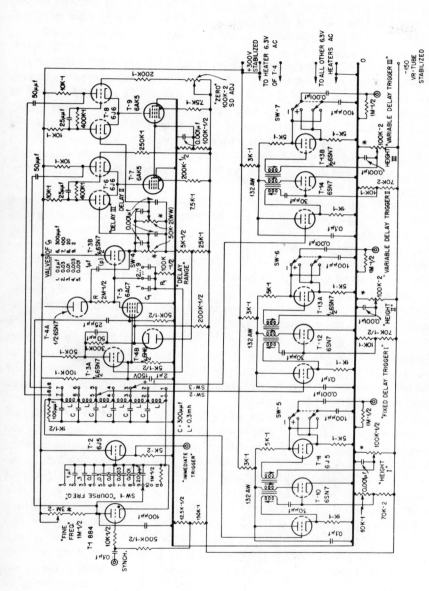

Fig. 6.18—Multiple-trigger generator.

The thyratron relaxation oscillator based on tube T-1 serves the purpose of establishing the repetition rate at which pulses are generated. Both fine and coarse frequency controls are provided to enable a range of frequencies from about 0.3 cycle per second to 30 kilocycles per second to be covered continuously. An external "Synch." connection enables the relaxation oscillator to be synchronized with an external frequency source when this mode of operation seems desirable. If switch SW-1 is thrown to position 11 and the control in the plate circuit of the thyratron is advanced toward a lower plate-load resistance, the thyratron is biased off but is still capable of being triggered by an external signal applied through the "Synch." connector. Tube T-2 is a cathode follower that serves to couple out an "Immediate Trigger"—one of the four output pulses provided by the circuit.

Standard pulses generated by the thyratron oscillator are obtained from the thyratron cathode and impressed on a tapped delay line having a range of 1.8 μsec in 0.3-μsec steps. Pulses from the delay line can be selected independently by SW-2 and SW-3 to trigger two identical biased blocking oscillators that generate positive or negative pulses available at the two delayed-trigger output connectors.

The amplitude of the output pulses is controlled by varying the biasing of the two phase inverters that couple out the blocking-oscillator pulses. Output pulses having a rise time of about 0.2 μsec and amplitudes in the range 0 to 75 volts are made available in this way. A third blocking oscillator is permanently coupled to the far end of the delay line, in order to supply pulses that are always delayed the same fixed time (1.8 μsec) following the immediate trigger obtained from the cathode of the thyratron.

When pulses having a range of delays longer than that provided by the tapped delay line are required, the switches SW-2 and SW-3 are placed in position 8. The two biased blocking oscillators furnishing output pulses of variable delay are now connected to two amplitude discriminators that are triggered by the signal from a self-gating saw-tooth generator. The slope of the saw-toothed wave can be varied by switch SW-4 for coarse steps in the range of delays. Continuous control of the timing of the delayed pulses is provided by the two potentiometers in the cathode circuit of tube T-3B.

For an understanding of the operation of this portion of the circuit, let us first consider the saw-tooth generator comprising tubes T-3, T-4, and T-5. Normally tube T-5, which constitutes a clamp, is drawing grid current, and the current through T-3A is cut off. Current is flowing through the diode T-4A, the 2-megohm resistor R, and the clamp, which are all in series. When tube T-5 receives from the

thyratron a large negative pulse at its suppressor, the current transfers to the capacitor C_1 selected by SW-4 and returns to ground
through resistor R_1. The resulting positive step in potential across
R_1 is coupled to the grid of T-3A, which now draws current and temporarily biases off the clamp tube. The signal at the grid of the cathode follower T-3B consists of the positive step in potential appearing
across R_1, followed by an almost linear increase in potential. Indeed,
the operation of the circuit is now identical to that of the saw-tooth
generator described in Chap. 2, Sec. 3.7. When the linearly increasing signal reaches a certain level, the diode T-4B causes the grid of
T-5 to return to zero potential, thus automatically restoring the circuit to its initial condition.

Tubes T-6 and T-7, with associated components, constitute one of
two similar amplitude discriminators of the Schmitt trigger variety
[see Chap. 2, Sec. 4.3(c)]. Each circuit element serves to trigger
one of the blocking oscillators generating output pulses. The discriminators are direct-coupled to the saw-tooth generator so that the
absolute spacing of the output pulses is independent of the primary
repetition frequency. With this feature, delays can be set at a frequency that allows visual observation of an oscillograph. The frequency can then be decreased to a very low value for testing circuits
that cannot be operated at high regular pulse rates. The range of
total delays made available by switch SW-4 goes from 3 μsec to 0.1
sec. A continuous control covering each step in the range is provided
by the two potentiometers in the cathode circuit of T-3B.

The method of using the multiple-trigger generator requires little
discussion. Any one of the four output pulses can serve to start the
oscillograph sweep, leaving the other three output pulses available
for triggering circuits under study. For short delays the tapped delay
line affords a stable control of the delay time. For long delays the
sweep is normally started by the pulse having a fixed delay with respect to the firing of the thyratron. This enables the two pulses of
variable delay to be placed anywhere on the sweep of the oscillograph,
since the minimum delay of the saw-tooth delay circuit is less than
the delay of the delay line (1.8 μsec). Other methods of using the
multiple-trigger generator can be chosen to meet particular needs
that arise. It should be noted that any two of the output connections
can be placed in parallel if double pulses are required.

5.2 A Low-range Capacitance Bridge. The presence of stray (or
parasitic) capacitance in an electronic circuit often has an important
influence on the operation of the circuit. This is particularly true in
the case of wide-band amplifiers and in the case of trigger circuits
designed for fast operation. Although it is often possible to estimate

with sufficient accuracy the capacitance that is present, it is convenient to have a portable instrument available for actually measuring the
capacitance.

The low-range capacitance bridge shown in Fig. 6.19 has been designed to measure values of capacitances in the range 0 to about 100
$\mu\mu$f. The absolute accuracy that can be obtained depends on the calibration of a standard variable capacitor, since the bridge makes use
of the method of substitution. Sensitivity of adjustment for balance
is about 0.1 $\mu\mu$f. Any resistance greater than about 5×10^4 ohms in
parallel with the capacitance under measurement can be balanced out
by means of variable resistances in one of the arms of the bridge.
In addition to the bridge, the complete instrument contains an RC oscillator (10 kilocycles per second) and a detector for indicating when
the bridge is balanced. If desired, an external detector—for instance,
a cathode-ray oscillograph—can be used.

Tube T-1 and associated parts constitute an RC oscillator that is
stabilized by a tungsten-lamp inverse-feedback element [see Chap. 2,
Sec. 3.6(a)]. Tube T-2 serves to couple the oscillator to the bridge.
A General Radio type 578-A shielded transformer is used to isolate
the bridge from the detector. Both shields in the transformer are
connected to ground. The output signal from the transformer is amplified by a two-stage amplifier, one stage of which contains an LC
plate load tuned to 10 kilocycles per second. The tuned plate load
prevents hum, and also higher harmonics of the oscillator waveform,
from interfering with the balancing of the bridge. The null indicator
consists of a milliammeter, the current through which is cut off when
the bridge is out of balance.

The bridge proper contains two arms that are essentially capacitive and two arms that consist of resistance and capacitance in parallel. (It has been found necessary to insert a resistance of 97 ohms in
series with the 0.0035-μf capacitor to compensate for losses in the
1-μf paper capacitor used in the adjacent bridge arm.) The three
variable capacitors present in the arm where the unknown capacitance
is connected serve the following purpose: The 20- and 100-$\mu\mu$f variable capacitors are set to nearly full capacitance, and their dials are
arranged to read zero in this position. The bridge is then brought
into balance by adjusting the remaining capacitor and the variable
resistors in the adjacent arm. When an unknown capacitance is connected to the bridge, a new balance is obtained by reducing one or the
other of the variable capacitors and by adjusting the variable capacitor used to balance the bridge. This dial, of course, must be calibrated to read directly in capacitance.

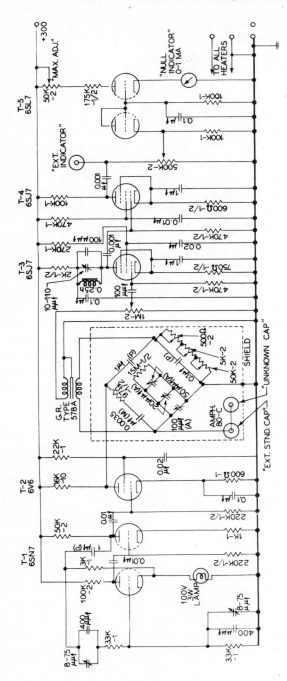

Fig. 6.19—Low-range capacitance bridge.

For measuring the wiring capacitance existing in a circuit, the best technique seems to consist in connecting a coaxial cable to the bridge, the other end of which has perhaps 1 cm of the central conductor exposed. The end of this cable is placed near the circuit to be measured, and the bridge is balanced. The central conductor is then temporarily soldered to the circuit, and a new balance is obtained. It is necessary, of course, to arrange the geometry of the connection in such a way as to avoid increasing the parasitic capacitance of the circuit under measurement. In addition, care must be taken to ensure that the network under measurement consists solely of a resistance greater than 50,000 ohms and the unknown capacitance in parallel. If the interstage parasitic capacitance of a wide-band amplifier is being measured, it is usually necessary to connect a jumper across the plate-to-grid coupling capacitor.

Chapter 7

POWER SUPPLIES AND CONTROL CIRCUITS

By William C. Elmore

1. INTRODUCTION

The first part of this chapter gives descriptions of a number of typical power supplies, most of them electronically stabilized. These supplies, or simple modifications of them, have been used with the various circuits described in preceding chapters. No discussion is given of ordinary unstabilized supplies, since their design is adequately treated in most electronics texts and handbooks.

Considerable experience with different voltage-stabilizing circuits indicates that those of the simple degenerative type are the most generally satisfactory.* A sufficient number of circuits of this type will be given to enable the reader to choose power supplies suitable for the circuits described in earlier chapters. Specific transformers, chokes, and certain other components will be given in diagrams, but the substitution of components of comparable ratings, made by other manufacturers, will not normally affect the operation of the supply. It has been found that certain components, notably transformers, occasionally appear to be overrated by their manufacturers, particularly in regard to power dissipation. These components, however, will perform satisfactorily at perhaps three-quarters of the listed rating.

The second part of this chapter is devoted to several control circuits that are useful in certain types of laboratory work.

2. SIMPLE THEORY OF VOLTAGE-STABILIZING CIRCUITS OF DEGENERATIVE TYPE

A voltage-stabilized power supply accomplishes more than simply furnishing a d-c voltage of a fairly stable value. It affords a low

---

*For a discussion of various types of voltage-stabilizing circuits, see F. V. Hunt and R. W. Hickman, Rev. Sci. Instruments, 10: 6 (1939).

source impedance, considerably reducing the interaction between various parts of a circuit for which it furnishes plate power, and the stabilizing circuit itself acts as an excellent filter for ripple voltages. In order to compare different stabilized power supplies, it is convenient to define the stabilization factor

$$S = \frac{E_o}{E_s} \frac{dE_s}{dE_o} \tag{1}$$

where E_s is the supply-mains voltage and E_o is the stabilized d-c output voltage; and to define the output, or source impedance,

$$R_o = -\frac{dE_o}{dI_o} = -\frac{e_o}{i_o} \tag{2}$$

where I_o is the current supplied the load. The most interesting property of the stabilizing circuit itself is expressed by the smoothing factor

$$\alpha = \frac{dE_o}{dE_1} = \frac{e_o}{e_1} \tag{3}$$

where E_1 is the output voltage of the transformer-rectifier-filter circuit preceding the stabilizing circuit.

It is evident that the quantities defined in Eqs. 1 and 2 specify the most important features of a voltage-stabilized supply. The smoothing factor, defined in Eq. 3, enables an estimate to be made of the ripple voltage at the output, if the ripple voltage at the input of the stabilizing circuit is known. Within the range of stabilization, all three quantities will not generally be constants, but their value will depend somewhat on the loading of the supply, the value of the supply-mains voltage, etc. To compare the performance of different circuits, it is usually sufficient to obtain only approximate values for S, R_o, and α.

The basic circuit of most stabilized supplies of the degenerative type is indicated in Fig. 7.1(a). The circuit consists of a conventional transformer-rectifier-filter supply, indicated by the block T-R-F, followed by a triode connected in series with the positive supply bus. A fraction β of the output voltage is compared with a fixed voltage E, obtained either from a VR tube or from a battery of dry cells. The difference between the two voltages is amplified by a difference amplifier (see Chap. 2, Sec. 3.3) of gain G and is used to control the grid bias of the series triode, so as to afford a degenerative compensation for any change in circuit conditions that tends to alter the existing output voltage. All circuit voltages must be so arranged that d-c coupling can be used throughout the amplifier. Where this type of coupling results in a loss in gain, resistors can be by-passed by capacitors so that a greater degeneration is obtained for a-c signals —in particular, for ripple voltages.

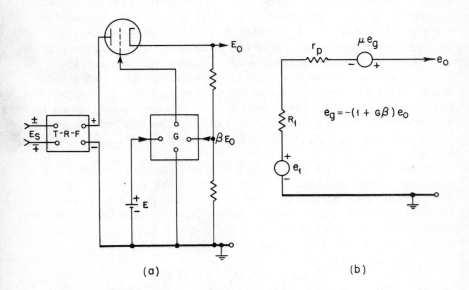

(a)   (b)

Fig. 7.1 — Basic circuit of a stabilized supply of the degenerative type.

A simplified equivalent circuit is shown in Fig. 7.1(b), where R_1 is the source impedance of the transformer-rectifier-filter combination, and r_p and μ are the plate resistance and the amplification factor, respectively, of the triode. By means of a simple circuit analysis, it is found that

$$S \approx \frac{E_o}{E_1} \mu\beta G \tag{4}$$

$$R_o \approx \frac{R_1 + r_p}{\mu\beta G} \tag{5}$$

$$\alpha \approx \frac{1}{\mu\beta G} \tag{6}$$

when $\beta G \gg 1$.

In the case of practical power supplies the plate-load resistor of the final stage of the difference amplifier is often connected to the plate side of the series triode instead of to the cathode side. This arrangement is chosen in order to maintain an adequate gain for the difference amplifier as the grid bias of the series triode approaches zero. An unfortunate result of this arrangement is a net reduction in the gain of the difference amplifier. One may attribute the reduction in gain to a form of Miller effect in which the effective resistance of the plate-load resistor is reduced by feedback between the plate and grid of the series triode. Exact expressions for S, R_o, and α show that the approximate expressions for S and α, Eqs. 4 and 6, are in error to an extent different from the error in the expression for R_o, Eq. 5. In the case of power supplies to be described, it turns out that the discrepancy in all three expressions can be roughly taken into account by assuming a value for the gain G of the difference amplifier that is one-half the value computed on the basis of a fixed plate-supply voltage.

Let us now consider what values of S, R_o and α can be obtained in practical power supplies. One of the simplest types of stabilizing circuits, such as the circuit used in the Model 200 supply, Fig. 7.5, employs a single 6SJ7 pentode as a difference amplifier, and the comparison voltage is about one-third of the output voltage. Reasonable values for the various quantities involved are

E_0 = 300 volts, E_1 = 550 volts, R_1 = 800 ohms,
G = 125, μ = 5, r_p = 750 ohms, $\beta = \frac{1}{3}$ (for steady voltages)

$\beta = 1$ (for ripple voltages)

Hence we find that

$$S \approx 115$$

$$R_o \approx 7.4 \text{ ohms}$$

$$\alpha \approx 1.6 \times 10^{-3} \quad \text{(for ripple voltages)}$$

For the sake of comparison, let us make the same computation for the Model 50 supply, Fig. 7.3, which contains a more elaborate difference amplifier. Reasonable values for this circuit are

$$R_1 = 800 \text{ ohms, } G = 850, \; \mu = 5, \; r_p = 375 \text{ ohms}$$

with the same values for E_0, E_1, and β as before.

We now find that

$$S \approx 770$$

$$R_o \approx 0.83 \text{ ohms}$$

$$\alpha \approx 2.3 \times 10^{-4} \quad \text{(for ripple voltages)}$$

The theoretical performance of this supply constitutes a certain improvement over that of the simpler supply. For many applications, however, the better performance may represent an unnecessary refinement.

Measurements made on the two supplies tend to confirm the results of these computations. Usually, however, the performance of a stabilized supply employing a VR tube to furnish a comparison voltage will not be so good as that predicted from the values computed. The discrepancy can be accounted for in terms of the behavior of the average VR tube, which cannot be considered as an ideal constant-voltage source or even as a constant-voltage source in series with a low resistance. Some of the complexities in the behavior of VR tubes are pointed out in the next section. A stabilized supply based on a VR-tube comparison voltage is usually adequate for all but the most exacting applications, and it is somewhat more convenient than one in which a comparison voltage is obtained from dry cells.

Another important characteristic of a stabilized power supply is the manner of its response to a sudden change in load. Since the gain of the difference amplifier falls off rapidly at frequencies much above those in the audio range and since a progressively increasing phase shift sets in, the output impedance will no longer be a few ohms at high frequencies or for sudden changes in load but will, instead, be much higher. For this reason it is essential to connect a capacitor of high value, usually of the electrolytic type, across the output of the supply. The impedance of the capacitor becomes low in the frequency range where the feedback stabilization begins to fail. Indeed, without the capacitor most circuits having a difference amplifier of two or more stages will oscillate at some high frequency.

3. VR-TUBE STABILIZED POWER SUPPLIES

In applications where the current load is relatively small and subject to limited variations, it is more economical to employ simple VR-tube stabilization than to construct an electronically stabilized supply. In practical circuits it is usually found that a negative bias supply, when used, can be stabilized in this way. The degree of stabilization obtained with a VR tube is considerably less than that obtained with a simple stabilized supply of the degenerative type and a VR tube for the comparison voltage.

Before considering the design of a VR-tube supply, it is worth while to point out some properties of VR tubes that do not seem to be generally recognized. Although information in tube handbooks correctly indicates the degree of stabilization that can be obtained if steady current through the tube is restricted to the specified limits (5 to 40 ma for the VR-75, VR-105, and VR-150), the voltage across the tube is not found to be a simple function of the value of the current. For slow changes in current there are several limited regions where the tubes may possess a negative-resistance characteristic and other regions where discontinuous changes in the current-voltage characteristic take place. The discontinuities may be as large as a few tenths of a volt; associated with them may be a marked hysteresis effect between voltage and current when the current is varied cyclically in the vicinity of a discontinuity. When the current through the tube is varied over a major portion of its operating range, the entire voltage-current characteristic widens into a type of hysteresis loop of the sort illustrated in Fig. 7.2. This figure has been drawn from a cathode-ray-tube presentation of the phenomenon.

It is impossible here to do more than point out the existence of these effects and indicate their order of magnitude. The position and magnitude of the discontinuities and the shape of the hysteresis loop differ from tube to tube. The hysteresis effect is dependent on the frequency at which the current is varied. The occurrence of a voltage discontinuity is usually associated with a sudden redistribution of part of the glow over the area of the cathode of the VR tube.

Evidently the effects that have been described may be undesirable in certain types of circuits. If a VR tube is used to furnish a comparison voltage in an electronically stabilized supply, for the sake of good stability the current through the tube should be drawn from the stabilized side of the supply. Some care may have to be exercised in choosing the value of the steady current to avoid locating it near a discontinuity. In the case of simple VR-tube stabilized supplies, the hysteresis effect, which is usually most marked for current changes in the lower half of the operating range, means that the tube will be less effective as a filter for ripple voltages than might be expected from its average static characteristic. Experience shows that placing a capacitor of 1 μf or more in parallel with a VR tube often causes trouble in the form of relaxation oscillations. These oscillations are very likely associated with the regions of negative resistance of the VR tube. No careful study, however, has been made of this behavior.

A capacitance of 0.1 μf has always been found to be a safe value to place in parallel with a VR tube.

Let us now consider some quantitative aspects in the design of a simple VR-tube stabilized supply. If the load current always remains in the range I_{min} to I_{max}, the VR-tube current must accommodate the change in current, $\Delta I = I_{max} - I_{min}$. The current I_o is defined by the relation $I_o = (I_{max} + I_{min})/2$.

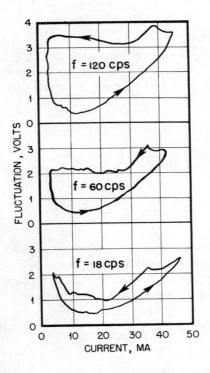

Fig. 7.2—Current-voltage characteristics of a VR-105.

Current through the VR tube will also change when the supply-mains voltage varies. It is usual to allow for a symmetrical variation of the supply-mains voltage, which may be expressed as $\pm 100r$ per cent of the normal value. For ordinary conditions a value of $r = 0.125$ is sufficient. If E_o is the normal d-c source voltage of the transformer-rectifier-filter circuit supplying the VR-tube stabilizer,*

*It is assumed that, to a sufficiently good approximation, the power supply proper can be replaced by its Thevenin equivalent, a constant-voltage generator E_o, and a series resistance R_o.

its value will suffer a maximum variation, $\Delta E = 2rE_o$. Let us now define R_s as the total series resistance between the VR tube and the equivalent source E_o of the power supply. In practice R_s will be the sum of a series dropping resistance and the effective internal resistance R_o of the power supply. When the voltage source changes its value by ΔE, the current change through the VR tube will be

$$\frac{\Delta E}{R_s} = \frac{2rE_o}{R_s}$$

Now the operating range of the most-used VR tubes (VR-75, VR-105, and VR-150) is 5 to 40 ma. Hence, to accommodate changes both in load current and in supply voltage, we must satisfy the relation

$$\frac{2rE_o}{R_s} + \Delta I \leq 0.035 \text{ amp} \tag{7}$$

The current through the VR tube itself is evidently

$$I_v = \frac{E_o - V}{R_s} - I_o \tag{8}$$

where V is the VR-tube potential difference. Since E_o and I_o represent mean values of the supply voltage and load-current extremes, respectively, it is clear that the value of I_v should be $(5 + 40)/2 = 22.5$ ma. On combining Eqs. 7 and 8, we find that

$$R_s \geq \frac{V}{0.117 - 4\Delta I - I_o} \tag{9}$$

for $r = 0.125$ and $I_v = 0.0225$ amp.

To illustrate the use of this relation, suppose that in a certain circuit the load current can vary from 5 to 25 ma. Then $I_o = 15$ ma and $\Delta I = 20$ ma, requiring that $R_s \geq 6,800$ ohms for a VR-150. The current through R_s will be 37.5 ma when $I_o = 15$ ma, so the effective source voltage of the power supply (Eq. 8) must be 405 volts. To the extent that R_s is greater than 6,800 ohms, there will exist a margin of safety in the design. It is evident that there is no need for the power supply proper to possess good regulation, since poor regulation means a larger output resistance, which in turn is absorbed in the value for R_s.

4. MEDIUM-VOLTAGE STABILIZED SUPPLIES

Most of the circuits described in earlier chapters have been designed for a plate-supply voltage of 300 volts and a bias-supply voltage of −150 volts when a bias supply is required. Although the choice of these values is somewhat arbitrary, it is found that they represent about the best compromise when properties of vacuum tubes, convenient signal levels, etc., are all taken into account. The standardization of supply voltages has the merit that certain circuit elements, such as a flip-flop, do not have to be redesigned each time they are used in a different circuit. Only for circuits where a power limitation exists has a plate-supply voltage lower than 300 volts been used. For a time, bias supplies giving −105 volts were in common use, but they were largely superseded when the greater flexibility of design afforded by a supply voltage of −150 volts was recognized.

The plate current required for most of the circuits that have been described is considerably in excess of the value that can be adequately furnished by a simple VR-tube stabilizer. The current required from the negative bias supply, in contrast, usually lies in a range from a few to 20 ma. Currents in this range can be stabilized adequately by a VR tube, provided a sufficiently high primary-supply voltage is available. In the case of most circuits the degree of stabilization required for a bias supply is found to be less than that required for the plate supply.

The various power-supply circuits to be described represent only a few basic circuits that have been adapted for specific output voltages and currents. It should be pointed out that, by substituting power transformers and chokes of higher current rating, and by placing additional triodes in parallel with the series triode of the stabilizing circuit, the current rating of any supply can be increased as much as desired.

The type 6Y6 tube, triode-connected, has become the standard series triode in all medium-voltage stabilizing circuits. To avoid parasitic oscillations, it is customary to use suppressor resistors of a few hundred ohms in series with the screen lead, and in series with grid leads if more than one tube is used. Ordinarily a maximum current of 75 ma is allowed for each 6Y6. It appears likely that the newly developed 6AS7 double triode will supplant the 6Y6 where currents in excess of 75 ma must be supplied by one stabilizing circuit. This tube requires a greater range of grid-voltage variation, so it unfortunately cannot be substituted for two or three 6Y6's in circuits already designed, unless other circuit changes are made also.

All the circuits described here can be used to supply any value of current up to the maximum value specified for the circuit. The range of input voltage (60 cycles per second) over which stabilization is operative is at least 105 to 125 volts and will be greater when the supply is not fully loaded.

4.1 <u>Model 50 Power Supply</u>. The Model 50 power supply, shown in Fig. 7.3, has been designed primarily for use with amplifiers that require less than 150 ma of plate current. When delivering a current of 100 ma to an external resistive load, it has an rms ripple voltage of 1.5 mv and presents an output impedance of 0.5 ohm for slow changes in load. The measured stabilization factor (the fractional change in input voltage divided by the fractional change in output voltage) is about 1,200.

The Model 50 supply includes a variable dropping resistor of 20,000 ohms and a large by-pass capacitor (16 μf) for furnishing plate-supply voltage to a preamplifier.

The difference amplifier in the stabilizing circuit is based on the double-triode difference amplifier described in Chap. 2, Sec. 3.3, followed by a single-triode amplifier. Both plates of the 6SL7 difference amplifier are biased at approximately the same potential (200 volts) to obtain a symmetry in currents and voltages between the two halves of the amplifier. It may be shown by straightforward circuit analysis that any change in the effective contact difference potential between grid and cathode, common to both tubes of the difference amplifier, suffers a degeneration of nearly $1/\mu$ in comparison with a signal impressed on the amplifier between grid and ground. For this reason the stabilized output voltage of the supply shows very little drift when the heater voltage is varied ±10 per cent. The triode amplifier stage following the difference amplifier uses a 6SL7 tube, and not a 6SF5, which might appear to be a logical choice. It is found that the 6SF5 is so much more microphonic than the 6SL7 that it is not ordinarily used.

It will be noticed that in all the stabilized supplies that are described in this section, including the Model 50, current for the VR tube is obtained from the output side of the supply. This arrangement ensures that the comparison voltage will not be subject to changes caused by a varying current through the VR tube. Another point worth noting in all the supplies is that the plate-load resistor of the amplifier stage that couples to the grid of the series triode is returned to the unstabilized side of the power supply. This enables the potential of the grid of the series triode to approach that of its cathode without causing the current through the amplifier stage to become very small and the gain, therefore, to become much reduced.

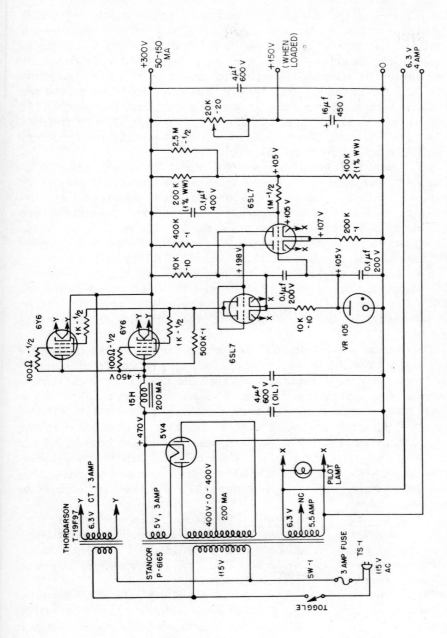

Fig. 7.3 — Model 50 power supply.

4.2 Model 100 Power Supply. The Model 100 power supply, Fig. 7.4, illustrates the design of a stabilized power supply capable of delivering 225 ma at 450 volts. The stabilizing circuit represents a variant of the type of circuit used in the Model 50 supply. The plate-load resistor in the right-hand member of the 6SL7 difference amplifier serves the purpose of keeping the amplifier voltages symmetrical. The transformer, UTC PA429, has been extensively used for supplies furnishing somewhat greater currents than are required for the average electronic circuit. The use of the type 5R4-GY rectifier tube is to be noted. The performance of the Model 100 supply is very similar to that of the Model 50 supply.

4.3 Model 200 Power Supply. The Model 200 supply, Fig. 7.5, is intended to be used with circuits (such as the Model 300 sweep circuit, Fig. 5.3) that require a VR-tube stabilized bias supply of −150 volts as well as a stabilized plate power supply. Connections are shown for obtaining + 105 volts from the VR tube used in the stabilizing circuit, and +450 volts from the unstabilized side of the supply. (These voltages are required in the Model 300 sweep circuit.)

With an external load of 75 ma, the rms ripple voltage is 24 mv, the output impedance about 19 ohms, and the stabilization factor 37. The difference amplifier consists of a single 6SJ7, which is the type of tube normally used in a supply of this sort, i.e., a sharp-cutoff pentode.

The method of obtaining the bias-supply voltage should be especially noted. The two halves of a 6X5 rectifier are connected in parallel to give half-wave rectification from one side of the high-voltage winding of the power transformer. An input capacitance of 1 μf in the filter gives a sufficiently high voltage to operate the VR-150. Following this capacitor are two stages of filtering, a variable dropping resistor, and finally the VR tube by-passed by a capacitance of 0.1 μf. The value of the resistor is set empirically so that the normal current through the VR tube is sufficient to accommodate reasonable changes in supply-mains voltage (e.g., ±12.5 per cent) and changes in the load current.

4.4 Model 500 Power Supply. The Model 500 power supply, Fig. 7.6, is intended for laboratory use where a large range in voltage must be provided. It is particularly suitable for obtaining static characteristics of vacuum tubes since two independently variable voltages from 0 to 300 volts can be obtained.

The circuit illustrates the combined use of dry cells and a VR-tube stabilized negative supply for obtaining reference voltages. It is evident that only a limited variation in supply voltage can be obtained in conventional supplies employing one VR tube for the reference

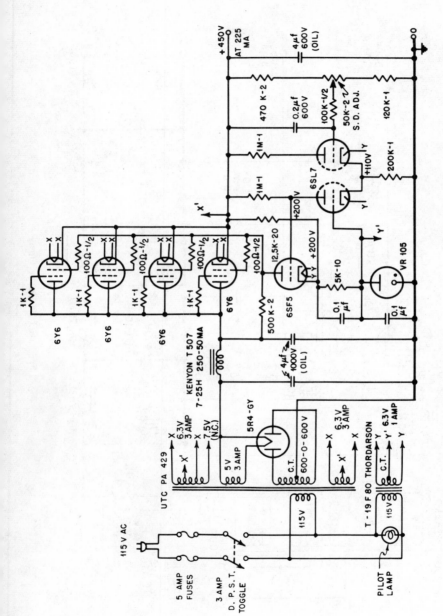

Fig. 7.4 — Model 100 power supply. When paralleling the two XX windings, be careful to get the proper phase.

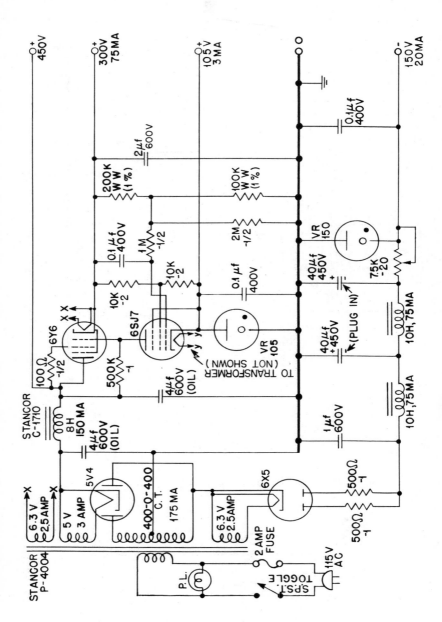

Fig. 7.5 — Model 200 power supply.

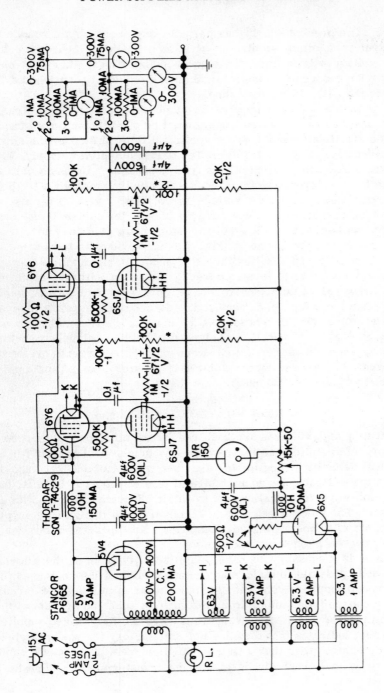

Fig. 7.6 — Model 500 power supply.

voltage. The present supply has considerably more ripple voltage in its output than other supplies that have been described, since the ripple voltage will be essentially equal to that on the -150-volt bias supply. To reduce the ripple, another section of filtering could be added to the filter in the bias supply.

4.5 Model 600 Power Supply. In some applications an electronically stabilized negative bias supply must be used instead of a simple VR-tube stabilized supply, whose applicability is limited by the small range of currents it can furnish. The Model 600 power supply, Fig. 7.7, illustrates one solution of this type of problem. Unless a battery is used for a reference voltage, it is essential to employ a VR-75 in the circuit when the output voltage is only 150 volts. Otherwise it may not be possible to reduce the grid bias of the series triode sufficiently, without having the amplifier stage draw grid current.

The power supply shown in Fig. 7.7 has an output impedance of about 17 ohms, a stabilization factor of about 70, and a ripple voltage of about 3 mv when it is supplying 25 ma to an external resistive load. These values do not represent as good a performance as might be expected from Eqs. 4, 5, and 6. The discrepancy appears to arise in the use of a VR-75, whose voltage-current characteristic is not so flat as that of a VR-105. A type 6AG7 tube, triode-connected, makes an excellent series triode when moderate currents are to be stabilized. It has a mu factor somewhat greater than 20 and a plate resistance of about 2,000 ohms.

5. HIGH-VOLTAGE SUPPLIES

Relatively high voltages are required for certain types of electrical detectors of radiation and for cathode-ray tubes. The current for an electrical detector is negligible, and that for a cathode-ray tube is 1 ma at most. Hence, for an unstabilized type of supply it is sufficient to use half-wave rectification and to obtain adequate filtering with an RC filter. The chief precaution to be observed in designing a supply of this sort is to ensure that all components are operated within their voltage, current, and power ratings.

When it is necessary to have stabilized voltages in the kilovolt range, it is possible to build stabilizing circuits of the sort used for plate power supplies. The vacuum tubes used in this type of circuit must be chosen from among transmitting-type tubes on account of the high voltages involved. However, experience with stabilized supplies of this sort indicates that they are not satisfactory for use with electrical detectors other than a Geiger-Mueller tube. The chief trouble seems to be that brush discharges in the transformer, or elsewhere

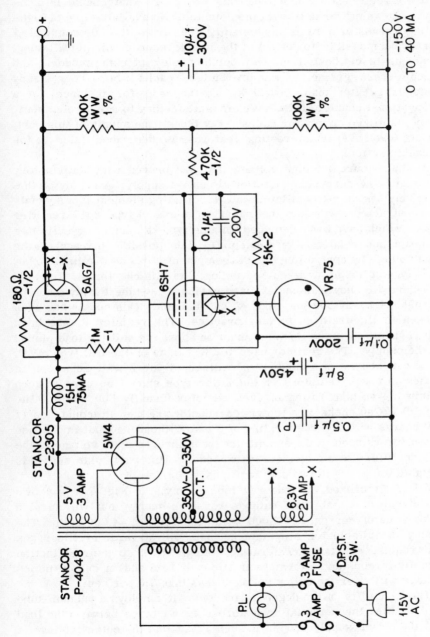

Fig. 7.7 — Model 600 power supply.

in the circuit, excite high-frequency transients that couple into the high-gain amplifier used with the detector. No available line of high-voltage transformers is consistently free from this defect, and it appears impossible to get rid of the interference by simple filtering. It seems to be best, from the point of view of both economy and trouble-free service, to employ battery packs where very steady voltages greater than about 1 kv are needed—for instance, for a proportional counter. It is, however, satisfactory to use an electronically stabilized supply for cathode-ray tubes. One supply of this sort, possessing several interesting features, is described later in the present section.

Another source of high voltage that has proved very satisfactory for many low-current applications is an r-f supply. A supply of this type employs an r-f oscillator whose oscillating element is a specially constructed step-up transformer. The use of type 8016 rectifier tubes, which have been designed for this type of service, results in a compact and relatively efficient unit. It is possible to regulate the high voltage by controlling the screen potential of the oscillator tube. This type of supply is discussed in Sec. 6 of this chapter.

Figure 7.8 shows an unstabilized cathode-ray-tube supply that will furnish +4 kv at 500 μa, and −2 kv at 2 ma. This supply has been chosen to illustrate customary practice. The resistor R_1 has been left unspecified, since its value must be chosen to suit the load placed on the supply. The resistor used for R_1 can be of the IRC type MVP, or it can consist of a number of ordinary 1- or 2-watt resistors in series. Enough resistors of the latter type should be used to keep within the voltage rating of each resistor (usually 500 volts). The type T-17C40 choke is a television reactor and has an inductance of 500 henrys with a current rating of 3 ma. Without the input impedance to the filters used in the circuit, the peak inverse plate voltage of the 2X2 rectifiers would be slightly exceeded. This particular supply is suitable for use with two oscillographs.

5.1 A Stabilized Cathode-ray-tube Supply. In Fig. 7.9 is shown the circuit of a stabilized cathode-ray-tube supply that will furnish up to 4 ma of current at −2,000 volts and 1 ma at +4,000 volts. The supply is suitable for simultaneous use with several oscillographs that require constant accelerating voltages to keep their deflection sensitivity constant. Normal variations in load and in supply-mains voltage will alter the output voltages less than 0.5 per cent.

The circuit is of the degenerative type. It employs a vacuum-tube load to alter the potential drop across a resistance between the load and the power supply proper in such a way that the output voltage is stabilized. A simple analysis of a stabilizing circuit of this type

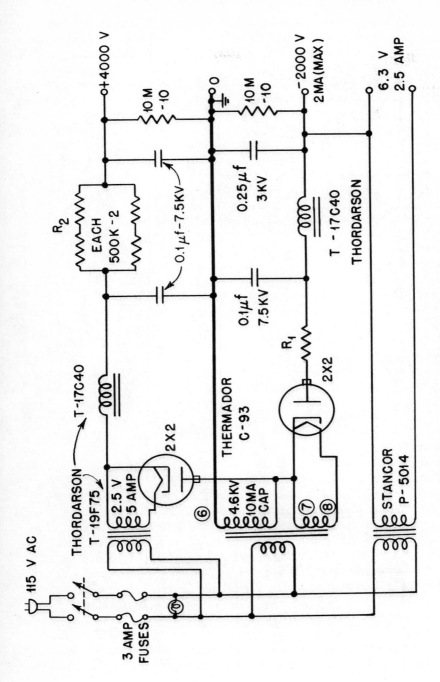

Fig. 7.8 — An unstabilized high-voltage supply for cathode-ray tubes.

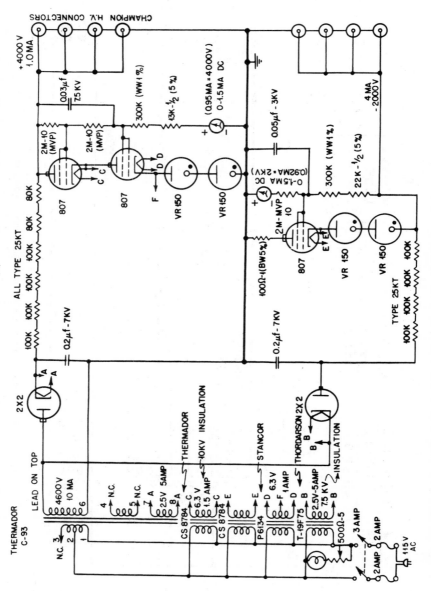

Fig. 7.9 — A stabilized high-voltage supply for cathode-ray tubes.

shows that the approximate values of stabilization factor S, of output impedance R_o, and of smoothing factor α, defined in Eqs. 1, 2, and 3, respectively, are

$$S \approx \frac{E_o}{E_1} \beta R g_m \tag{10}$$

$$R_o \approx \frac{1}{\beta g_m} \tag{11}$$

$$\alpha \approx \frac{1}{\beta R g_m} \tag{12}$$

where β is the fraction of the output voltage impressed on the grid of the control tube, g_m is the tube transconductance, R is the series dropping resistance, E_o is the stabilized output voltage, and E_1 is the unstabilized power-supply voltage.

To make a satisfactory stabilizing circuit of this type it is necessary to obtain a vacuum tube (triode) that will stand a very high plate voltage and possess a reasonable value of g_m for currents in the milliampere range. If grids G_1 and G_2 of an 807 tube are connected in parallel to serve as the control grid, a triode is obtained that has an amplification factor around 350 and a plate resistance around 1.6×10^5 ohms, i.e., a transconductance of about 2,000 μmhos. These values pertain to currents and voltages encountered under the conditions of operation in the high-voltage supply shown in Fig. 7.9.

In the case of the 4,000-volt supply, it is necessary to employ two 807 tubes in series, in order that the plate voltage may be reduced to a safe value. The additional 807 tube serves mainly to couple the current through the control tube to the high-voltage supply bus and to drop the voltage at the plate of the control tube to 1,850 volts. Electrically, the additional 807 tube is equivalent to a battery of 1,850 volts having an internal resistance of $1/g_m \approx 500$ ohms connected between the plate of the control tube and the 4,000-volt bus. Since the internal resistance simply adds to the already high plate resistance of the control tube, the operation of the circuit is practically identical with that of the circuit used in the $-2,000$-volt supply.

If reasonable values are substituted in the expression for S, R_o, and α given in Eqs. 10, 11, and 12, respectively, it is found that

$$S \approx 40$$

$$R_o \approx 3,000 \text{ ohms}$$

$$\alpha \approx 10^{-3} \quad \text{(for ripple voltages)}$$

It is evident from these values that the output voltage should remain constant to 0.5 per cent for reasonable variations in supply-mains voltage and for permissible changes in load. Measurements made on a particular supply confirm these estimates of stability.

Undoubtedly the weakest part of the supply lies in the use of VR-150 regulator tubes with currents in the range of a few milliamperes. It is not known what long-time stability can be expected when the tubes are so operated, but tests made over a period of eight hours indicate a drift of less than 0.5 per cent. Although the 807 tubes are considerably overvolted, no trouble has been experienced with tube failure. When new tubes are first used, some sparking from points may occur, but these discharges clear up in a short time and cause no trouble in the operation of an oscillograph powered by the supply. The a-c ripple voltage on the output is about 1 volt on the negative supply and 0.5 volt on the positive supply.

6. R-F HIGH-VOLTAGE SUPPLIES

A high-voltage power supply based on an oscillator operating at a frequency of a few hundred kilocycles per second has proved to be a very practical source of d-c voltages for cathode-ray tubes and for Geiger-Mueller counters. A supply of this sort appears to have the following advantages: (1) It can be constructed compactly. (2) It is very safe to work with since it employs low-value capacitors for filtering and is capable of delivering only a very limited amount of power. (3) Its output voltage can be readily stabilized by controlling the screen voltage of the oscillator. (4) Its cost compares favorably with that of a conventional 60-cycles-per-second high-voltage supply. Since an account of the theory and design of r-f supplies is readily available,* only a brief discussion of the principle of operation of such a supply will be given here. Two practical r-f supplies will be described at the end of this section.

The basic oscillator circuit normally employed in an r-f supply is indicated in Fig. 7.10. The frequency of oscillation is determined chiefly by the resonant frequency of the secondary winding. The capacitance C_s that tunes this winding includes the distributed capacitance of the winding, the capacitance of the rectifying tubes, and the stray wiring capacitance. The primary winding of the step-up transformer is tuned by a fixed mica capacitor and a variable air capacitor to approximately the resonant frequency of the secondary. The coefficient of coupling between the two windings is normally made

*O. H. Schade, Proc. I.R.E. 31: 158 (April, 1943).

somewhat greater than critical. A third winding of the transformer, located at the end of the secondary winding opposite from the end occupied by the primary, is loosely coupled to the secondary and provides grid excitation for the oscillator tube. For efficiency the oscillator is operated Class C.

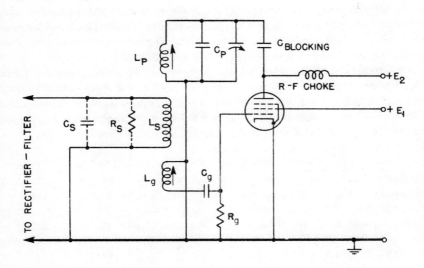

Fig. 7.10 — Basic circuit of a high-voltage supply of the r-f type.

The voltage, stability, and efficiency of an r-f supply hinge on the design of the transformer. Although it is possible to make a simple analysis indicating the most important factors in the design,* without some experience in constructing transformers it is usually necessary to wind several different transformers before a suitable one is obtained. Transformers for the two r-f supplies described in the present section have been developed primarily by a cut-and-try method and may not represent an optimum design. It is to be hoped that a number of well-designed transformers for various applications will become available commercially.

The construction of practical r-f high-voltage supplies depends on the use of the RCA type 8016 rectifier tube, which has been developed specifically for this type of service. The 8016 tube has a directly heated cathode which consumes only one-quarter watt of power and

*Ibid.

which will tolerate a relatively wide range of heater-voltage variation. Power for the heater is normally obtained from a coil of a few
turns coupled to the oscillator transformer. It is not difficult to obtain adequate insulation for a potential difference of several thousand
volts by spacing the heater winding a moderate distance from the
main windings of the transformer. When an output voltage higher than
a few thousand volts is required, it is usually more efficient to employ
a voltage-doubling or voltage-tripling circuit. The problem of heating
several rectifier cathodes at widely differing voltage levels is solved
by adding more heater windings to the transformer.

An attractive feature of an r-f supply is the smallness of filter
capacitors required. A capacitance of 1 μf at 60 cycles per second
has a reactance of 2,700 ohms, whereas a capacitance of 0.003 μf at
100 kc/sec has a reactance of only 500 ohms. It is obviously a simple
matter to construct a very efficient RC filter for an r-f supply from
parts requiring only a small space.

6.1 A Supply for Geiger-Mueller Counters. Figure 7.11 shows
the circuit diagram and the constructional details of the transformer
for an r-f supply designed to be used with Geiger-Mueller counters.
The unit has ordinarily been built in a metal shield box 5 by 4½ by
4½ in. mounted on an octal plug. The external connections made to
the octal plug are shown in the circuit diagram of the Model 400
counter, Fig. 4.7, which employs this particular power supply. The
total current taken by the 6SJ7 oscillator is 9 ma or less, and the
normal load on the supply is a 20-megohm bleeder used in series
with a microammeter reading 0 to 100 μa. The positive output voltage
can be varied from 600 to 1,500 volts by varying the screen potential.
After a warm-up period of 15 min, the high voltage remains sufficiently constant so that no need exists for a stabilizing circuit other than
that used for the 300-volt plate-supply voltage.

The transformer is wound with litz wire in order to reduce losses
due to skin effect. The various sections of the transformer are uni-
versal-wound, since this mode of winding not only reduces the capacitance shunting the secondary but also makes the sections self-sup-
porting. It is necessary to impregnate the transformer with glyptal
varnish and bake it. This procedure protects the fine wire used for
the windings and reduces coil losses caused in part by the absorption
of moisture. In the construction of an r-f supply, the coil should not
be mounted too close to the shield, since the shield can absorb power
and decrease the efficiency of the device. It is best to keep the shield
a distance of at least one coil diameter away from the primary and
secondary windings.

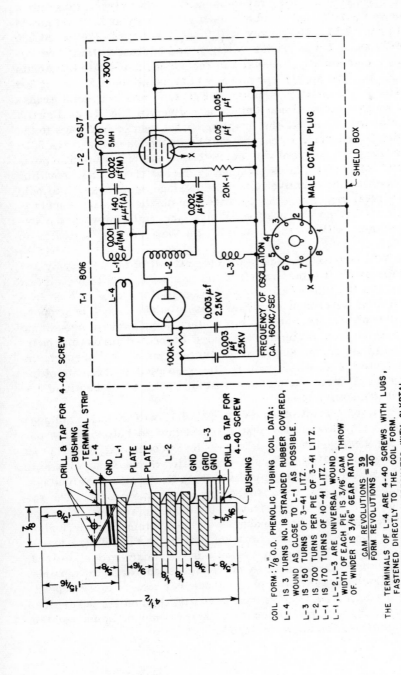

Fig. 7.11 — A high-voltage supply for a Geiger–Mueller counter.

6.2 <u>A Stabilized Cathode-ray-tube Supply</u>. The circuit diagram of
an r-f power supply that has been used extensively at Los Alamos is
shown in Fig. 7.12. The supply will furnish voltages of +4 kv at 200
μa, and −2 kv at 1 ma. These voltages and current ratings are required by a cathode-ray tube used in recording fast single transients
(see Chap. 5). The supply consumes a current of about 35 ma at 300
volts. The r-f oscillator employs a 6V6 tube and a special transformer whose constructional details are given in Fig. 7.12. Usually
it is necessary to adjust the coupling of the heater windings to the
rest of the transformer to ensure that the cathodes of the three 8016
rectifier tubes are supplied with correct amounts of power. The positive output voltage of 4 kv is obtained by means of a voltage-doubling
circuit, whereas the negative voltage is obtained by means of a simple
half-wave rectifier. Since the current load on the negative supply is
greater than that on the positive supply, the ratio between the two
output voltages will be more nearly 2.4 than 2.0, as indicated in
Fig. 7.12.

Figure 7.12 contains, in addition to the circuit of the r-f supply and
the specifications for the transformer, a simple stabilizing circuit
for controlling the screen current of the oscillator. Tube T-6 constitutes a simple difference amplifier whose output signal is proportional to the difference between the voltage supplied by a neon lamp
and that coming from a point on a bleeder connected across the positive high-voltage terminals. Screen current must pass through the
cathode follower T-5, whose grid is direct-coupled to the plate of the
difference amplifier. The method of stabilization is evidently of the
ordinary degenerative type.

The stabilizing circuit indicated in Fig. 7.12 will maintain voltages
applied to a cathode-ray tube that are constant to better than 1 per
cent for any changes in load likely to be encountered. The output
voltage, however, will show a long-time drift, which is due in part to
the use of a small neon lamp for furnishing the comparison voltage.
The voltage of the lamp tends to change as the lamp ages. The resistance bleeder used in the circuit also tends to alter its value as
the resistors age. Another weakness in the system of stabilization
employed is the fact that the positive voltage is the voltage that is
directly stabilized. The negative voltage is only indirectly stabilized,
by virtue of the common source of voltage used for both supplies.
Since the deflection sensitivity of a cathode-ray tube is more dependent on the predeflection accelerating potential than on the postdeflec-
tion potential (by a factor of about 3), there would be some point in
directly stabilizing the negative supply.

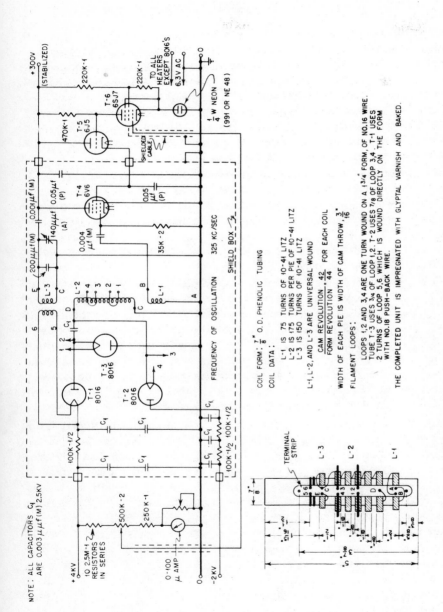

Fig. 7.12 — A stabilized high-voltage supply for a cathode-ray tube.

7. A CONSTANT-CURRENT MAGNET SUPPLY

The electromagnet of a mass spectrograph for heavy ions must be supplied with a very steady current free from ripple. The supply described in the present section is designed for a magnet having a coil of resistance 1,200 ohms and requiring a current that can be varied continuously from 50 to 350 ma. After a warm-up period of ½ hr, the circuit will supply a current of 350 ma steady to 1 part in 20,000 over a period of 15 min. It will maintain this current to 1 part in 5,000 over an 8-hr period. The ripple in the current is less than 0.002 per cent when the magnet has an inductance of 40 henrys.

A simplified circuit diagram of the supply is shown in Fig. 7.13. The complete wiring diagram is shown in Fig. 7.14.

An examination of Fig. 7.13 indicates that the circuit is of the degenerative type, somewhat similar in operation to the power supplies discussed in Secs. 2 and 4 of this chapter. Here the voltage drop across an adjustable precision resistor is stabilized, thereby stabilizing the current through it.

Tube T-1 serves as a difference amplifier, employing a battery of 27.5 volts in its grid lead to furnish a reference voltage. The output from the amplifier is coupled through a bias battery to the grid of T-2, and also to the screen of T-2 by means of the cathode follower T-3. A type 1B4-P tube is used for T-1, with its filament supplied from a 1.5-volt dry cell. This mode of operation tends to keep the effective contact difference in potential between grid and cathode very constant, as compared with that of a pentode having a cathode indirectly heated by a-c power from the supply mains.

To obtain sufficient stabilization with the circuit, the signal from T-1 to the series regulator tube T-2 is in effect applied both to the control grid and to the screen. If an 807 tube is connected as a triode, with the plate and screen tied together, it has a mu factor of only 8. If it is connected as a pentode (by keeping the screen-cathode potential difference constant), it has a mu factor of about 150. By keeping the potential difference of the screen-control grid nearly constant, a somewhat higher mu factor is obtained. This method is the one actually used, although it requires a separate 6AG7 cathode follower to furnish screen bias to each 807 tube. It may be that the improvement in circuit performance does not warrant this refinement and that it would be satisfactory to connect the 807 tubes simply as pentodes. In this case the separate stabilized power supply would be connected directly between cathodes and screens of the 807 tubes.

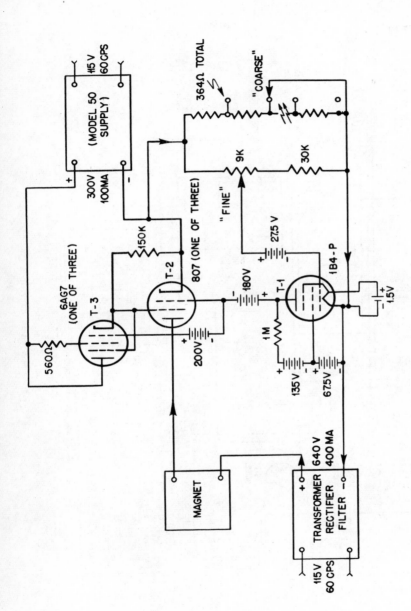

Fig. 7.13 — Simplified diagram of the constant-current magnet supply.

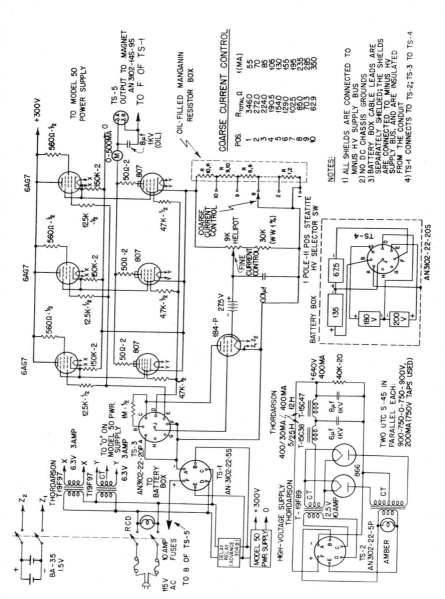

Fig. 7.14 — A constant-current magnet supply.

Referring now to the complete circuit diagram, Fig. 7.14, it will be noticed that suppressor resistors are placed in various leads to the 807 and the 6AG7 tubes. These are necessary to prevent parasitic oscillations. The manganin resistors used for coarse control of current have been specially made for the circuit. It will be observed that the coarse steps of control are so chosen that it is always possible to fill in the steps with the fine control, which is a Helipot, in order to permit an accurate setting of the magnet current to be made. Other details of the circuit require no further comment.

8. A STABILIZED HEATER POWER SUPPLY

The stability of unfed-back amplifiers, and of certain other electronic devices, depends on tubes maintaining constant characteristics, such as constant values of g_m and r_p, and a constant effective contact potential difference between grid and cathode. These quantities may change when the heater voltage is subject to the usual fluctuations in supply-mains voltage. To reduce trouble from this cause, the rms value of the heater voltage can be stabilized.

One practical method of stabilization amounts to rectifying the heater voltage with suitable rectifiers of the copper-oxide type and using a storage battery as a ballast device to reduce any fluctuations in voltage arising in the primary power source. The continuous use of storage batteries in the vicinity of electronic and other laboratory equipment is certainly inconvenient because of maintenance requirements, and may be objectionable because of gases and fumes that are given off. This situation has prompted the development of an a-c heater-voltage stabilizing circuit of the degenerative type.

The circuit of the stabilizer is shown in Fig. 7.15. Measurements made with the stabilizer supplying 15 amp at 6.3 volts indicate that it has a stabilization factor of about 40 for the rms value of the output voltage (6.3 volts). With no modification the circuit will stabilize any current load from 0 to 15 amp for line-voltage variations in the range 105 to 125 volts.

The operation of the circuit depends on the change in resistance of tungsten lamps when the current through them is altered in value. Since the change in resistance depends on the heating of the lamp filaments, the stabilizing action is not sensitive to the waveform of the current but is sensitive only to its rms value. Two groups of six lamps in series (6.3 volts, type 40, brown beads) are placed in opposite arms of a Wheatstone bridge, which is powered directly by the 6.3-volt supply voltage undergoing stabilization. Low-temperature-coefficient resistors in the other two arms of the bridge are so chosen

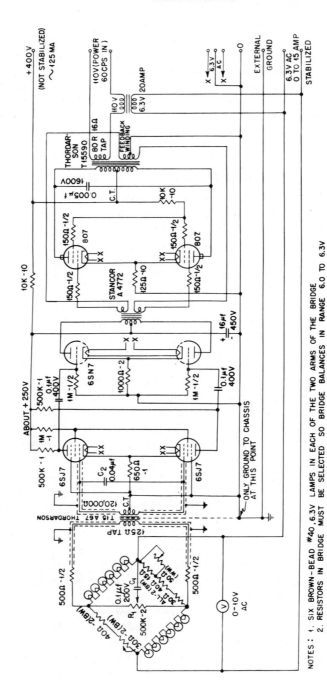

Fig. 7.15 — A stabilized heater-voltage supply.

NOTES : 1. SIX BROWN-BEAD #40, 6.3V LAMPS IN EACH OF THE TWO ARMS OF THE BRIDGE
2. RESISTORS IN BRIDGE MUST BE SELECTED SO BRIDGE BALANCES IN RANGE 6.0 TO 6.3V

that the bridge balances in the range 6.0 to 6.3 volts. If the input voltage is higher than the voltage for exact balance, the output voltage from the bridge will have one phase, whereas if the input voltage is low, it will have the opposite phase. The magnitude of the output voltage will be approximately proportional to the difference between the applied voltage and the voltage for exact balance.

To obtain a stabilizing action, the output signal from the bridge is amplified considerably and used to add to, or subtract from, the supply-mains voltage that furnishes the major amount of power to the primary of the heater-supply transformer. Evidently when phases are correctly arranged the system is degenerative.

To make a practical circuit based on the method of operation that has been described, it is necessary to provide an adjustment for the reactive balance of the bridge. This is provided in the circuit of Fig. 7.15 by the high-resistance potentiometer R_1 and the capacitor C_1, which enable a reactive component of a variable amount to be thrown in parallel with one or the other of two adjacent arms of the bridge. Not only is this adjustment necessary to balance out stray capacitances in the circuit, but it turns out that there is an optimum setting of the reactive balance to obtain stabilization over the largest possible range of supply-voltage variation. This adjustment is made after the circuit is installed.

Some provision must also be made in the amplifier to suppress, to a certain extent, the second harmonic component in the output signal of the bridge. This has been done in the circuit of Fig. 7.15 by inserting 500-ohm resistors in each lead to the input transformer of the amplifier and by tuning the secondary of the transformer to 60 cycles per second the capacitor C_2. Evidently it would be more efficient to use a lower impedance tap on the input transformer than 125 ohms, and to reduce or omit the 500-ohm resistors. If a correct impedance match exists between the bridge and the grids of the 6SJ7 tubes, no selective tuning of the transformer is practicable.

The use of an audio output transformer in the circuit is uneconomical, and it could be replaced by a 60-cycles-per-second power transformer if suitable windings were available to provide an impedance match to the pair of 807 tubes. Since fairly high voltages may be developed across the primary winding, good insulation is imperative. Type 616 tubes cannot be substituted for type 807 tubes, on account of the high plate voltages encountered. The use of inverse feedback in the output stages of the amplifier considerably improves the waveform of the output voltage that is mixed with the 110-volt supply voltage.

In evaluating the behavior of a circuit of the type described, it is necessary to employ either a wattmeter or a voltmeter of the electro-dynamometer type. Ordinary a-c voltmeters of the copper-oxide rectifier type will not indicate properly, since a certain amount of waveform distortion occurs in the output of the stabilizer. In practical applications of the stabilizer, the heater transformer is normally mounted near the tubes whose heater voltage is being stabilized.

9. CONTROL CIRCUITS

9.1 Model 600 Ion-gauge Control. An ionization manometer, or ion gauge, constitutes one of the most convenient devices for measuring pressures in the range 10^{-3} to 10^{-8} mm of mercury. The manometer contains a filament that emits electrons, a grid that serves as an anode, and a plate that collects positive ions formed by the bombardment of the residual gases by electrons flowing from the filament to the grid. When the electron current and the electrode potentials are maintained constant, the relation between pressure and ion current can be sufficiently linear for practical measurements of pressure. The proportionality constant, however, depends on the ion gauge, and somewhat on the nature of the residual gas in the system. Hence an ionization manometer is usually calibrated in the range 10^{-3} to 10^{-4} mm of mercury against a McLeod gauge, with the use of the type of gas that is found in the vacuum system. The linear relationship is then used to extrapolate its calibration to lower pressures.

While making measurements with an ion gauge, it is necessary to keep the electrode potentials constant and, more particularly, to keep the electron current constant by controlling the filament current. Since the amount of filament current required to give a certain electron current—for instance, 5 ma—depends both on the existing pressure and on the previous history of the filament, i.e., the state of its emissive properties, a rather wide range of control is necessary. The ion current that may occur in the entire range of operation may vary from 10^{-4} to 10^{-9} amp.

A satisfactory ion-gauge control circuit should (1) keep the electron current as constant as possible (against changes in emissive properties of the filament, line-voltage fluctuations, etc.); (2) afford a convenient means of reading a range of ion currents; (3) provide a safety cutoff that will prevent the gauge from being damaged if a leak should occur in the vacuum system; and (4) provide a means of out-gassing the ion gauge when low pressures are to be measured. The Model 600 ion-gauge control, Fig. 7.16, performs all these functions in a satisfactory manner. This particular circuit is intended to be

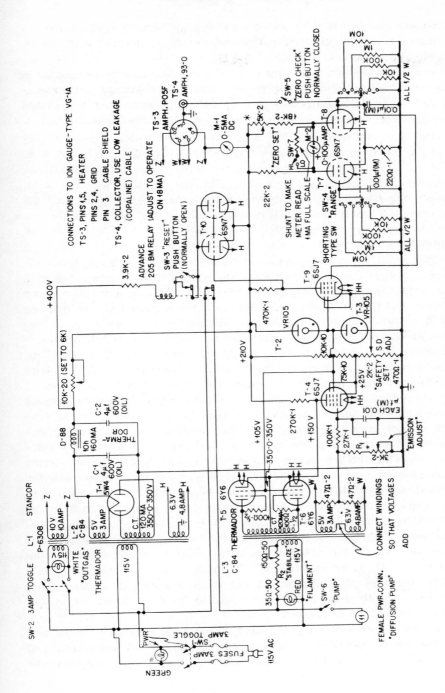

Fig. 7.16 — Model 600 ion-gauge control.

used with the Distillation Products Company type VG-1A ionization manometer. If slight modifications are made in the circuit, it can be used with manometers of other makes.

The operation of the circuit can be best presented by discussing in turn the four functions it performs. The power supply, comprising transformer L-2, tubes T-1, T-2, and T-3, and other associated components, requires no discussion since it is conventional in design.

The part of the circuit that stabilizes the emission current of the ion gauge utilizes transformer L-3 and the tubes T-4, T-5, and T-6. The collector in the ion gauge is essentially at ground potential, the filament at slightly less than +25 volts, and the grid at +210 volts. Hence the filament-grid potential difference is +185 volts, and the filament-collector potential difference −25 volts. These values are within the range recommended by the manufacturer of the gauge. An emission current of 5 ma is normally used.

The negative-emission current flows from ground through the resistance R_1 to the winding of L-3, which heats the filament, thence to the grid (anode) of the gauge, and finally through a milliammeter (0 to 5 ma) to the +210-volt supply bus. The potential at the high end of R_1 depends on the magnitude of the emission current and is impressed on the grid of the difference amplifier T-4, which serves to control the grid-cathode bias of the two 6Y6 tubes, T-5 and T-6. These tubes constitute a variable resistive load on the high-voltage winding of transformer L-3, which has, in series with its primary, the resistance R_2 part of which is variable. If the emission current is too high, an increased load is placed on the transformer L-3 by the circuit just described. Hence the primary voltage drops on account of the greater potential drop in the resistance R_2, and the voltage supplied the ion-gauge filament is accordingly reduced. If the emission current is too low, the reverse action takes place, and the voltage supplied to the filament is increased. The control action is of the negative feedback, or degenerative, type. It serves to hold the emission current constant to about 1 per cent for normal changes in emissive properties of the filament and for normal line-voltage fluctuations. To set the actual value of the emission current, part of the resistance R_1 is made variable. To bring the circuit into the middle of its range of stabilization, part of the resistance R_2 is also made variable. Both these adjustments should be made available on the front panel of the instrument.

It should be noted not only that the emission current is stabilized by the circuit described, but also that the potential of the filament of the ion gauge is held fixed within very narrow limits, slightly less than 25 volts. This, of course, is the potential of the grid of T-4 when the circuit is within its range of stabilizing action. Typical charac- teristics of the VG-1A ion gauge, under the conditions of operation in the Model 600 circuit, are shown in Fig. 7.17.

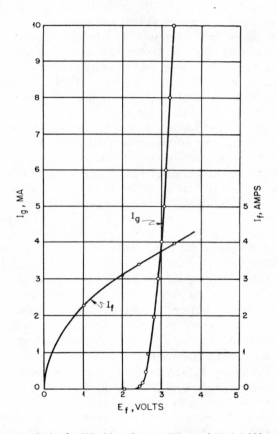

Fig. 7.17 — Characteristic of a VG-1A under conditions of Model 600 ion-gauge control.

The negative-ion current to the collector of the ion gauge is passed through a suitable high resistance, and the voltage developed is read by a vacuum-tube voltmeter based on the balanced difference ampli- fier (see Chap. 2, Sec. 3.3). Since great sensitivity is required, a meter that reads 0 to 100 μa is connected directly between the plates T-7 and T-8. Normally the meter is provided with a shunt, so that it reads 1 ma full scale, and in this condition a full-scale deflection indicates ion currents of about 10^{-4}, 10^{-5}, 10^{-6}, and 10^{-7} amp for positions 2, 3, 4, and 5, respectively, of the range switch. If, in position 5, the shunt is switched out, full scale corresponds to 10^{-8} amp. These values of ion current correspond, approximately, to pressures of 10^{-3}, 10^{-4}, ..., 10^{-7} mm of mercury, respectively. For accurate measurements it is necessary to calibrate the entire setup in the high-pressure range against an absolute standard.

Since the meter without the shunt can be damaged by a sudden increase in ion current, the shunt should never be disconnected except while readings are being made on the most sensitive scale. A pushbutton switch is provided to enable the zero of the meter to be checked readily. On account of grid currents in the two halves of the 6SN7 tube that constitutes the difference amplifier, equal resistances are switched in both grid circuits by the range switch. Individual type 6SN7 tubes are found occasionally to have such great grid currents that they are unsuitable for use in the vacuum-tube voltmeter. Position 1 of the range switch is used when the ion gauge is outgassed.

The portion of the circuit used for a safety cutoff employs tubes T-9 and T-10 and a relay that is set to operate if the current through it drops below 18 ma. The operation of the safety cutoff should be obvious on inspection of Fig. 7.16. The potentiometer, denoted "Safety Set," is adjusted so that the relay will open if the meter exceeds its full-scale reading (except when the meter shunt is temporarily switched out). The range switch should always be left in the position desired to provide the safety cutoff. The safety circuit is easily reset by pushing the "Reset" button. A connection is provided to supply 110 volts (60 cycles per second) to operate an external relay that can be used to control power reaching the diffusion pumps. The safety cutoff will then turn off these pumps when it operates.

The outgassing of the VG-1A is affected by passing current through the anode grid and simultaneously flaming the tube to outgas the collector. Current for heating the grid is furnished by transformer L-1. During outgassing, the range switch should be set in position 1.

If it is desired to modify the Model 600 ion-gauge control for use with another type of ionization manometer, the following points should be kept in mind: (1) It is necessary to ensure that the filament winding of L-3 will provide current and voltage in the correct range. (2) Usually it is necessary to provide a different means of outgassing the manometer, such as use of the electron current to bombard the anode grid and, possibly, the collector. The heat developed by the electron current will then bring about the outgassing. (3) Suitable operating voltages and currents of another manometer may differ from those of the VG-1A, requiring further modifications in the circuit. The basic principles of operation used in the Model 600 ion-gauge control have proved to be satisfactory.

9.2 Model 4 Valve Control for Toepler Pump. The circuit to be described here, Fig. 7.18, has been extensively used to permit the automatic operation of a Toepler pump in gas-microanalysis systems. The circuit serves to open and close a solenoid valve* in an air line when the mercury in the pump reaches predetermined levels. The current drawn at the contacts in the mercury column is small, about 100 μa or less, and the maximum voltage appearing across a contact that is being broken is 10 volts, in series with 2×10^5 ohms. It is essential to keep both voltage and current low to avoid sparking at the contacts and fouling of the mercury.

The operation of the circuit may best be understood by following through one pumping cycle. At the start of the cycle the mercury is at its lowest position, and only the input lead marked "1" is in contact with the mercury. In this condition both T-1 and T-2 are conducting, and the potential drop in the plate-load resistor of T-2 biases off the FG17 thyratron, T-3. Hence the solenoid valve is closed, and a slow leak in the Toepler pump furnishes pressure to the lower surface of the mercury column, which therefore rises and makes contact with input lead "2." Although this puts a negative bias of 10 volts on T-2, the tube continues to conduct, and no change in the circuit takes place. When the mercury finally makes contact with input lead "3," negative bias is applied to both T-1 and T-2, so that the tube T-1 is biased off and the thyratron T-2 extinguishes. Since negative bias is now removed from the grid of T-3, this tube conducts and the solenoid valve is energized. A vacuum line is thereby connected to the system, and the mercury column begins to fall, first breaking contact with input lead "3." Nothing happens at this time since tube T-2 is still biased off. The RC filter in the grid of T-1 prevents a high voltage from appearing immediately between input lead "3" and the mercury surface. As soon as the mercury breaks contact with lead "2," the thyratron T-2 will fire after a few seconds' delay. Both T-1 and T-2 are now conducting, and the cycle repeats itself. The adjustable delay provided in the firing of T-2 enables the operator to determine the minimum level reached by the mercury column before it begins to rise again.

The method of obtaining d-c voltages in the circuit is simple. Since no isolation is provided between the circuit and the 110-volt supply mains, care must be taken to avoid contact with the input leads.

9.3 Model 100 Plating-cell Control. The technique of selectively plating out one metal in the presence of other metals in an electrolyte requires careful control of the magnitude of the back emf, or cathode

*The G.E. solenoid valve, Model CR9507-C1B, has been used for this purpose.

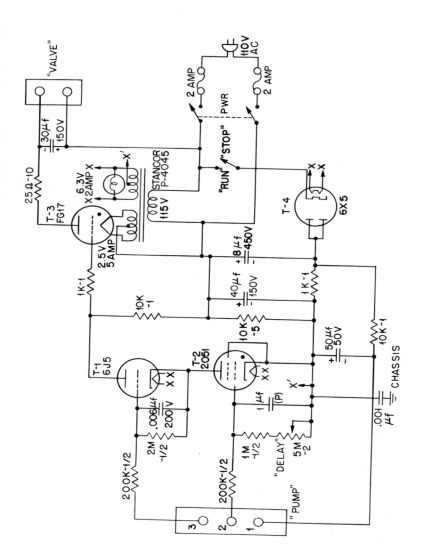

Fig. 7.18—Valve control for a Toepler pump.

potential, at the plating cathode. Under suitable conditions there exists a narrow range of emf's where only the desired metal is deposited. This technique can be used, for instance, to prepare radioactive sources of one particular metal that occurs associated with other, contaminating, elements. Conditions in the electrolyte must be so chosen that the desired metal is the first one to plate out when the back emf at the cathode is increased by passing current through the cell. It is evident that the magnitude of the back emf, and therefore the process of selective deposition, can be controlled by controlling the voltage across the cell.

The magnitude of the emf at the cathode is determined in the usual manner by employing a calomel reference cell. Experience with a given plating operation will indicate what voltage between the plating cathode and the electrode in the reference cell is most suitable for an optimum plating condition. There then arises the problem of automatically controlling the voltage across the cell in such a way as to maintain a constant voltage between the plating cathode and the calomel reference electrode. The Model 100 plating-cell control is an electronic device to perform this function automatically for a small laboratory plating cell.

The circuit of the Model 100 plating-cell control is shown in Fig. 7.19. It consists essentially of a difference amplifier followed by a one-stage triode amplifier and a cathode follower to supply current and voltage to the plating cell. The voltage existing between the plating cathode (at ground potential) and the electrode of the calomel reference cell is impressed on one grid of the difference amplifier, whereas a steady adjustable comparison voltage is impressed on the other grid of the amplifier. If the calomel reference voltage is low, the output potential of the difference amplifier (at the plate of T-2) is low, and the potential of the plate of the amplifier T-3 is high. Hence the cathode follower T-4 will place a relatively high voltage across the cell. This will increase the cell current and also the value of the calomel reference voltage. Evidently the system is degenerative, and the circuit will tend to maintain a definite value for the calomel reference voltage. The over-all stabilization in the instrument is of the order of 2,000 times. By adjusting the comparison voltage at the grid of T-2, the operator can set the calomel reference voltage at the desired operating value as read by a vacuum-tube voltmeter connected between the plating cathode and the calomel reference electrode.

Part of the cathode resistance of the difference amplifier is made adjustable to afford a means of bringing the circuit into its operating

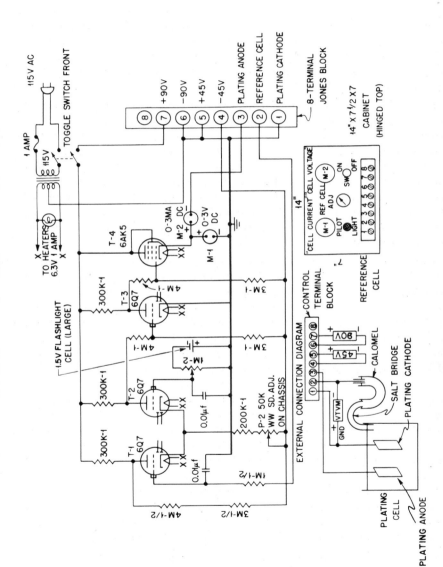

Fig. 7.19 — A plating-cell control.

range. Normally the resistance is set in such a way that the differ-ence in potential between the control grids of the difference amplifier is zero when the plating-cell current is approximately correct.

Type 6Q7 tubes have been used for the voltage amplifiers on account of their relatively low grid current. Some resistance, however, needs to be inserted between the reference-cell electrode and the plating-cell cathode. It is assumed that this resistance will be furnished by the internal resistance of the vacuum-tube voltmeter always used with the circuit. This resistance should not be greater than 20 megohms.

9.4 An On-Off Thermostat Control. The control circuit shown in Fig. 7.20 is of interest chiefly for its extreme simplicity. It is used, in conjunction with a sensitive on-off thermoregulator of the mercury thermometer type, to operate a relay, which in turn can control 1,000 watts of heater power.

A type 117L7 GT tube is used in the circuit both to furnish a negative bias voltage and to operate a 1,500-ohm relay requiring 60 volts d-c for reliable closure. The relay tube acts as its own rectifier. When the connections to the thermoregulator are open, enough negative bias is furnished the grid of the relay tube to enable it to pass the correct average current (40 ma) to close the relay. When the connections are closed, the current through the relay tube is reduced and the relay remains open. The current through the thermoregulator is about 20 μa when it is closed.

9.5 A Current Integrator. In certain nuclear experiments involving accelerators of positive ions it is necessary to know the target current, or, more precisely, to know the average target current during the course of an experiment. Since the target current may be subject to fluctuations, it is desirable to measure the integral of the current and to compute from it the average current. In this section a circuit will be described that integrates currents in the range 10^{-5} to 10^{-7} amp. The output signal from the integrator consists of a series of pulses, or counts. Each count corresponds to a definite amount of charge — about 0.10 microcoulomb. The total number of counts can be recorded with a standard counting circuit.

The principle of operation of an integrating circuit for small currents coming from a high-impedance source is very simple. The current is allowed to charge a capacitor, and when the potential across the capacitor reaches a definite value a trigger circuit is set in operation. The trigger circuit rapidly discharges the capacitor to some lower potential and then allows the cycle to be repeated. If ΔV is the change in potential across the capacitance C, the integrated

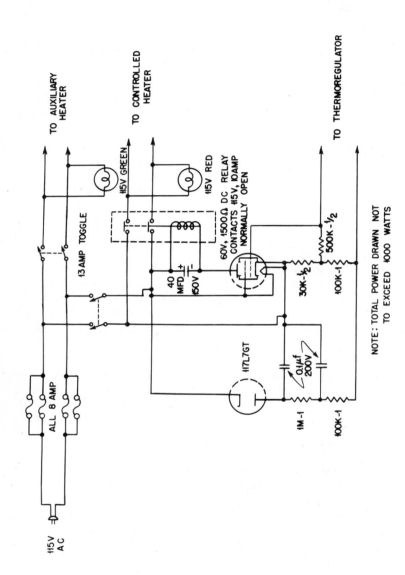

Fig. 7.20 — An off-on thermostat control.

current for each cycle of operation is simply $C \, \Delta V$. Since the discharging of the capacitor requires a finite time t_1, then for an accuracy of 1 per cent the maximum repetition rate of discharging the capacitor must be less than $1/100t_1$.

The problem of designing an accurate current integrator based on the principle just stated hinges on obtaining a trigger circuit that has the requisite voltage stability in its triggering characteristics. The current integrator shown in Fig. 7.21 is based on the Schmitt trigger circuit discussed in Chap. 2, Sec. 4.3(c). It is much used as a stable amplitude discriminator for pulses. In its present application the hysteresis of the discriminator has been increased to about 50 volts by increasing the appropriate resistances in the circuit. The range of hysteresis is used to set the lower and upper limits of potentials reached in the discharging and charging of the capacitor C_1.

The target, or collector, in the accelerator must be well insulated from its surroundings. It is connected to the input connector of the current integrator through a coaxial cable having very high leakage resistance. Potential builds up across the 10-megohm isolating resistor R_1, and current through the resistor charges the capacitor C_1. When the grid of T-2 reaches the critical potential at which the Schmitt trigger circuit, comprising T-2, T-3, and T-4, is triggered, a positive gate signal from the plate circuit of T-4 raises the grid potential of the clamp tube, T-1, which starts to discharge the capacitor C_1. When the potential at the grid of T-2 has dropped about 50 volts, the circuit is triggered back into its original state, the gate signal ends, and C_1 is ready to be charged again by the target current. The discharge of the capacitor C_1 requires about 100 μsec, so the repetition rate should be limited to 100 cycles per second for a maximum error of 1 per cent. The capacitor C_1 should be increased if larger currents are to be measured.

The Schmitt trigger circuit employs the tube T-3 in its cathode circuit as a constant-current device (see Chap. 2, Sec. 3.7). Its presence enables the cathode potential of T-2 and T-4 to vary through the 50-volt hysteresis cycle without appreciable change of the current through the tubes. The grid bias of T-2 therefore remains substantially constant during the discharge part of the cycle, and it is always negative enough to minimize grid-current flow. Even so, it is usually necessary to select the 6SH7 tube used for T-2 to obtain one having low grid current.

Each time the circuit is triggered, a positive pulse of about 50 volts is obtained at the plate of T-4. Tube T-5 serves as a low-impedance, cathode-follower output stage for coupling this pulse to an external counting circuit.

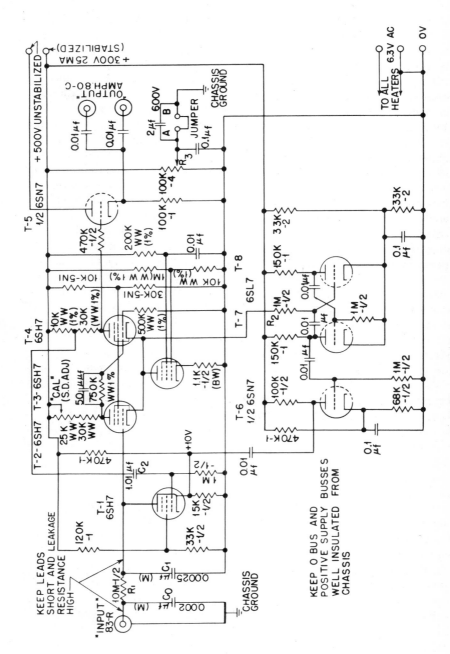

Fig. 7.21 — An integrating-current meter.

The portion of the circuit thus far described constitutes the funda-mental part of the current integrator. When the circuit is first turned on, it is possible for the potential of the grid of T-2 to rise so that the trigger circuit is in the state where T-2 is conducting but the grid of T-1 is below cutoff. This is a stable state, and the circuit is completely inoperative. This difficulty arises from the capacitive coupling used between the plate circuit of T-4 and the grid of T-1. Obviously it is necessary to change the state of charge on C_2 before the circuit can operate normally.

The portion of the circuit comprising tubes T-6, T-7, and T-8 serves automatically to correct the situation just described. Tubes T-7 and T-8 constitute a trigger circuit of the multivibrator type. This circuit element, however, remains in a stable state, with T-7 conducting and T-8 nonconducting as long as the resistor R_2 is re-turned to an external potential a few volts lower than the cathode potential of T-7 and T-8, about +160 volts. Since this resistor is con-nected to the cathodes of T-2 and T-4, whose potential varies between 70 and 120 volts during the normal operation of the circuit, the sub-sidiary trigger circuit is normally inactive. If, when the circuit is first turned on, the abnormal state that has been described should occur, the cathode potential to T-2 and T-4 will rise to a point where tubes T-7 and T-8 will multivibrate. A negative signal is therefore generated at the plate of T-6, and it is coupled to the cathode of T-1. The negative signal there serves to discharge the capacitor C_1, and by the time the Schmitt trigger circuit is called on to function again, the capacitor C_2 has recovered the charge it requires for the normal operation of the circuit.

The circuit used for correcting the abnormal condition could be avoided by employing a negative bias supply and coupling the plate of T-4 to the grid of T-1 through a suitable resistance divider. How-ever, fewer tubes and parts are required by the system adopted in the circuit of Fig. 7.21.

The precise role assumed by the resistor R_1 and the capacitor C_0 requires some explanation. The resistor R_1 serves mainly to make the calibration of the circuit independent of the capacitance of the target and connecting cable. This capacitance and the capacitance of C_0 are not discharged by the clamp tube T-1, and only the capaci-tance of C_1 is left to determine the calibration of the circuit. The capacitor C_0 serves to reduce fluctuations of the potential of the target, without otherwise affecting the operation of the circuit.

It will be noticed that the power-supply lead, denoted by 0 volts, is not at ground or chassis potential, but that the entire circuit can be lowered in potential any amount up to 300 volts by means of the poten-tiometer R_3. This provision enables the mean potential of the col-lector to be so fixed that the effect of secondary electron emission and of stray ion leakages is minimized. If the 300-volt adjustment of collector potential is not sufficient, the jumper connecting points A and B can be replaced by an external battery to afford a greater range of adjustment. Except for leakage currents, all current entering the circuit through the input connector must pass between points A and B. Hence, if internal leakage in the circuit is kept low, a slow-acting galvanometer can be connected between these points to read the mean input current.

The circuit is normally calibrated by passing a known current into it. For convenience in operation, part of the plate-load resistor of T-2 can be adjusted to enable a minor change to be made in the hys-teresis of the trigger circuit. The current integrator, therefore, can be calibrated for exactly 10^{-7} coulombs per output pulse in the operat-ing range. All resistors affecting the calibration of the circuit are wire-wound, and the 300-volt plate supply should be highly stabilized. Day-to-day tests of the circuit indicate that it will maintain its cali-bration to at least 1 per cent.

Linearity of response depends on how well all sources of leakage current are removed. In the range 1 to 20 μa, a particular circuit of this type showed a departure from linearity of 2 per cent. That is, when the current was maintained at 1 μa and then at 20 μa, each count corresponded to the same amount of charge to within this tolerance. On account of leakage currents, a somewhat greater departure from linearity can be expected for currents as low as 0.1 μa.

INDEX